A HISTORY OF NEW YORK
and
THE SKETCH BOOK

A HISTORY
OF NEW YORK

and

THE SKETCH BOOK

by

Washington Irving

THE BOOK LEAGUE OF AMERICA

New York

CONTENTS

A HISTORY OF NEW YORK

A

HISTORY OF NEW YORK,

FROM

THE BEGINNING OF THE WORLD TO THE END OF THE DUTCH DYNASTY,

CONTAINING, AMONG MANY SURPRISING AND CURIOUS MATTERS,

THE UNUTTERABLE PONDERINGS OF WALTER THE DOUBTER, THE DISASTROUS PROJECTS OF WILLIAM THE TESTY, AND THE CHIVALRIC ACHIEVEMENTS OF PETER THE HEAD-STRONG——THE THREE DUTCH GOVERNORS OF NEW AMSTERDAM;

BEING THE ONLY AUTHENTIC HISTORY OF THE TIMES THAT EVER HATH BEEN, OR EVER WILL BE, PUBLISHED.

BY

DIEDRICH KNICKERBOCKER.

De waarheid die in duister lag,
De komt mit klaarheid aan den dag.

First published in 1809

NOTICES

WHICH APPEARED IN THE NEWSPAPERS PREVIOUS TO THE
PUBLICATION OF THIS WORK.

———◆———

From the Evening Post of October 26, 1809.

DISTRESSING.

Left his lodgings some time since, and has not since been heard of, a small elderly gentleman, dressed in an old black coat and cocked hat, by the name of *Knickerbocker*. As there are some reasons for believing he is not entirely in his right mind, and as great anxiety is entertained about him, any information concerning him left either at the Columbian Hotel, Mulberry Street, or at the office of this paper, will be thankfully received.

P. S. Printers of newspapers would be aiding the cause of humanity in giving an insertion to the above.

————

From the same, November 6, 1809.

To the Editor of the Evening Post:

Sir,—Having read in your paper of the 26th October last, a paragraph respecting an old gentleman by the name of *Knickerbocker*, who was missing from his lodgings; if it would be any relief to his friends, or furnish them with any clew to discover where he is, you may inform them that a person answering the description given, was seen by the passengers of the Albany stage, early in the morning, about four or five weeks since, resting himself by the side of the road, a little above King's Bridge. He had in his hand a small bundle tied in a red bandanna handkerchief: he appeared to be travelling northward, and was very much fatigued and exhausted.   A TRAVELLER.

————

From the same, November 16, 1809.

To the Editor of the Evening Post:

Sir,—You have been good enough to publish in your paper a paragraph about Mr. *Diedrich Knickerbocker*, who was missing so strangly some time since. Nothing satisfactory has been heard of the old gentleman since; but *a very curious kind of a written book* has been found in his room, in his own hand-

3

writing. Now I wish you to notice him, if he is still alive, that if he does not return and pay off his bill for boarding and lodging, I shall have to dispose of his book to satisfy me for the same.

I am, Sir, your humble servant,

SETH HANDASIDE,

Landlord of the Independent Columbian Hotel, Mulberry Street.

———

From the same, November 28, 1809.

LITERARY NOTICE.

INSKEEP & BRADFORD have in the press, and will shortly publish,

A H i s t o r y o f N e w Y o r k ,

In two volumes, duodecimo. Price three dollars.

Containing an account of its discovery and settlement, with its internal policies, manners, customs, wars, etc., etc., under the Dutch government, furnishing many curious and interesting particulars never before published, and which are gathered from various manuscript and other authenticated sources, the whole being interspersed with philosophical speculations and moral precepts.

This work was found in the chamber of Mr. Diedrich Knickerbocker, the old gentleman whose sudden and mysterious disappearance has been noticed. It is published in order to discharge certain debts he has left behind.

———

From the American Citizen, December 6, 1809.

Is this day published

By INSKEEP & BRADFORD, No. 128 Broadway,

A H i s t o r y o f N e w Y o r k ,

etc., etc.,

(Containing same as above.)

ACCOUNT OF THE AUTHOR.

It was some time, if I recollect right, in the early part of the autumn of 1808, that a stranger applied for lodgings at the Independent Columbian Hotel in Mulberry-street, of which I am landlord. He was a small, brisk-looking old gentleman, dressed in a rusty black coat, a pair of olive velvet breeches, and a small cocked hat. He had a few gray hairs plaited and clubbed behind, and his beard seemed to be of some eight-and-forty hours' growth. The only piece of finery which he bore about him, was a bright pair of square silver shoe-buckles, and all his baggage was contained in a pair of saddle-bags, which he carried under his arm. His whole appearance was something out of the common run; and my wife, who is a very shrewd body, at once set him down for some eminent country schoolmaster.

As the Independent Columbian Hotel is a very small house, I was a little puzzled at first where to put him; but my wife, who seemed taken with his looks, would needs put him in her best chamber, which is genteelly set off with the profiles of the whole family, done in black, by those two great painters, Jarvis and Wood; and commands a very pleasant view of the new grounds on the Collect, together with the rear of the Poor-House and Bridewell, and a full front of the Hospital; so that it is the cheerfulest room in the whole house.

During the whole time that he stayed with us, we found him a very worthy, good sort of an old gentleman, though a little queer in his ways. He would keep in his room for days together, and if any of the children cried, or made a noise about his door, he would bounce out in a great passion, with his hands full of papers, and say something about "deranging his ideas;" which made my wife believe sometimes that he was not altogether *compos*. Indeed, there was more than one reason to make her think so, for his room was always covered with scraps of paper and old mouldy books, laying about at sixes and sevens, which he would never let anybody touch; for he said he had laid them all away in their proper places, so that he might know where to find them; though for that matter, he was half his time worrying about the house in search of some book or writing which he had carefully put out of the way. I shall never forget what a pother he once made, because my wife cleaned out his room when his back was turned, and put every thing to rights; for he swore he would never be able to get his papers in order again in a twelvemonth. Upon this my wife ventured to ask him what he did with so many books and papers? and he told her that he was "seeking for immortality;" which made her think, more than ever, that the poor old gentleman's head was a little cracked.

He was a very inquisitive body, and when not in his room was continually poking about town, hearing all the news, and prying into every thing that was going on: this was particularly the case about election time, when he did nothing but bustle about from poll to poll, attending all ward meetings and committee rooms; though I could never find that he took part with either side of the question. On the contrary, he would come home and rail at both parties with great wrath—and plainly proved one day, to the satisfaction of my wife and three old ladies who were drinking tea with her, that the two parties were like two rogues, each tugging at a skirt of the nation; and that in the end they would tear the very coat off its back, and expose its nakedness. Indeed, he was an oracle among the neighbors, who would collect around him to hear him talk of an afternoon, as he smoked his pipe on the bench before the door; and I really believe he would have brought over the whole neighborhood to his own side of the question, if they could ever have found out what it was.

He was very much given to argue, or as he called it, *philosophize*, about the most trifling matter; and to do him justice, I never knew anybody that was a match for him, except it was a grave-looking old gentleman who called now and then to see him, and often posed him in an argument. But this is nothing surprising, as I have since found out this stranger is the city librarian; who, of course, must be a man of great learning: and I have my doubts, if he had not some hand in the following history.

As our lodger had been a long time with us, and we had never received any pay, my wife began to be somewhat uneasy, and curious to find out who and what he was. She accordingly made bold to put the question to his friend, the librarian, who replied in his dry way that he was one of the *literati*, which she supposed to mean some new party in politics. I scorn to push a lodger for his pay; so I let day after day pass on without dunning the old gentleman for a farthing: but my wife, who always takes these matters on herself, and is, as I said, a shrewd kind of a woman, at last got out of patience, and hinted, that she thought it high time "some people should have a sight of some people's money." To which the old gentleman replied, in a mighty touchy manner, that she need not make herself uneasy, for that he had a treasure there, (pointing to his saddle-bags,) worth her whole house put together. This was the only answer we could ever get from him; and as my wife, by some of those odd ways in which women find out every thing, learnt that he was of very great connections, being related to the Knickerbockers of Scaghtikoke, and cousin-german to the Congressman of that name, she did not like to treat him uncivilly. What is more, she even offered, merely by way of making things easy, to let him live scot-free, if he would teach the children their letters; and to try her best and get her neighbors to send their children also; but the old gentleman took it in such dudgeon, and seemed so affronted at being taken for a schoolmaster, that she never dared to speak on the subject again.

About two months ago, he went out of a morning, with a bundle in his hand —and has never been heard of since. All kinds of inquiries were made after him, but in vain. I wrote to his relations at Scaghtikoke, but they sent for answer, that he had not been there since the year before last, when he had a great dispute with the Congressman about politics, and left the place in a huff, and they had neither heard nor seen any thing of him from that time to this. I must own I felt very much worried about the poor old gentleman, for I thought something bad must have happened to him, that he should be missing so long, and never return to pay his bill. I therefore advertised him in the newspapers, and though my melancholy advertisement was published by several humane printers, yet I have never been able to learn any thing satisfactory about him.

My wife now said it was high time to take care of ourselves, and see if he had left any thing behind in his room, that would pay us for his board and lodging. We found nothing, however, but some old books and musty writings, and his saddle-bags, which, being opened in the presence of the librarian, contained only a few articles of worn-out clothes, and a large bundle of blotted paper. On looking over this, the librarian told us, he had no doubt it was the treasure which the old gentleman had spoken about; as it proved to be a most excellent and faithful HISTORY OF NEW YORK, which he advised us by all means to publish: assuring us that it would be so eagerly bought up by a discerning public, that he had no doubt it would be enough to pay our arrears ten times over. Upon this we got a very learned schoolmaster, who teaches our children, to prepare it for the press, which he accordingly has done; and has, moreover, added to it a number of valuable notes of his own.

This, therefore, is a true statement of my reasons for having this work printed, without waiting for the consent of the author: and I here declare, that if he ever returns, (though I much fear some unhappy accident has befallen him,) I stand ready to account with him like a true and honest man. Which is all at present,

From the public's humble servant,

SETH HANDASIDE.

Independent Columbian Hotel, New-York.

THE foregoing account of the author was prefixed to the first edition of this work. Shortly after its publication a letter was received from him, by Mr. Handaside, dated at a small Dutch village on the banks of the Hudson, whither he had travelled for the purpose of inspecting certain ancient records. As this was one of those few and happy villages into which newspapers never find their way, it is not a matter of surprise, that Mr. Knickerbocker should never have seen the numerous advertisements that were made concerning him; and that he should learn of the publication of his history by mere accident.

He expressed much concern at its premature appearance, as thereby he was prevented from making several important corrections and alterations; as well as from profiting by many curious hints which he had collected during his travels along the shores of the Tappan Sea, and his sojourn at Haverstraw and Esopus.

Finding that there was no longer any immediate necessity for his return to New York, he extended his journey up to the residence of his relations at Scaghtikoke. On his way thither, he stopped for some days at Albany, for which city he is known to have entertained a great partiality. He found it, however, considerably altered, and was much concerned at the inroads and improvements which the Yankees were making, and the consequent decline of the good old Dutch manners. Indeed, he was informed that these intruders were making sad innovations in all parts of the State; where they had given great trouble and vexation to the regular Dutch settlers, by the introduction of turnpike gates and country school-houses. It is said also, that Mr. Knickerbocker shook his head sorrowfully at noticing the gradual decay of the great

Vander Heyden palace; but was highly indignant at finding that the ancient Dutch church, which stood in the middle of the street, had been pulled down, since his last visit.

The fame of Mr. Knickerbocker's history having reached even to Albany, he received much flattering attention from its worthy burghers, some of whom, however, pointed out two or three very great errors he had fallen into, particularly that of suspending a lump of sugar over the Albany tea-tables, which, they assured him, had been discontinued for some years past. Several families, moreover, were somewhat piqued that their ancestors had not been mentioned in his work, and showed great jealousy of their neighbors who had thus been distinguished; while the latter, it must be confessed, plumed themselves vastly thereupon: considering these recordings in the light of letters-patent of nobility, establishing their claims to ancestry—which, in this republican country, is a matter of no little solicitude and vainglory.

It is also said, that he enjoyed high favor and countenance from the governor, who once asked him to dinner, and was seen two or three times to shake hands with him, when they met in the street; which certainly was going great lengths, considering that they differed in politics. Indeed, certain of the governor's confidential friends, to whom he could venture to speak his mind freely on such matters, have assured us, that he privately entertained a considerable good-will for our author—nay, he even once went so far as to declare, and that openly, too, and at his own table, just after dinner, that "Knickerbocker was a very well-meaning sort of an old gentleman, and no fool." From all which, many have been led to suppose, that had our author been of different politics, and written for the newspapers, instead of wasting his talents on histories, he might have risen to some post of honor and profit: peradventure, to be a notary public, or even a justice in the Ten Pound Court.

Beside the honors and civilities already mentioned, he was much caressed by the literati of Albany; particularly by Mr. John Cook, who entertained him very hospitably at his circulating library and reading-room, where they used to drink Spa water, and talk about the ancients. He found Mr. Cook a man after his own heart—of great literary research, and a curious collector of books. At parting, the latter, in testimony of friendship, made him a present of the two oldest works in his collection; which were the earliest edition of the Heidelberg Catechism, and Adrian Vander Donck's famous account of the New Netherlands; by the last of which, Mr. Knickerbocker profited greatly in this his second edition.

Having passed some time very agreeably at Albany, our author proceeded to Scaghtikoke; where, it is but justice to say, he was received with open arms, and treated with wonderful loving-kindness. He was much looked up to by the family, being the first historian of the name; and was considered almost as great a man as his cousin the Congressman—with whom, by-the-by, he became perfectly reconciled, and contracted a strong friendship.

In spite, however, of the kindness of his relations, and their great attention to his comforts, the old gentleman soon became restless and discontented. His history being published, he had no longer any business to occupy his thoughts, or any scheme to excite his hopes and anticipations. This, to a busy mind like his, was a truly deplorable situation; and, had he not been a man of inflexible morals and regular habits, there would have been great danger of his taking to politics, or drinking—both which pernicious vices we daily see men driven to, by mere spleen and idleness.

It is true, he sometimes employed himself in preparing a second edition of his history, wherein he endeavored to correct and improve many passages with which he was dissatisfied, and to rectify some mistakes that had crept into it; for he was particularly anxious that his work should be noted for its authenticity, which, indeed, is the very life and soul of history. But the glow of composition had departed—he had to leave many places untouched, which he would fain have altered; and even where he did make alterations, he seemed always in doubt whether they were for the better or the worse.

After a residence of some time at Scaghtikoke, he began to feel a strong desire to return to New York, which he ever regarded with the warmest affection, not merely because it was his native city, but because he really considered it the very best city in the whole world. On his return, he entered into the full enjoyment of the advantages of a literary reputation. He was continually importuned to write advertisements, petitions, hand-bills, and productions of similar import; and, although he never meddled with the public papers, yet had he the credit of writing innumerable essays, and smart things, that appeared on all subjects, and all sides of the question; in all which he was clearly detected "by his style."

He contracted, moreover, a considerable debt at the post-office, in consequence of the numerous letters he received from authors and printers soliciting his subscription; and he was applied to by every charitable society for yearly donations, which he gave very cheerfully, considering these applications as so many compliments. He was once invited to a great corporation dinner; and was even twice summoned to attend as a juryman at the court of quarter sessions. Indeed, so renowned did he become, that he could no longer pry about, as formerly, in all holes and corners of the city, according to the bent of his humor, unnoticed and uninterrupted; but several times when he has been sauntering the streets, on his usual rambles of observation, equipped with his cane and cocked hat, the little boys at play have been known to cry, "there goes Diedrich!"—at which the old gentleman seemed not a little pleased, looking upon these salutations in the light of the praise of posterity.

In a word, if we take into consideration all these various honors and distinctions, together with an exuberant eulogium passed on him in the Port Folio—(with which, we are told, the old gentleman was so much overpowered, that he was sick for two or three days)—it must be confessed, that few authors have ever lived to receive such illustrious rewards, or have so completely enjoyed in advance their own immortality.

After his return from Scaghtikoke, Mr. Knickerbocker took up his residence at a little rural retreat, which the Stuyvesants had granted him on the family domain, in gratitude for his honorable mention of their ancestor. It was pleasantly situated on the borders of one of the salt marshes beyond Corlear's Hook:

subject, indeed, to be occasionally overflowed, and much infested, in the summer-time, with mosquitoes; but otherwise very agreeable, producing abundant crops of salt grass and bulrushes.

Here, we are sorry to say, the good old gentleman fell dangerously ill of a fever, occasioned by the neighboring marshes. When he found his end approaching, he disposed of his worldly affairs, leaving the bulk of his fortune to the New York Historical Society; his Heidelberg Catechism, and Vander Donck's work to the city library; and his saddle-bags to Mr. Handaside. He forgave all his enemies,—that is to say, all who bore any enmity towards him; for as to himself, he declared he died in good-will with all the world. And, after dictating several kind messages to his relations at Scaghtikoke, as well as to certain of our most substantial Dutch citizens, he expired in the arms of his friend the librarian.

His remains were interred, according to his own request, in St. Mark's churchyard, close by the bones of his favorite hero, Peter Stuyvesant: and it is rumored, that the Historical Society have it in mind to erect a wooden monument to his memory in the Bowling-Green.

HISTORY OF NEW YORK.

By DIEDRICH KNICKERBOCKER.

De waarheid die in duister lag,
De komt met klaarheid aan den dag.

BOOK I.

CONTAINING DIVERS INGENIOUS THEORIES AND PHILOSOPHIC SPECU-
LATIONS, CONCERNING THE CREATION AND POPULATION OF THE
WORLD, AS CONNECTED WITH THE HISTORY OF NEW YORK.

CHAPTER I.

DESCRIPTION OF THE WORLD.

ACCORDING to the best authorities, the world in which we dwell is a huge,
opaque, reflecting, inanimate mass, floating in the vast ethereal ocean of infinite
space. It has the form of an orange, being an oblate spheroid, curiously flattened
at opposite parts, for the insertion of two imaginary poles, which are supposed
to penetrate and unite at the centre; thus forming an axis on which the mighty
orange turns with a regular diurnal revolution.

The transitions of light and darkness, whence proceed the alternations of
day and night, are produced by this diurnal revolution successively presenting
the different parts of the earth to the rays of the sun. The latter is, according
to the best, that is to say, the latest accounts, a luminous or fiery body, of a
prodigious magnitude, from which this world is driven by a centrifugal or
repelling power, and to which it is drawn by a centripetal or attractive force,
otherwise called the attraction of gravitation; the combination, or rather the
counteraction, of these two opposing impulses producing a circular and annual
revolution. Hence result the different seasons of the year, viz., spring, summer,
autumn, and winter.

This I believe to be the most approved modern theory on the subject—
though there be many philosophers who have entertained very different
opinions; some, too, of them entitled to much deference from their great
antiquity and illustrious characters. Thus it was advanced by some of the
ancient sages, that the earth was an extended plain, supported by vast pillars;
and by others, that it rested on the head of a snake, or the back of a huge
tortoise—but as they did not provide a resting place for either the pillars or
the tortoise, the whole theory fell to the ground, for want of proper foundation.

The Brahmins assert, that the heavens rest upon the earth, and the sun and
moon swim therein like fishes in the water, moving from east to west by day,
and gliding along the edge of the horizon to their original stations during

night;[1] while, according to the Pauranicas of India, it is a vast plain, encircled by seven oceans of milk, nectar, and other delicious liquids; that it is studded with seven mountains, and ornamented in the centre by a mountainous rock of burnished gold; and that a great dragon occasionally swallows up the moon, which accounts for the phenomena of lunar eclipses.[2]

Beside these, and many other equally sage opinions, we have the profound conjectures of ABOUL-HASSAN-ALY, son of Al Khan, son of Aly, son of Abder-rahman, son of Abdallah, son of Masoud-el-Hadheli, who is commonly called MASOUDI, and surnamed Cothbiddin, but who takes the humble title of Laheb-ar-rasoul, which means the companion of the ambassador of God. He has written a universal history, entitled "Mouroudge-ed-dharab, or the Golden Meadows, and the Mines of Precious Stones."[3] In this valuable work he has related the history of the world, from the creation down to the moment of writing; which was under the Caliphate of Mothi Billah, in the month Dgioumadi-el-aoual of the 336th year of the Hegira or flight of the Prophet. He informs us that the earth is a huge bird, Mecca and Medina constituting the head, Persia and India the right wing, the land of Gog the left wing, and Africa the tail. He informs us, moreover, that an earth has existed before the present, (which he considers as a mere chicken of 7,000 years,) that it has undergone divers deluges, and that, according to the opinion of some well-informed Brahmins of his acquaintance, it will be renovated every seventy-thousandth hazarouam; each hazarouam consisting of 12,000 years.

These are a few of the many contradictory opinions of philosophers concerning the earth, and we find that the learned have had equal perplexity as to the nature of the sun. Some of the ancient philosophers have affirmed that it is a vast wheel of brilliant fire;[4] others, that it is merely a mirror or sphere of transparent crystal;[5] and a third class, at the head of whom stands Anaxagoras, maintained that it was nothing but a huge ignited mass of iron or stone—indeed, he declared the heavens to be merely a vault of stone—and that the stars were stones whirled upward from the earth, and set on fire by the velocity of its revolutions.[6] But I give little attention to the doctrines of this philosopher, the people of Athens having fully refuted them, by banishing him from their city; a concise mode of answering unwelcome doctrines, much resorted to in former days. Another sect of philosophers do declare, that certain fiery particles exhale constantly from the earth, which, concentrating in a single point of the firmament by day, constitute the sun, but being scattered and rambling about in the dark at night, collect in various points, and form stars. These are regu-

---

[1]Faria y Souza. Mick. Lus. note b. 7.   [2]Sir W. Jones, Diss. Antiq. Ind. Zod.
[3]MSS. Bibliot. Roi. Fr.

[4]Plutarch de Placitis Philosoph. lib. ii. cap. 20.

[5]Achill. Tat. Isag. cap. 19. Ap. Petav. t. iii. p. 81. Stob. Eclog. Phys. lib. i. p. 56. Plut. de Plac. Phi.

[6]Diogenes Laertius in Anaxag. 1. ii. sec. 8. Plat. Apol. t. i. p. 26. Plut. de Plac. Philo. Xenoph. Mem. l. iv. p. 815.

larly burnt out and extinguished, not unlike to the lamps in our streets, and require a fresh supply of exhalations for the next occasion.[7]

It is even recorded, that at certain remote and obscure periods, in consequence of a great scarcity of fuel, the sun has been completely burnt out, and sometimes not rekindled for a month at a time;—a most melancholy circumstance, the very idea of which gave vast concern to Heraclitus, that worthy weeping philosopher of antiquity. In addition to these various speculations, it was the opinion of Herschel, that the sun is a magnificent, habitable abode; the light it furnishes arising from certain empyreal, luminous or phosphoric clouds, swimming in its transparent atmosphere.[8]

But we will not enter farther at present into the nature of the sun, that being an inquiry not immediately necessary to the development of this history; neither will we embroil ourselves in any more of the endless disputes of philosophers touching the form of this globe, but content ourselves with the theory advanced in the beginning of this chapter, and will proceed to illustrate, by experiment, the complexity of motion therein ascribed to this our rotatory planet.

Professor Von Poddingcoft (or Puddinghead, as the name may be rendered into English) was long celebrated in the university of Leyden, for profound gravity of deportment, and a talent of going to sleep in the midst of examinations, to the infinite relief of his hopeful students, who thereby worked their way through college with great ease and little study. In the course of one of his lectures, the learned professor, seizing a bucket of water, swung it around his head at arm's-length. The impulse with which he threw the vessel from him being a centrifugal force, the retention of his arm operating as a centripetal power, and the bucket, which was a substitute for the earth, describing a circular orbit round about the globular head and ruby visage of Professor Von Poddingcoft, which formed no bad representation of the sun. All of these particulars were duly explained to the class of gaping students around him. He apprised them, moreover, that the same principle of gravitation, which retained the water in the bucket, restrains the ocean from flying from the earth in its rapid revolutions; and he farther informed them, that should the motion of the earth be suddenly checked, it would incontinently fall into the sun, through the centripetal force of gravitation; a most ruinous event to this planet, and one which would also obscure, though it most probably would not extinguish, the solar luminary. An unlucky stripling, one of those vagrant geniuses who seem sent into the world merely to annoy worthy men of the puddinghead order, desirous of ascertaining the correctness of the experiment, suddenly arrested the arm of the professor, just at the moment the bucket was in its zenith, which immediately descended with astonishing precision upon the philosophic head of the instructor of youth. A hollow sound, and a red-hot hiss, attended the contact; but the theory was in the amplest manner illustrated, for

[7] Aristot. Meteor. l. ii. c. 2. Idem. Probl. sec. 15. Stob. Ecl. Phys. l. i. p. 55. Bruck. Hist. Phil. t. i. p. 1154, &c.

[8] Philos. Trans. 1795, p. 72. Idem. 1801, p. 265. Nich. Philos. Journ. i. p. 13.

the unfortunate bucket perished in the conflict; but the blazing countenance of Professor Von Poddingcoft emerged from amidst the waters, glowing fiercer than ever with unutterable indignation, whereby the students were marvellously edified, and departed considerably wiser than before.

It is a mortifying circumstance, which greatly perplexes many a painstaking philosopher, that nature often refuses to second his most profound and elaborate efforts; so that after having invented one of the most ingenious and natural theories imaginable, she will have the perverseness to act directly in the teeth of his system, and flatly contradict his most favorite positions. This is a manifest and unmerited grievance, since it throws the censure of the vulgar and unlearned entirely upon the philosopher; whereas the fault is not to be ascribed to his theory, which is unquestionably correct, but to the waywardness of dame nature, who, with the proverbial fickleness of her sex, is continually indulging in coquetries and caprices, and seems really to take pleasure in violating all philosophic rules, and jilting the most learned and indefatigable of her adorers. Thus it happened with respect to the foregoing satisfactory explanation of the motion of our planet; it appears that the centrifugal force has long since ceased to operate, while its antagonist remains in undiminished potency: the world, therefore, according to the theory as it originally stood, ought in strict propriety to tumble into the sun; philosophers were convinced that it would do so, and awaited in anxious impatience the fulfilment of their prognostics. But the untoward planet pertinaciously continued her course, notwithstanding that she had reason, philosophy, and a whole university of learned professors opposed to her conduct. The philosophers took this in very ill part, and it is thought they would never have pardoned the slight and affront which they conceived put upon them by the world, had not a good-natured professor kindly officiated as a mediator between the parties, and effected a reconciliation.

Finding the world would not accommodate itself to the theory, he wisely determined to accommodate the theory to the world: he therefore informed his brother philosophers, that the circular motion of the earth round the sun was no sooner engendered by the conflicting impulses above described, than it became a regular revolution, independent of the causes which gave it origin. His learned brethren readily joined in the opinion, being heartily glad of any explanation that would decently extricate them from their embarrassment— and ever since that memorable era the world has been left to take her own course, and to revolve around the sun in such orbit as she thinks proper.

CHAPTER II.

Cosmogony, or Creation of the World; with a Multitude of Excellent Theories, by Which the Creation of a World Is Shown to be No Such Difficult Matter as Common Folk Would Imagine.

Having thus briefly introduced my reader to the world, and given him some idea of its form and situation, he will naturally be curious to know from whence it came, and how it was created. And, indeed, the clearing up of these points is absolutely essential to my history, inasmuch as if this world had not been formed, it is more than probable that this renowned island on which is situated the city of New York, would never have had an existence. The regular course of my history, therefore, requires that I should proceed to notice the cosmogony, or formation of this our globe.

And now I give my readers fair warning, that I am about to plunge, for a chapter or two, into as complete a labyrinth as ever historian was perplexed withal; therefore, I advise them to take fast hold of my skirts, and keep close at my heels, venturing neither to the right hand nor to the left, lest they get bemired in a slough of unintelligible learning, or have their brains knocked out by some of those hard Greek names which will be flying about in all directions. But should any of them be too indolent or chicken-hearted to accompany me in this perilous undertaking, they had better take a short cut round, and wait for me at the beginning of some smoother chapter.

Of the creation of the world, we have a thousand contradictory accounts; and though a very satisfactory one is furnished us by divine revelation, yet every philosopher feels himself in honor bound to furnish us with a better. As an impartial historian, I consider it my duty to notice their several theories, by which mankind have been so exceedingly edified and instructed.

Thus it was the opinion of certain ancient sages, that the earth and the whole system of the universe was the deity himself;[1] a doctrine most strenuously maintained by Zenophanes and the whole tribe of Eleatics, as also by Strabo and the sect of peripatetic philsophers. Pythagoras likewise inculcated the famous numerical system of the monad, dyad, and triad, and by means of his sacred quaternary elucidated the formation of the world, the arcana of nature, and the principles both of music and morals.[2] Other sages adhered to the mathematical system of squares and triangles; the cube, the pyramid, and the sphere, the tetrahedron, the octahedron, the icosahedron, and the dodeca-hedron.[3] While others advocated the great elementary theory, which refers

[1] Aristot. ap. Cic. lib. i. cap. 3.

[2] Aristot. Metaph. lib. i. c. 5. Idem. de Cœlo, l. iii. c. i. Rousseau Mém. sur Musique ancien, p. 39. Plutarch de Plac. Philos. lib. i. cap. 3.

[3] Tim. Locr. ap. Plato. t. iii. p. 90.

the construction of our globe, and all that it contains, to the combinations of four material elements—air, earth, fire, and water; with the assistance of a fifth, an immaterial and vivifying principle.

Nor must I omit to mention the great atomic system, taught by old Moschus, before the siege of Troy; revived by Democritus, of laughing memory; improved by Epicurus, that king of good fellows, and modernized by the fanciful Descartes.

But I decline inquiring, whether the atoms, of which the earth is said to be composed, are eternal or recent; whether they are animate or inanimate; whether, agreeably to the opinion of the atheists, they were fortuitously aggregated, or, as the theists maintain, were arranged by a supreme intelligence.[4] Whether, in fact, the earth be an insensate clod, or whether it be animated by a soul;[5] which opinion was strenuously maintained by a host of philosophers, at the head of whom stands the great Plato, that temperate sage, who threw the cold water of philosophy on the form of sexual intercourse, and inculcated the doctrine of Platonic love—an exquisitely refined intercourse, but much better adapted to the ideal inhabitants of his imaginary island of Atlantis than to the sturdy race, composed of rebellious flesh and blood, which populates the little matter-of-fact island we inhabit.

Beside these systems, we have, moreover, the poetical theogony of old Hesiod, who generated the whole universe in the regular mode of procreation; and the plausible opinion of others, that the earth was hatched from the great egg of night, which floated in chaos, and was cracked by the horns of the celestial bull. To illustrate this last doctrine, Burnet, in his theory of the earth,[6] has favored us with an accurate drawing and description, both of the form and texture of this mundane egg; which is found to bear a marvellous resemblance to that of a goose. Such of my readers as take a proper interest in the origin of this our planet, will be pleased to learn, that the most profound sages of antiquity, among the Egyptians, Chaldeans, Persians, Greeks, and Latins, have alternately assisted at the hatching of this strange bird, and that their cacklings have been caught, and continued in different tones and inflections, from philosopher to philosopher, unto the present day.

But while briefly noticing long-celebrated systems of ancient sages, let me not pass over with neglect those of other philosophers; which, though less universal and renowned, have equal claims to attention, and equal chance for correctness. Thus it is recorded by the Brahmins, in the pages of their inspired Shastah, that the angel Bistnoo, transforming himself into a great boar, plunged into the watery abyss, and brought up the earth on his tusks. Then issued from him a mighty tortoise, and a mighty snake; and Bistnoo placed the snake erect upon

---

[4] Aristot. Nat. Auscult. l. ii. cap. 6. Aristoph. Metaph. lib. i. cap. 3. Cic. de Nat. Deor. lib. i. cap. 10. Justin Mart. orat. ad gent. p. 20.

[5] Mosheim in Cudw. lib. i. cap. 4. Tim. de anim. mund ap. Plat. lib. iii. Mém. de l'Acad. des Belles-Lettr. t. xxxii. p. 19, et al.

[6] Book i. ch. 5.

the back of the tortoise, and he placed the earth upon the head of the snake.[7]

The negro philosophers of Congo affirm that the world was made by the hands of angels, excepting their own country, which the Supreme Being constructed himself, that it might be supremely excellent. And he took great pains with the inhabitants, and made them very black, and beautiful; and when he had finished the first man, he was well pleased with him, and smoothed him over the face; and hence his nose, and the nose of all his descendants, became flat.

The Mohawk philosophers tell us, that a pregnant woman fell down from heaven, and that a tortoise took her upon its back, because every place was covered with water; and that the woman, sitting upon the tortoise, paddled with her hands in the water, and raked up the earth, whence it finally happened that the earth became higher than the water.[8]

But I forbear to quote a number more of these ancient and outlandish philosophers, whose deplorable ignorance, in despite of all their erudition, compelled them to write in languages which but few of my readers can understand; and I shall proceed briefly to notice a few more intelligible and fashionable theories of their modern successors.

And, first, I shall mention the great Buffon, who conjectures that this globe was originally a globe of liquid fire, scintillated from the body of the sun, by the percussion of a comet, as a spark is generated by the collision of flint and steel. That at first it was surrounded by gross vapors, which, cooling and condensing in process of time, constituted, according to their densities, earth, water, and air; which gradually arranged themselves, according to their respective gravities, round the burning or vitrified mass that formed their centre.

Hutton, on the contrary, supposes that the waters at first were universally paramount; and he terrifies himself with the idea that the earth must be eventually washed away by the force of rain, rivers, and mountain torrents, until it is confounded with the ocean, or, in other words, absolutely dissolves into itself. Sublime idea! far surpassing that of the tender-hearted damsel of antiquity, who wept herself into a fountain; or the good dame of Narbonne in France, who, for a volubility of tongue unusual in her sex, was doomed to peel five hundred thousand and thirty-nine ropes of onions, and actually run out at her eyes before half the hideous task was accomplished.

Whiston, the same ingenious philosopher who rivalled Ditton in his researches after the longitude, (for which the mischief-loving Swift discharged on their heads a most savory stanza,) has distinguished himself by a very admirable theory respecting the earth. He conjectures that it was originally a *chaotic comet*, which being selected for the abode of man, was removed from its eccentric orbit, and whirled round the sun in its present regular motion; by which change of direction, order succeeded to confusion in the arrangement of its component parts. The philosopher adds, that the deluge was produced by an uncourteous salute from the watery tail of another comet;

[7]Holwell, Gent. Philosophy.
[8]Johannes Megapolensis, Jun. Account of Maquaas or Mohawk Indians.

doubtless through sheer envy of its improved condition: thus furnishing a melancholy proof that jealousy may prevail, even among the heavenly bodies, and discord interrupt that celestial harmony of the spheres so melodiously sung by the poets.

But I pass over a variety of excellent theories, among which are those of Burnet, and Woodward, and Whitehurst; regretting extremely that my time will not suffer me to give them the notice they deserve—and shall conclude with that of the renowned Dr. Darwin. This learned Theban, who is as much distinguished for rhyme as reason, and for good-natured credulity as serious research, and who has recommended himself wonderfully to the good graces of the ladies, by letting them into all the gallantries, amours, debaucheries, and other topics of scandal of the court of Flora, has fallen upon a theory worthy of his combustible imagination. According to his opinion, the huge mass of chaos took a sudden occasion to explode, like a barrel of gunpowder, and in that act exploded the sun—which in its flight, by a similar convulsion, exploded the earth—which in like guise exploded the moon—and thus by a concatenation of explosions, the whole solar system was produced, and set most systematically in motion! [9]

By the great variety of theories here alluded to, every one of which, if thoroughly examined, will be found surprisingly consistent in all its parts, my unlearned readers will perhaps be led to conclude, that the creation of a world is not so difficult a task as they at first imagined. I have shown at least a score of ingenious methods in which a world could be constructed; and I have no doubt that had any of the philosophers above quoted the use of a good manageable comet, and the philosophical warehouse *chaos* at his command, he would engage to manufacture a planet as good, or, if you would take his word for it, better than this we inhabit.

And here I cannot help noticing the kindness of Providence, in creating comets for the great relief of bewildered philosophers. By their assistance more sudden evolutions and transitions are effected in the system of nature, than are wrought in a pantomimic exhibition, by the wonder-working sword of Harlequin. Should one of our modern sages, in his theoretical flights among the stars, ever find himself lost in the clouds, and in danger of tumbling into the abyss of nonsense and absurdity, he has but to seize a comet by the beard, mount astride of its tail, and away he gallops in triumph, like an enchanter on his hippogriff, or a Connecticut witch on her broomstick, "to sweep the cobwebs out of the sky."

It is an old and vulgar saying about a "beggar on horseback," which I would not for the world have applied to these reverend philosophers; but I must confess that some of them, when they are mounted on one of those fiery steeds, are as wild in their curvetings as was Phaëton of yore, when he aspired to manage the chariot of Phœbus. One drives his comet at full speed against the sun, and knocks the world out of him with the mighty concussion; another, more moderate, makes his comet a kind of beast of burden, carrying the sun

[9] Darw. Bot. Garden, Part I. Cant. i. l. 105.

a regular supply of food and fagots; a third, of more combustible disposition, threatens to throw his comet, like a bombshell, into the world and blow it up like a powder-magazine; while a fourth, with no great delicacy to this planet and its inhabitants, insinuates that some day or other his comet—my modest pen blushes while I write it—shall absolutely turn tail upon our world and deluge it with water!—Surely, as I have already observed, comets were bountifully provided by Providence for the benefit of philosophers, to assist them in manufacturing theories.

And now, having adduced several of the most prominent theories that occur to my recollection, I leave my judicious readers at full liberty to choose among them. They are all serious speculations of learned men—all differ essentially from each other—and all have the same title to belief. It has ever been the task of one race of philosophers to demolish the works of their predecessors, and elevate more splendid fantasies in their stead, which in their turn are demolished and replaced by the air-castles of a succeeding generation. Thus it would seem that knowledge and genius, of which we make such great parade, consist but in detecting the errors and absurdities of those who have gone before, and devising new errors and absurdities, to be detected by those who are to come after us. Theories are the mighty soap-bubbles with which the grown-up children of science amuse themselves—while the honest vulgar stand gazing in stupid admiration, and dignify these learned vagaries with the name of wisdom!—Surely, Socrates was right in his opinion, that philosophers are but a soberer sort of madmen, busying themselves in things totally incomprehensible, or which, if they could be comprehended, would be found not worthy the trouble of discovery.

For my own part, until the learned have come to an agreement among themselves, I shall content myself with the account handed down to us by Moses; in which I do but follow the example of our ingenious neighbors of Connecticut; who at their first settlement proclaimed that the colony should be governed by the laws of God—until they had time to make better.

One thing, however, appears certain—from the unanimous authority of the before-quoted philosophers, supported by the evidence of our own senses, (which, though very apt to deceive us, may be cautiously admitted as additional testimony,) it appears, I say, and I make the assertion deliberately, without fear of contradiction, that this globe really *was created*, and that it is composed of *land and water*. It farther appears that it is curiously divided and parcelled out into continents and islands, among which I boldly declare the renowned ISLAND OF NEW YORK will be found by any one who seeks for it in its proper place.

CHAPTER III.

How That Famous Navigator, Noah, Was Shamefully Nick-
named; and How He Committed an Unpardonable Oversight in
Not Having Four Sons. With the Great Trouble of Philosophers
Caused Thereby, and the Discovery of America.

Noah, who is the first sea-faring man we read of, begat three sons, Shem, Ham,
and Japhet. Authors, it is true, are not wanting who affirm that the patriarch
had a number of other children. Thus Berosus makes him father of the gigantic
Titans; Methodius gives him a son called Jonithus, or Jonicus, and others have
mentioned a son named Thuiscon, from whom descended the Teutons or
Teutonic, or, in other words, the Dutch nation.

I regret exceedingly that the nature of my plan will not permit me to gratify
the laudable curiosity of my readers, by investigating minutely the history of
the great Noah. Indeed, such an undertaking would be attended with more
trouble than many people would imagine; for the good old patriarch seems
to have been a great traveller in his day, and to have passed under a different
name in every country that he visited. The Chaldeans, for instance, give us his
story, merely altering his name into Xisuthrus—a trivial alteration, which, to
an historian skilled in etymologies, will appear wholly unimportant. It appears,
likewise, that he had exchanged his tarpaulin and quadrant among the Chaldeans for the gorgeous insignia of royalty, and appears as a monarch in their
annals. The Egyptians celebrate him under the name of Osiris; the Indians, as
Menu; the Greek and Roman writers confound him with Ogyges, and the
Theban with Deucalion and Saturn. But the Chinese, who deservedly rank
among the most extensive and authentic historians, inasmuch as they have
known the world much longer than any one else, declare that Noah was no
other than Fohi; and what gives this assertion some air of credibility is, that
it is a fact, admitted by the most enlightened literati, that Noah travelled into
China at the time of the building of the tower of Babel, (probably to improve
himself in the study of languages,) and the learned Dr. Shackford gives us the
additional information, that the ark rested on a mountain on the frontiers of
China.

From this mass of rational conjectures and sage hypotheses, many satisfactory
deductions might be drawn; but I shall content myself with the simple fact
stated in the Bible, viz., that Noah begat three sons, Shem, Ham, and Japhet.
It is astonishing on what remote and obscure contingencies the great affairs of
this world depend, and how events the most distant, and to the common
observer unconnected, are inevitably consequent the one to the other. It
remains for the philosopher to discover these mysterious affinities, and it is the
proudest triumph of his skill to detect and drag forth some latent chain of
causation, which at first sight appears a paradox to the inexperienced observer.
Thus many of my readers will doubtless wonder what connection the family

of Noah can possibly have with this history—and many will stare when informed that the whole history of this quarter of the world has taken its character and course from the simple circumstance of the patriarch's having but three sons—but to explain:

Noah, we are told by sundry very credible historians, becoming sole surviving heir and proprietor of the earth in fee simple, after the deluge, like a good father, portioned out his estate among his children. To Shem he gave Asia; to Ham, Africa; and to Japhet, Europe. Now it is a thousand times to be lamented that he had but three sons, for had there been a fourth, he would doubtless have inherited America; which, of course, would have been dragged forth from its obscurity on the occasion; and thus many a hard-working historian and philosopher would have been spared a prodigious mass of weary conjecture respecting the first discovery and population of this country. Noah, however, having provided for his three sons, looked in all probability upon our country as mere wild unsettled land, and said nothing about it; and to this unpardonable taciturnity of the patriarch, may we ascribe the misfortune that America did not come into the world as early as the other quarters of the globe.

It is true, some writers have vindicated him from this misconduct towards posterity, and asserted that he really did discover America. Thus it was the opinion of Mark Lescarbot, a French writer, possessed of that ponderosity of thought and profoundness of reflection so peculiar to his nation, that the immediate descendants of Noah peopled this quarter of the globe, and that the old patriarch himself, who still retained a passion for the sea-faring life, superintended the transmigration. The pious and enlightened father, Charlevoix, a French Jesuit, remarkable for his aversion to the marvellous, common to all great travellers, is conclusively of the same opinion; nay, he goes still farther, and decides upon the manner in which the discovery was effected, which was by sea, and under the immediate direction of the great Noah. "I have already observed," exclaims the good father, in a tone of becoming indignation, "that it is an arbitrary supposition that the grand-children of Noah were not able to penetrate into the new world, or that they never thought of it. In effect, I can see no reason that can justify such a notion. Who can seriously believe that Noah and his immediate descendants knew less than we do, and that the builder and pilot of the greatest ship that ever was, a ship which was formed to traverse an unbounded ocean, and had so many shoals and quicksands to guard against, should be ignorant of, or should not have communicated to his descendants, the art of sailing on the ocean?" Therefore, they did sail on the ocean—therefore, they sailed to America—therefore, America was discovered by Noah.

Now all this exquisite chain of reasoning, which is so strikingly characteristic of the good father, being addressed to the faith, rather than the understanding, is flatly opposed by Hans de Laet, who declares it a real and most ridiculous paradox, to suppose that Noah ever entertained the thought of discovering America; and as Hans is a Dutch writer, I am inclined to believe he must have been much better acquainted with the worthy crew of the ark than his competitors, and of course possessed of more accurate sources of information.

It is astonishing how intimate historians do daily become with the patriarchs and other great men of antiquity. As intimacy improves with time, and as the learned are particularly inquisitive and familiar in their acquaintance with the ancients, I should not be surprised if some future writers should gravely give us a picture of men and manners as they existed before the flood, far more copious and accurate than the Bible; and that, in the course of another century, the log-book of the good Noah should be as current among historians, as the voyages of Captain Cook, or the renowned history of Robinson Crusoe.

I shall not occupy my time by discussing the huge mass of additional suppositions, conjectures, and probabilities, respecting the first discovery of this country, with which unhappy historians overload themselves, in their endeavors to satisfy the doubts of an incredulous world. It is painful to see these laborious wights panting, and toiling, and sweating under an enormous burden, at the very outset of their works, which, on being opened, turns out to be nothing but a mighty bundle of straw. As, however, by unwearied assiduity, they seem to have established the fact, to the satisfaction of all the world, that this country *has been discovered*, I shall avail myself of their useful labors to be extremely brief upon this point.

I shall not, therefore, stop to inquire, whether America was first discovered by a wandering vessel of that celebrated Phœnician fleet, which, according to Herodotus, circumnavigated Africa; or by that Carthaginian expedition, which Pliny, the naturalist, informs us, discovered the Canary Islands; or whether it was settled by a temporary colony from Tyre, as hinted by Aristotle and Seneca. I shall neither inquire whether it was first discovered by the Chinese, as Vossius with great shrewdness advances; nor by the Norwegians in 1002, under Biorn; nor by Behem, the German navigator, as Mr. Otto has endeavored to prove to the savants of the learned city of Philadelphia.

Nor shall I investigate the more modern claims of the Welsh, founded on the voyage of Prince Madoc in the eleventh century, who having never returned, it has since been wisely concluded that he must have gone to America, and that for a plain reason—if he did not go there, where else could he have gone?—a question which most Socratically shuts out all farther dispute.

Laying aside, therefore, all the conjectures above mentioned, with a multitude of others, equally satisfactory, I shall take for granted the vulgar opinion, that America was discovered on the 12th of October, 1492, by Christoval Colon, a Genoese, who has been clumsily nicknamed Columbus, but for what reason I cannot discern. Of the voyages and adventures of this Colon, I shall say nothing, seeing that they are already sufficiently known; nor shall I undertake to prove that this country should have been called Colonia, after his name, that being notoriously self-evident.

Having thus happily got my readers on this side of the Atlantic, I picture them to myself, all impatience to enter upon the enjoyment of the land of promise, and in full expectation that I will immediately deliver it into their possession. But if I do, may I ever forfeit the reputation of a regular-bred historian! No—no—most curious and thrice learned readers, (for thrice learned ye are, if ye have read all that has gone before, and nine times learned shall ye be, if ye read that which comes after,) we have yet a world of work before us. Think you the first discoverers of this fair quarter of the globe had nothing to do but go on shore and find a country ready laid out and cultivated like a garden, wherein they might revel at their ease? No such thing—they had forests to cut down, underwood to grub up, marshes to drain, and savages to exterminate.

In like manner, I have sundry doubts to clear away, questions to resolve, and paradoxes to explain, before I permit you to range at random; but these difficulties once overcome, we shall be enabled to jog on right merrily through the rest of our history. Thus my work shall, in a manner, echo the nature of the subject, in the same manner as the sound of poetry has been found by certain shrewd critics to echo the sense—this being an improvement in history, which I claim the merit of having invented.

CHAPTER IV.

SHOWING THE GREAT DIFFICULTY PHILOSOPHERS HAVE HAD IN PEOPLING AMERICA—AND HOW THE ABORIGINES CAME TO BE BE-GOTTEN BY ACCIDENT—TO THE GREAT RELIEF AND SATISFACTION OF THE AUTHOR.

THE NEXT INQUIRY at which we arrive in the regular course of our history, is to ascertain, if possible, how this country was originally peopled—a point fruitful of incredible embarrassments; for unless we prove that the aborigines did absolutely come from somewhere, it will be immediately asserted in this age of scepticism that they did not come at all; and if they did not come at all, then was this country never populated—a conclusion perfectly agreeable to the rules of logic, but wholly irreconcilable to every feeling of humanity, inasmuch as it must syllogistically prove fatal to the innumerable aborigines of this populous region.

To avert so dire a sophism, and to rescue from logical annihilation so many millions of fellow-creatures, how many wings of geese have been plundered! what oceans of ink have been benevolently drained! and how many capacious heads of learned historians have been addled, and forever confounded! I pause with reverential awe, when I contemplate the ponderous tomes, in different languages, with which they have endeavored to solve this question, so important to the happiness of society, but so involved in clouds of impenetrable obscurity. Historian after historian has engaged in the endless circle of hypothetical argument, and after leading us a weary chase through octavos, quartos, and folios, has let us out at the end of his work just as wise as we were at the beginning. It was doubtless some philosophical wild-goose chase of the kind that made the old poet Macrobius rail in such a passion at curiosity, which he anathematizes most heartily, as "an irksome, agonizing care, a superstitious industry about unprofitable things, an itching humor to see what is not to be seen, and to be doing what signifies nothing when it is done." But to proceed:

Of the claims of the children of Noah to the original population of this country, I shall say nothing, as they have already been touched upon in my last chapter. The claimants next in celebrity, are the descendants of Abraham. Thus Christoval Colon (vulgarly called Columbus) when he first discovered the gold mines of Hispaniola, immediately concluded, with a shrewdness that would have done honor to a philosopher, that he had found the ancient Ophir, from whence Solomon procured the gold for embellishing the temple at Jerusalem; nay, Colon even imagined that he saw the remains of furnaces of veritable Hebraic construction, employed in refining the precious ore.

So golden a conjecture, tinctured with such fascinating extravagance, was too tempting not to be immediately snapped at by the gudgeons of learning; and accordingly, there were divers profound writers, ready to swear to its correctness, and to bring in their usual load of authorities, and wise surmises, wherewithal to prop it up. Vetablus and Robertus Stephens declared nothing could be more clear—Arius Montanus, without the least hesitation, asserts that Mexico was the true Ophir, and the Jews the early settlers of the country. While Possevin, Becan, and several other sagacious writers, lug in a *supposed* prophecy of the fourth book of Esdras, which being inserted in the mighty hypothesis, like the keystone of an arch, gives it, in their opinion, perpetual durability.

Scarce, however, have they completed their goodly superstructure, than in trudges a phalanx of opposite authors, with Hans de Laet, the great Dutchman, at their head, and at one blow tumbles the whole fabric about their ears. Hans, in fact, contradicts outright all the Israelitish claims to the first settlement of this country, attributing all those equivocal symptoms, and traces of Christianity and Judaism, which have been said to be found in divers provinces of the new world, to the *Devil*, who has always affected to counterfeit the worship of the true deity. "A remark," says the knowing old Padre d'Acosta, "made by all good authors who have spoken of the religion of nations newly discovered, and founded besides on the authority of the *fathers of the church*."

Some writers again, among whom it is with great regret I am compelled to mention Lopez de Gomara, and Juan de Leri, insinuate that the Canaanites, being driven from the land of promise by the Jews, were seized with such a panic that they fled without looking behind them, until, stopping to take breath, they found themselves safe in America. As they brought neither their national language, manners, nor features with them, it is supposed they left them behind in the hurry of their flight—I cannot give my faith to this opinion.

I pass over the supposition of the learned Grotius, who being both an ambassador and a Dutchman to boot, is entitled to great respect; that North America was peopled by a strolling company of Norwegians, and that Peru was founded by a colony from China—Manco or Mango Capac, the first Incas, being himself a Chinese. Nor shall I more than barely mention, that Father Kircher ascribes the settlement of America to the Egyptians, Rudbeck to the Scandinavians, Charron to the Gauls, Juffredus Petri to a skating party from Friesland, Milius to the Celtæ, Marinocus the Sicilian to the Romans, Le Compte to the Phœnicians, Postel to the Moors, Martyn d'Angleria to the Abyssinians, together with the sage surmise of de Laet, that England, Ireland, and the Orcades may contend for that honor.

Nor will I bestow any more attention or credit to the idea that America is the fairy region of Zipangri, described by that dreaming traveller, Marco Polo, the Venetian; or that it comprises the visionary island of Atlantis, described by Plato. Neither will I stop to investigate that heathenish assertion of Paracelsus, that each hemisphere of the globe was originally furnished with an Adam and Eve—or the more flattering opinion of Dr. Romayne, supported by many nameless authorities, that Adam was of the Indian race—or the startling conjecture of Buffon, Helvetius, and Darwin, so highly honorable to mankind, that the whole human species is accidentally descended from a remarkable family of monkeys!

This last conjecture, I must own, came upon me very suddenly and very ungraciously. I have often beheld the clown in a pantomime, while gazing in stupid wonder at the extravagant gambols of a harlequin, all at once electrified by a sudden stroke of the wooden sword across his shoulders. Little did I think at such times, that it would ever fall to my lot to be treated with equal discourtesy; and that while I was quietly beholding these grave philosophers, emulating the eccentric transformations of the hero of pantomime, they would on a sudden turn upon me and my readers, and with one hypothetical flourish metamorphose us into beasts! I determined from that moment not to burn my fingers with any more of their theories, but content myself with detailing the different methods by which they transported the descendants of these ancient and respectable monkeys to this great field of theoretical warfare.

This was done either by migrations by land or transmigrations by water. Thus, Padre Joseph d'Acosta enumerates three passages by land—first by the north of Europe, secondly by the north of Asia, and thirdly by regions southward of the straits of Magellan. The learned Grotius marches his Norwegians by a pleasant route across frozen rivers and arms of the sea, through Iceland, Greenland, Estotiland, and Naremberga: and various writers, among whom are Angleria, De Hornn, and Buffon, anxious for the accommodation of these travellers, have fastened the two continents together by a strong chain of deductions—by which means they could pass over dry-shod. But should even this fail, Pinkerton, that industrious old gentleman who compiles books and manufactures geographies, has constructed a natural bridge of ice, from continent to continent, at the distance of four or five miles from Behring's straits —for which he is entitled to the grateful thanks of all the wandering aborigines who ever did or ever will pass over it.

It is an evil much to be lamented, that none of the worthy writers above quoted could ever commence his work, without immediately declaring hostilities against every writer who had treated of the same subject. In this particular, authors may be compared to a certain sagacious bird, which, in building its nest, is sure to pull to pieces the nests of all the birds in its neighborhood. This unhappy propensity tends grievously to impede the progress of sound knowledge. Theories are at best but brittle productions, and when once committed to the stream, they should take care that, like the notable pots which were fellow-voyagers, they do not crack each other.

My chief surprise is, that among the many writers I have noticed, no one has attempted to prove that this country was peopled from the moon—or that the first inhabitants floated hither on islands of ice, as white bears cruise about the northern oceans—or that they were conveyed hither by balloons, as modern aeronauts pass from Dover to Calais—or by witchcraft, as Simon Magus posted among the stars—or after the manner of the renowned Scythian Abaris, who, like the New England witches on full-blooded broomsticks, made most unheard-of journeys on the back of a golden arrow, given him by the Hyperborean Apollo.

But there is still one mode left by which this country could have been peopled, which I have reserved for the last, because I consider it worth all the rest: it is—*by accident!* Speaking of the islands of Solomon, New Guinea, and New Holland, the profound father Charlevoix observes, "in fine, all these countries are peopled, and *it is possible* some have been so *by accident.* Now if it could have happened in that manner, why might it not have been at the *same time,* and by the *same means,* with *the other* parts of the globe?" This ingenious mode of deducing certain conclusions from possible premises, is an improvement in syllogistic skill, and proves the good father superior even to Archimedes, for he can turn the world without any thing to rest his lever upon. It is only surpassed by the dexterity with which the sturdy old Jesuit, in another place, cuts the gordian knot—"Nothing," says he, "is more easy. The inhabitants of both hemispheres are certainly the descendants of the same father. The common father of mankind received an express order from Heaven to people the world, and *accordingly it has been peopled.* To bring this about, it was necessary to overcome all difficulties in the way, *and they have also been overcome!*" Pious logician! How does he put all the herd of laborious theorists to the blush, by explaining, in five words, what it has cost them volumes to prove they knew nothing about.

From all the authorities here quoted, and a variety of others which I have consulted, but which are omitted through fear of fatiguing the unlearned reader—I can only draw the following conclusions, which luckily, however, are sufficient for my purpose—First, that this part of the world has actually *been peopled,* (Q. E. D.,) to support which we have living proofs in the numerous tribes of Indians that inhabit it. Secondly, that it has been peopled in five hundred different ways, as proved by a cloud of authors, who, from the positiveness of their assertions, seem to have been eye-witnesses to the fact. Thirdly, that the people of this country had a *variety of fathers,* which, as it may not be thought much to their credit by the common run of readers, the less we say on the subject the better. The question, therefore, I trust, is forever at rest.

CHAPTER V.

In Which the Author Puts a Mighty Question to the Rout by the Assistance of the Man in the Moon—Which Not Only Delivers Thousands of People from Great Embarrassment, but Likewise Concludes this Introductory Book.

The writer of a history may, in some respects, be likened unto an adventurous knight, who having undertaken a perilous enterprise, by way of establishing his fame, feels bound, in honor and chivalry, to turn back for no difficulty nor hardship, and never to shrink or quail, whatever enemy he may encounter. Under this impression, I resolutely draw my pen, and fall to, with might and main, at those doughty questions and subtle paradoxes, which, like fiery dragons and bloody giants, beset the entrance to my history, and would fain repulse me from the very threshold. And at this moment a gigantic question has started up, which I must needs take by the beard and utterly subdue, before I can advance another step in my historic undertaking; but I trust this will be the last adversary I shall have to contend with, and that in the next book I shall be enabled to conduct my readers in triumph into the body of my work.

The question which has thus suddenly arisen, is, what right had the first discoverers of America to land and take possession of a country, without first gaining the consent of its inhabitants, or yielding them an adequate compensation for their territory?—a question which has withstood many fierce assaults, and has given much distress of mind to multitudes of kind-hearted folk. And, indeed, until it be totally vanquished, and put to rest, the worthy people of America can by no means enjoy the soil they inhabit, with clear right and title, and quiet, unsullied consciences.

The first source of right, by which property is acquired in a country, is discovery. For as all mankind have an equal right to any thing which has never before been appropriated, so any nation that discovers an uninhabited country, and takes possession thereof, is considered as enjoying full property, and absolute, unquestionable empire therein.[1]

This proposition being admitted, it follows clearly that the Europeans who first visited America were the real discoverers of the same; nothing being necessary to the establishment of this fact, but simply to prove that it was totally uninhabited by man. This would, at first, appear to be a point of some difficulty, for it is well known that this quarter of the world abounded with certain animals that walked erect on two feet, had something of the human countenance, uttered certain unintelligible sounds very much like language; in short, had a marvellous resemblance to human beings. But the

[1]Grotius. Puffendorff, b. v. c. 4. Vattel, b. i. c. 18, &c.

zealous and enlightened fathers, who accompanied the discoverers, for the purpose of promoting the kingdom of heaven, by establishing fat monasteries and bishoprics on earth, soon cleared up this point, greatly to the satisfaction of his holiness the Pope, and of all Christian voyagers and discoverers.

They plainly proved, and as there were no Indian writers arose on the other side, the fact was considered as fully admitted and established, that the two-legged race of animals before mentioned were mere cannibals, detestable monsters, and many of them giants—which last description of vagrants have, since the times of Gog, Magog, and Goliath, been considered as outlaws, and have received no quarter in either history, chivalry, or song. Indeed, even the philosophic Bacon declared the Americans to be people proscribed by the laws of nature, inasmuch as they had a barbarous custom of sacrificing men, and feeding upon man's flesh.

Nor are these all the proofs of their utter barbarism; among many other writers of discernment, Ulloa tells us, "their imbecility is so visible, that one can hardly form an idea of them different from what one has of the brutes. Nothing disturbs the tranquillity of their souls, equally insensible to disasters and to prosperity. Though half naked, they are as contented as a monarch in his most splendid array. Fear makes no impression on them, and respect as little." All this is furthermore supported by the authority of M. Bouguer: "It is not easy," says he, "to describe the degree of their indifference for wealth and all its advantages. One does not well know what motives to propose to them, when one would persuade them to any service. It is vain to offer them money; they answer they are not hungry." And Vanegas confirms the whole, assuring us that "ambition they have none, and are more desirous of being thought strong than valiant. The objects of ambition with us—honor, fame, reputation, riches, posts, and distinctions—are unknown among them. So that this powerful spring of action, the cause of so much *seeming* good and *real* evil in the world, has no power over them. In a word, these unhappy mortals may be compared to children, in whom the development of reason is not completed."

Now all these peculiarities, although in the unenlightened states of Greece they would have entitled their possessors to immortal honor, as having reduced to practise those rigid and abstemious maxims, the mere talking about which acquired certain old Greeks the reputation of sages and philosophers;— yet, were they clearly proved in the present instance to betoken a most abject and brutified nature, totally beneath the human character. But the benevolent fathers, who had undertaken to turn these unhappy savages into dumb beasts, by dint of argument, advanced still stronger proofs; for as certain divines of the sixteenth century, and among the rest, Lullus, affirm— the Americans go naked, and have no beards!—"They have nothing," says Lullus, "of the reasonable animal, except the mask."—And even that mask was allowed to avail them but little, for it was soon found that they were of a hideous copper complexion—and being of a copper complexion, it was all the same as if they were negroes—and negroes are black, "and black," said the pious fathers, devoutly crossing themselves, "is the color of the Devil!" Therefore, so far from being able to own property, they had no right even to personal freedom—for liberty is too radiant a deity to inhabit such gloomy temples. All which circumstances plainly convinced the righteous followers of Cortes and Pizarro, that these miscreants had no title to the soil that they infested—that they were a perverse, illiterate, dumb, beardless, black-seed— mere wild beasts of the forests, and, like them, should either be subdued or exterminated.

From the foregoing arguments, therefore, and a variety of others equally conclusive, which I forbear to enumerate, it is clearly evident that this fair quarter of the globe, when first visited by Europeans, was a howling wilderness, inhabited by nothing but wild beasts, and that the transatlantic visitors acquired an incontrovertible property therein, by the *right of discovery*.

This right being fully established, we now come to the next, which is the right acquired by *cultivation*. "The cultivation of the soil," we are told, "is an obligation imposed by nature on mankind. The whole world is appointed for the nourishment of its inhabitants; but it would be incapable of doing it, was it uncultivated. Every nation is then obliged by the law of nature to cultivate the ground that has fallen to its share. Those people, like the ancient Germans and modern Tartars, who, having fertile countries, disdain to cultivate the earth, and choose to live by rapine, are wanting to themselves, and *deserve to be exterminated as savage and pernicious beasts*."[2]

Now it is notorious, that the savages knew nothing of agriculture, when first discovered by the Europeans, but lived a most vagabond, disorderly, unrighteous life,—rambling from place to place, and prodigally rioting upon the spontaneous luxuries of nature, without tasking her generosity to yield them any thing more; whereas it has been most unquestionably shown, that Heaven intended the earth should be ploughed and sown, and manured, and laid out into cities, and towns, and farms, and country-seats, and pleasure grounds, and public gardens, all which the Indians knew nothing about— therefore, they did not improve the talents Providence had bestowed on them—therefore, they were careless stewards—therefore, they had no right to the soil—therefore, they deserved to be exterminated.

It is true, the savages might plead that they drew all the benefits from the land which their simple wants required—they found plenty of game to hunt, which, together with the roots and uncultivated fruits of the earth, furnished a sufficient variety for their frugal repasts;—and that as Heaven merely designed the earth to form the abode, and satisfy the wants of man; so long as those purposes were answered, the will of Heaven was accomplished. —But this only proves how undeserving they were of the blessings around them—they were so much the more savages, for not having more wants; for knowledge is in some degree an increase of desires, and it is this superiority, both in the number and magnitude of his desires, that distinguishes the man from the beast. Therefore, the Indians, in not having more wants, were very unreasonable animals; and it was but just that they should make way for

[2]Vattel, b. i. ch. 17.

the Europeans, who had a thousand wants to their one, and, therefore, would turn the earth to more account, and by cultivating it, more truly fulfil the will of Heaven. Besides—Grotius and Lauterbach, and Puffendorff, and Titius, and many wise men beside, who have considered the matter properly, have determined that the property of a country cannot be acquired by hunting, cutting wood, or drawing water in it—nothing but precise demarcation of limits, and the intention of cultivation, can establish the possession. Now, as the savages (probably from never having read the authors above quoted) had never complied with any of these necessary forms, it plainly follows that they had no right to the soil, but that it was completely at the disposal of the first comers, who had more knowledge, more wants, and more elegant, that is to say, artificial desires than themselves.

In entering upon a newly discovered, uncultivated country, therefore, the new comers were but taking possession of what, according to the aforesaid doctrine, was their own property—therefore, in opposing them, the savages were invading their just rights, infringing the immutable laws of Nature, and counteracting the will of Heaven—therefore, they were guilty of impiety, burglary, and trespass on the case—therefore, they were hardened offenders against God and man—therefore, they ought to be exterminated.

But a more irresistible right than either that I have mentioned, and one which will be the most readily admitted by my reader, provided he be blessed with bowels of charity and philanthropy, is the right acquired by civilization. All the world knows the lamentable state in which these poor savages were found—not only deficient in the comforts of life, but what is still worse, most piteously and unfortunately blind to the miseries of their situation. But no sooner did the benevolent inhabitants of Europe behold their sad condition, than they immediately went to work to ameliorate and improve it. They introduced among them rum, gin, brandy, and the other comforts of life—and it is astonishing to read how soon the poor savages learned to estimate those blessings—they likewise made known to them a thousand remedies, by which the most inveterate diseases are alleviated and healed; and that they might comprehend the benefits and enjoy the comforts of these medicines, they previously introduced among them the diseases which they were calculated to cure. By these and a variety of other methods was the condition of these poor savages wonderfully improved; they acquired a thousand wants, of which they had before been ignorant; and as he has most sources of happiness who has most wants to be gratified, they were doubtlessly rendered a much happier race of beings.

But the most important branch of civilization, and which has most strenuously been extolled by the zealous and pious fathers of the Romish Church, is the introduction of the Christian faith. It was truly a sight that might well inspire horror, to behold these savages tumbling among the dark mountains of paganism, and guilty of the most horrible ignorance of religion. It is true, they neither stole nor defrauded; they were sober, frugal, continent, and faithful to their word; but though they acted right habitually, it was all in vain, unless they acted so from precept. The new comers, therefore, used

every method to induce them to embrace and practise the true religion—
except indeed that of setting them the example.

But notwithstanding all these complicated labors for their good, such was
the unparalleled obstinacy of these stubborn wretches, that they ungratefully
refused to acknowledge the strangers as their benefactors, and persisted in
disbelieving the doctrines they endeavored to inculcate; most insolently alleging, that from their conduct, the advocates of Christianity did not seem
to believe in it themselves. Was not this too much for human patience?—
would not one suppose that the benign visitants from Europe, provoked at
their incredulity, and discouraged by their stiff-necked obstinacy, would
forever have abandoned their shores, and consigned them to their original
ignorance and misery?—But no—so zealous were they to effect the temporal
comfort and eternal salvation of these pagan infidels, that they even proceeded
from the milder means of persuasion, to the more painful and troublesome
one of persecution, let loose among them whole troops of fiery monks and
furious bloodhounds—purified them by fire and sword, by stake and fagot;
in consequence of which indefatigable measures, the cause of Christian love
and charity was so rapidly advanced, that in a few years not one-fifth of the
number of unbelievers existed in South America that were found there at
the time of its discovery.

What stronger right need the European settlers advance to the country
than this? Have not whole nations of uninformed savages been made acquainted
with a thousand imperious wants and indispensable comforts, of which they
were before wholly ignorant? Have they not been literally hunted and smoked
out of the dens and lurking-places of ignorance and infidelity, and absolutely
scourged into the right path? Have not the temporal things, the vain baubles
and filthy lucre of this world, which were too apt to engage their worldly
and selfish thoughts, been benevolently taken from them? and have they
not, instead thereof, been taught to set their affections on things above?—
And finally, to use the words of a reverend Spanish father, in a letter to his
superior in Spain—"Can any one have the presumption to say, that these
savage pagans have yielded any thing more than an inconsiderable recompense
to their benefactors, in surrendering to them a little pitiful tract of this dirty
sublunary planet, in exchange for a glorious inheritance in the kingdom of
heaven?"

Here, then, are three complete and undeniable sources of right established,
any one of which was more than ample to establish a property in the newly
discovered regions of America. Now, so it has happened in certain parts
of this delightful quarter of the globe, that the right of discovery has been
so strenuously asserted—the influence of cultivation so industriously extended,
and the progress of salvation and civilization so zealously prosecuted, that,
what with their attendant wars, persecutions, oppressions, diseases, and other
partial evils that often hang on the skirts of great benefits—the savage aborigines
have, somehow or another, been utterly annihilated—and this all at once
brings me to a fourth right, which is worth all the others put together.—
For the original claimants to the soil being all dead and buried, and no one

remaining to inherit or dispute the soil, the Spaniards, as the next immediate occupants, entered upon the possession as clearly as the hangman succeeds to the clothes of the malefactor—and as they have Blackstone,[3] and all the learned expounders of the law on their side, they may set all actions of ejectment at defiance—and this last right may be entitled the RIGHT BY EXTERMINATION, or in other words, the RIGHT BY GUNPOWDER.

But lest any scruples of conscience should remain on this head, and to settle the question of right forever, his holiness Pope Alexander VI. issued a bull, by which he generously granted the newly discovered quarter of the globe to the Spaniards and Portuguese; who, thus having law and gospel on their side, and being inflamed with great spiritual zeal, showed the pagan savages neither favor nor affection, but prosecuted the work of discovery, colonization, civilization, and extermination, with ten times more fury than ever.

Thus were the European worthies who first discovered America, clearly entitled to the soil; and not only entitled to the soil, but likewise to the eternal thanks of these infidel savages, for having come so far, endured so many perils by sea and land, and taken such unwearied pains, for no other purpose but to improve their forlorn, uncivilized, and heathenish condition— for having made them acquainted with the comforts of life; for having introduced among them the light of religion; and, finally, for having hurried them out of the world, to enjoy its reward!

But as argument is never so well understood by us selfish mortals as when it comes home to ourselves, and as I am particularly anxious that this question should be put to rest forever, I will suppose a parallel case, by way of arousing the candid attention of my readers.

Let us suppose, then, that the inhabitants of the moon, by astonishing advancement in science, and by profound insight into that lunar philosophy, the mere flickerings of which have of late years dazzled the feeble optics, and addled the shallow brains of the good people of our globe—let us suppose, I say, that the inhabitants of the moon, by these means, had arrived at such a command of their *energies*, such an enviable state of *perfectibility*, as to control the elements, and navigate the boundless regions of space. Let us suppose a roving crew of these soaring philosophers, in the course of an aerial voyage of discovery among the stars, should chance to alight upon this outlandish planet.

And here I beg my readers will not have the uncharitableness to smile, as is too frequently the fault of volatile readers, when perusing the grave speculations of philosophers. I am far from indulging in any sportive vein at present; nor is the supposition I have been making so wild as many may deem it. It has long been a very serious and anxious question with me, and many a time and oft, in the course of my overwhelming cares and contrivances for the welfare and protection of this my native planet, have I lain awake whole nights debating in my mind, whether it were most probable we should first discover and civilize the moon, or the moon discover and civilize our globe.

[3]Bl. Com. b. ii. c. i.

Neither would the prodigy of sailing in the air and cruising among the stars be a whit more astonishing and incomprehensible to us, than was the European mystery of navigating floating castles, through the world of waters, to the simple natives. We have already discovered the art of coasting along the aerial shores of our planet, by means of balloons, as the savages had of venturing along their sea-coasts in canoes; and the disparity between the former, and the aerial vehicles of the philosophers from the moon, might not be greater than that between the bark canoes of the savages and the mighty ships of their discoverers. I might here pursue an endless chain of similar speculations; but as they would be unimportant to my subject, I abandon them to my reader, particularly if he be a philosopher, as matters well worthy of his attentive consideration.

To return then to my supposition—let us suppose that the aerial visitants I have mentioned, possessed of vastly superior knowledge to ourselves; that is to say, possessed of superior knowledge in the art of extermination—riding on hippogriffs—defended with impenetrable armor—armed with concentrated sunbeams, and provided with vast engines, to hurl enormous moon-stones: in short, let us suppose them, if our vanity will permit the supposition, as superior to us in knowledge, and consequently in power, as the Europeans were to the Indians, when they first discovered them. All this is very possible; it is only our self-sufficiency that makes us think otherwise; and I warrant the poor savages, before they had any knowledge of the white men, armed in all the terrors of glittering steel and tremendous gunpowder, were as perfectly convinced that they themselves were the wisest, the most virtuous, powerful, and perfect of created beings, as are at this present moment the lordly inhabitants of Old England, the volatile populace of France, or even the self-satisfied citizens of this most enlightened republic.

Let us suppose, moreover, that the aerial voyagers, finding this planet to be nothing but a howling wilderness, inhabited by us, poor savages and wild beasts, shall take formal possession of it in the name of his most gracious and philosophic excellency, the man in the moon. Finding, however, that their numbers are incompetent to hold it in complete subjection, on account of the ferocious barbarity of its inhabitants, they shall take our worthy President, the King of England, the Emperor of Hayti, the mighty Bonaparte, and the great King of Bantam, and returning to their native planet, shall carry them to court, as were the Indian chiefs led about as spectacles in the courts of Europe.

Then making such obeisance as the etiquette of the court requires, they shall address the puissant man in the moon, in, as near as I can conjecture, the following terms:

"Most serene and mighty Potentate, whose dominions extend as far as eye can reach, who rideth on the Great Bear, useth the sun as a looking-glass, and maintaineth unrivalled control over tides, madmen, and sea-crabs: We, thy liege subjects, have just returned from a voyage of discovery, in the course of which we have landed and taken possession of that obscure little dirty planet which thou beholdest rolling at a distance. The five uncouth monsters which we have brought into this august presence were once very important chiefs among their fellow-savages, who are a race of beings totally destitute of the common attributes of humanity; and differing in every thing from the inhabitants of the moon, inasmuch as they carry their heads upon their shoulders, instead of under their arms—have two eyes instead of one—are utterly destitute of tails, and of a variety of unseemly complexions, particularly of horrible whiteness—instead of pea-green.

"We have, moreover, found these miserable savages sunk into a state of the utmost ignorance and depravity, every man shamelessly living with his own wife, and rearing his own children, instead of indulging in that community of wives enjoined by the law of nature, as expounded by the philosophers of the moon. In a word, they have scarcely a gleam of true philosophy among them, but are, in fact, utter heretics, ignoramuses, and barbarians. Taking compassion, therefore, on the sad condition of these sublunary wretches, we have endeavored, while we remained on their planet, to introduce among them the light of reason—and the comforts of the moon. We have treated them to mouthfuls of moonshine, and draughts of nitrous oxide, which they swallowed with incredible voracity, particularly the females; and we have likewise endeavored to instill into them the precepts of lunar philosophy. We have insisted upon their renouncing the contemptible shackles of religion and common sense, and adoring the profound, omnipotent, and all-perfect energy, and the ecstatic, immutable, immovable perfection. But such was the unparalleled obstinacy of these wretched savages, that they persisted in cleaving to their wives, and adhering to their religion, and absolutely set at naught the sublime doctrines of the moon—nay, among other abominable heresies, they even went so far as blasphemously to declare, that this ineffable planet was made of nothing more nor less than green cheese!"

At these words, the great man in the moon (being a very profound philosopher) shall fall into a terrible passion, and possessing equal authority over things that do not belong to him, as did whilom his holiness the Pope, shall forthwith issue a formidable bull, specifying, "That, whereas a certain crew of Lunatics have lately discovered, and taken possession of, a newly-discovered planet called *the earth*—and that whereas it is inhabited by none but a race of two-legged animals, that carry their heads on their shoulders instead of under their arms; cannot talk the lunatic language; have two eyes instead of one; are destitute of tails, and of a horrible whiteness, instead of pea-green—therefore, and for a variety of other excellent reasons, they are considered incapable of possessing any property in the planet they infest, and the right and title to it is confirmed to its original discoverers.—And furthermore, the colonists who are now about to depart to the aforesaid planet are authorized and commanded to use every means to convert these infidel savages from the darkness of Christianity, and make them thorough and absolute Lunatics."

In consequence of this benevolent bull, our philosophic benefactors go to work with hearty zeal. They seize upon our fertile territories, scourge us from our rightful possessions, relieve us from our wives, and when we are unreasonable enough to complain, they will turn upon us, and say: "Miserable barbarians! ungrateful wretches! have we not come thousands of miles to improve your worthless planet? have we not fed you with moonshine? have we not intoxicated you with nitrous oxide? does not our moon give you light every night, and have you the baseness to murmur, when we claim a pitiful return for all these benefits? But finding that we not only persist in absolute contempt of their reasoning and disbelief in their philosophy, but even go so far as daringly to defend our property, their patience shall be exhausted, and they shall resort to their superior powers of argument; hunt us with hippogriffs, transfix us with concentrated sun-beams, demolish our cities with moon-stones; until having, by main force, converted us to the true faith, they shall graciously permit us to exist in the torrid deserts of Arabia, or the frozen regions of Lapland, there to enjoy the blessings of civilization and the charms of lunar philosophy, in much the same manner as the reformed and enlightened savages of this country are kindly suffered to inhabit the inhospitable forests of the north, or the impenetrable wildernesses of South America.

Thus, I hope, I have clearly proved, and strikingly illustrated, the right of the early colonists to the possession of this country; and thus is this gigantic question completely vanquished: so having manfully surmounted all obstacles, and subdued all opposition, what remains but that I should forthwith conduct my readers into the city which we have been so long in a manner besieging? But hold—before I proceed another step, I must pause to take breath, and recover from the excessive fatigue I have undergone, in preparing to begin this most accurate of histories. And in this I do but imitate the example of a renowned Dutch tumbler of antiquity, who took a start of three miles for the purpose of jumping over a hill, but having run himself out of breath by the time he reached the foot, sat himself quietly down for a few moments to blow, and then walked over it at his leisure.

BOOK II.

TREATING OF THE FIRST SETTLEMENT OF THE PROVINCE OF NIEW NEDERLANDTS.

CHAPTER I.

IN WHICH ARE CONTAINED DIVERS REASONS WHY A MAN SHOULD NOT WRITE IN A HURRY. ALSO, OF MASTER HENDRICK HUDSON, HIS DISCOVERY OF A STRANGE COUNTRY—AND HOW HE WAS MAGNIFICENTLY REWARDED BY THE MUNIFICENCE OF THEIR HIGH MIGHTINESSES.

MY GREAT-GRANDFATHER, by the mother's side, Hermanus Van Clattercop, when employed to build the large stone church at Rotterdam, which stands about three hundred yards to your left after you turn off from the Boomkeys, and which is so conveniently constructed, that all the zealous Christians of Rotterdam prefer sleeping through a sermon there to any other church in the city—my great-grandfather, I say, when employed to build that famous church, did, in the first place, send to Delft for a box of long pipes; then, having purchased a new spitting-box and a hundred weight of the best Virginia, he sat himself down, and did nothing for the space of three months but smoke most laboriously. Then did he spend full three months more in trudging on foot, and voyaging in trekschuit, from Rotterdam to Amsterdam—to Delft— to Haerlem—to Leyden—to the Hague, knocking his head and breaking his pipe against every church in his road. Then did he advance gradually nearer and nearer to Rotterdam, until he came in full sight of the identical spot whereon the church was to be built. Then did he spend three months longer in walking round it and round it, contemplating it, first from one point of view, and then from another—now would he be paddled by it on the canal— now would he peep at it through a telescope, from the other side of the Meuse, and now would he take a bird's-eye glance at it, from the top of one of those gigantic windmills which protect the gates of the city. The good folks of the place were on the tiptoe of expectation and impatience—notwithstanding all the turmoil of my great-grandfather, not a symptom of the church was yet to be seen; they even began to fear it would never be brought into the world, but that its great projector would lie down and die in labor of the mighty plan he had conceived. At length, having occupied twelve good months in puffing and paddling, and talking and walking—having travelled over all Holland, and even taken a peep into France and Germany— having smoked five hundred and ninety-nine pipes, and three hundred weight of the best Virginia tobacco—my great-grandfather gathered together all that knowing and industrious class of citizens who prefer attending to anybody's business sooner than their own, and having pulled off his coat and five pair of breeches, he advanced sturdily up, and laid the corner-stone of the church, in the presence of the whole multitude—just at the commencement of the thirteenth month.

In a similar manner, and with the example of my worthy ancestor full before my eyes, have I proceeded in writing this most authentic history. The honest Rotterdamers no doubt thought my great-grandfather was doing nothing at all to the purpose, while he was making such a world of prefatory bustle, about the building of his church—and many of the ingenious inhabitants of this fair city will unquestionably suppose that all the preliminary chapters, with the discovery, population, and final settlement of America, were totally irrelevant and superfluous—and that the main business, the history of New York, is not a jot more advanced than if I had never taken up my pen. Never were wise people more mistaken in their conjectures; in consequence of going to work slowly and deliberately, the church came out of my grandfather's hands one of the most sumptuous, goodly, and glorious edifices in the known world—excepting that, like our magnificent Capitol at Washington, it was begun on so grand a scale that the good folks could not afford to finish more than the wing of it. So, likewise, I trust, if ever I am able to finish this work on the plan I have commenced, (of which, in simple truth, I sometimes have my doubts,) it will be found that I have pursued the latest rules of my art, as exemplified in the writings of all the great American historians, and wrought a very large history out of a small subject—which nowadays is considered one of the great triumphs of historic skill. To proceed, then, with the thread of my story.

In the ever-memorable year of our Lord, 1609, on a Saturday morning, the five-and-twentieth day of March, old style, did that "worthy and irre-coverable discoverer, (as he has justly been called,) Master Henry Hudson," set sail from Holland in a stout vessel called the Half Moon, being employed by the Dutch East India Company, to seek a north-west passage to China.

Henry (or, as the Dutch historians call him, Hendrick) Hudson, was a sea-faring man of renown, who had learned to smoke tobacco under Sir Walter Raleigh, and is said to have been the first to introduce it into Holland, which gained him much popularity in that country, and caused him to find great favor in the eyes of their High Mightinesses, the Lords States General, and also of the honorable West India Company. He was a short, square, brawny old gentleman, with a double chin, a mastiff mouth, and a broad copper nose, which was supposed in those days to have acquired its fiery hue from the constant neighborhood of his tobacco-pipe.

He wore a true Andrea Ferrara, tucked in a leathern belt, and a commodore's cocked hat on one side of his head. He was remarkable for always jerking up his breeches when he gave out his orders; and his voice sounded not unlike the brattling of a tin trumpet—owing to the number of hard north-westers which he had swallowed in the course of his sea-faring.

Such was Hendrick Hudson, of whom we have heard so much, and know so little: and I have been thus particular in his description, for the benefit of modern painters and statuaries, that they may represent him as he was; and not, according to their common custom with modern heroes, make him look like Cæsar, or Marcus Aurelius, or the Apollo of Belvidere.

As chief mate and favorite companion, the commodore chose master Robert Juet, of Limehouse, in England. By some his name has been spelled *Chewit*, and ascribed to the circumstance of his having been the first man that ever chewed tobacco; but this I believe to be a mere flippancy; more especially as certain of his progeny are living at this day, who write their names Juet. He was an old comrade and early schoolmate of the great Hudson, with whom he had often played truant and sailed chip boats in a neighboring pond, when they were little boys—from whence it is said the commodore first derived his bias towards a sea-faring life. Certain it is, that the old people about Limehouse declared Robert Juet to be an unlucky urchin, prone to mischief, that would one day or other come to the gallows.

He grew up as boys of that kind often grow up, a rambling, heedless varlet, tossed about in all quarters of the world—meeting with more perils and wonders than did Sindbad the Sailor, without growing a whit more wise, prudent, or ill-natured. Under every misfortune, he comforted himself with a quid of tobacco, and the truly philosophic maxim, that "it will be all the same thing a hundred years hence." He was skilled in the art of carving anchors and true-lovers' knots on the bulk-heads and quarter-railings, and was considered a great wit on board ship, in consequence of his playing pranks on everybody around, and now and then even making a wry face at old Hendrick, when his back was turned.

To this universal genius are we indebted for many particulars concerning this voyage; of which he wrote a history, at the request of the commodore, who had an unconquerable aversion to writing himself, from having received so many floggings about it when at school. To supply the deficiencies of master Juet's journal, which is written with true log-book brevity, I have availed myself of divers family traditions, handed down from my great-great-grandfather, who accompanied the expedition in the capacity of cabin-boy.

From all that I can learn, few incidents worthy of remark happened in the voyage; and it mortifies me exceedingly that I have to admit so noted an expedition into my work, without making any more of it.

Suffice it to say, the voyage was prosperous and tranquil—the crew being a patient people, much given to slumber and vacuity, and but little troubled with the disease of thinking—a malady of the mind, which is the sure breeder of discontent. Hudson had laid in abundance of gin and sourkrout, and every man was allowed to sleep quietly at his post unless the wind blew. True it is, some slight disaffection was shown on two or three occasions, at certain unreasonable conduct of Commodore Hudson. Thus, for instance, he forbore to shorten sail when the wind was light, and the weather serene, which was considered, among the most experienced Dutch seamen, as certain *weather-breeders*, or prognostics, that the weather would change for the worse. He acted, moreover, in direct contradiction to that ancient and sage rule of the Dutch navigators, who always took in sail at night—put the helm a-port, and turned in—by which precaution they had a good night's rest—were sure of knowing where they were the next morning, and stood but little chance of running down a continent in the dark. He likewise prohibited the seamen from wearing more than five jackets and six pair of breeches, under pretence of rendering them more alert; and no man was permitted to go aloft, and hand in sails with a pipe in his mouth, as is the invariable Dutch custom at the present day. All these grievances, though they might ruffle for a moment the constitutional tranquillity of the honest Dutch tars, made but transient impression; they eat hugely, drank profusely, and slept immeasurably, and being under the especial guidance of Providence, the ship was safely conducted to the coast of America; where, after sundry unimportant touchings and standings off and on, she at length, on the fourth day of September, entered that majestic bay, which at this day expands its ample bosom before the city of New York, and which had never before been visited by any European.[1]

[1]True it is—and I am not ignorant of the fact, that in a certain apocryphal book of voyages, compiled by one Hakluyt, is to be found a letter written to Francis the First, by one Giovanne, or John Verazzani, on which some writers are inclined to found a belief that this delightful bay had been visited nearly a century previous to the voyage

It has been traditionary in our family, that when the great navigator was first blessed with a view of this enchanting island, he was observed, for the first and only time in his life, to exhibit strong symptoms of astonishment and admiration. He is said to have turned to master Juet, and uttered these remarkable words, while he pointed towards this paradise of the new world —"See! there!"—and thereupon, as was always his way when he was uncommonly pleased, he did puff out such clouds of dense tobacco-smoke, that in one minute the vessel was out of sight of land, and master Juet was fain to wait until the winds dispersed this impenetrable fog.

It was indeed—as my great-grandfather used to say—though in truth I never heard him, for he died, as might be expected, before I was born—"it was indeed a spot on which the eye might have revelled forever, in ever-new and never-ending beauties." The island of Manna-hata spread wide before them, like some sweet vision of fancy, or some fair creation of industrious magic. Its hills of smiling green swelled gently one above another, crowned with lofty trees of luxuriant growth; some pointing their tapering foliage towards the clouds, which were gloriously transparent; and others loaded with a verdant burden of clambering vines, bowing their branches to the earth, that was covered with flowers. On the gentle declivities of the hills were scattered, in gay profusion, the dog-wood, the sumach, and the wild brier, whose scarlet berries and white blossoms glowed brightly among the deep green of the surrounding foliage; and here and there a curling column of smoke rising from the little glens that opened along the shore, seemed to promise the weary voyagers a welcome at the hands of their fellow-creatures. As they stood gazing with entranced attention on the scene before them, a red man, crowned with feathers, issued from one of these glens, and after contemplating in silent wonder the gallant ship, as she sat like a stately swan swimming on a silver lake, sounded the war-whoop, and bounded into the

of the enterprising Hudson. Now this (albeit it has met with the countenance of certain very judicious and learned men) I hold in utter disbelief, and that for various good and substantial reasons: *First*, Because on strict examination it will be found, that the description given by this Verazzani applies about as well to the bay of New York as it does to my night-cap. *Secondly*, Because that this John Verazzani, for whom I already begin to feel a most bitter enmity, is a native of Florence: and everybody knows the crafty wiles of these losel Florentines, by which they filched away the laurels from the brows of the immortal Colon, (vulgarly called Columbus,) and bestowed them on their officious townsman, Amerigo Vespucci; and I make no doubt they are equally ready to rob the illustrious Hudson of the credit of discovering this beautiful island, adorned by the city of New York, and placing it beside their usurped discovery of South America. And, *thirdly,* I award my decision in favor of the pretensions of Hendrick Hudson, inasmuch as his expedition sailed from Holland, being truly and absolutely a Dutch enterprise—and though all the proofs in the world were introduced on the other side, I would set them at naught, as undeserving my attention. If these three reasons be not sufficient to satisfy every burgher of this ancient city—all I can say is, they are degenerate descendants from their venerable Dutch ancestors, and totally unworthy the trouble of convincing. Thus, therefore, the title of Hendrick Hudson to his renowned discovery is fully vindicated.

woods like a wild deer, to the utter astonishment of the phlegmatic Dutchmen, who had never heard such a noise, or witnessed such a caper, in their whole lives.

Of the transactions of our adventurers with the savages, and how the latter smoked copper pipes, and ate dried currants; how they brought great store of tobacco and oysters; how they shot one of the ship's crew, and how he was buried, I shall say nothing; being that I consider them unimportant to my history. After tarrying a few days in the bay, in order to refresh themselves after their sea-faring, our voyagers weighed anchor, to explore a mighty river which emptied into the bay. This river, it is said, was known among the savages by the name of the *Shatemuck;* though we are assured, in an excellent little history published in 1674, by John Josselyn, Gent., that it was called the *Mohegan,*[2] and master Richard Bloome, who wrote some time afterwards, asserts the same—so that I very much incline in favor of the opinion of these two honest gentlemen. Be this as it may, up this river did the adventurous Hendrick proceed, little doubting but it would turn out to be the much-looked-for passage to China!

The journal goes on to make mention of divers interviews between the crew and the natives, in the voyage up the river; but as they would be impertinent to my history, I shall pass over them in silence, except the following dry joke, played off by the old commodore and his school-fellow, Robert Juet, which does such vast credit to their experimental philosophy, that I cannot refrain from inserting it. "Our master and his mate determined to try some of the chiefe men of the countrey, whether they had any treacherie in them. So they tooke them downe into the cabin and gave them so much wine and aqua vitæ, that they were all merrie; and one of them had his wife with him, which sate so modestly, as any of our countrey women would do in a strange place. In the end one of them was drunke, which had been aboarde of our ship all the time that we had been there, and that was strange to them, for they could not tell how to take it."[3]

Having satisfied himself by this ingenious experiment, that the natives were an honest, social race of jolly roysters, who had no objection to a drinking bout, and were very merry in their cups, the old commodore chuckled hugely to himself, and thrusting a double quid of tobacco in his cheek, directed master Juet to have it carefully recorded, for the satisfaction of all the natural philosophers of the university of Leyden—which done, he proceeded on his voyage, with great self-complacency. After sailing, however, above an hundred miles up the river, he found the watery world around him began to grow more shallow and confined, the current more rapid, and perfectly fresh—phenomena not uncommon in the ascent of rivers, but which puzzled the honest Dutchmen prodigiously. A consultation was therefore called, and having deliberated full six hours, they were brought to a determination, by

[2] This river is likewise laid down in Ogilvy's map as Manhattan—Noordt—Montaigne and Mauritius river.

[3] Juet's Journ. Purch. Pil.

the ship's running aground—whereupon they unanimously concluded, that there was but little chance of getting to China in this direction. A boat, however, was despatched to explore higher up the river, which, on its return, confirmed the opinion—upon this the ship was warped off and put about, with great difficulty, being, like most of her sex, exceedingly hard to govern; and the adventurous Hudson, according to the account of my great-great-grandfather, returned down the river—with a prodigious flea in his ear!

Being satisfied that there was little likelihood of getting to China, unless, like the blind man, he returned from whence he set out, and took a fresh start, he forthwith recrossed the sea to Holland, where he was received with great welcome by the honorable East India Company, who were very much rejoiced to see him come back safe—with their ship; and at a large and respectable meeting of the first merchants and burgomasters of Amsterdam, it was unanimously determined, that as a munificent reward for the eminent services he had performed, and the important discovery he had made, the great river Mohegan should be called after his name!—and it continues to be called Hudson river unto this very day.

CHAPTER II.

CONTAINING AN ACCOUNT OF A MIGHTY ARK, WHICH FLOATED, UNDER
THE PROTECTION OF ST. NICHOLAS, FROM HOLLAND TO GIBBET ISLAND—
THE DESCENT OF THE STRANGE ANIMALS THEREFROM—A GREAT
VICTORY, AND A DESCRIPTION OF THE ANCIENT VILLAGE OF
COMMUNIPAW.

THE delectable accounts given by the great Hudson, and master Juet, of the country they had discovered, excited not a little talk and speculation among the good people of Holland. Letters-patent were granted by government to an association of merchants, called the West India Company, for the exclusive trade on Hudson river, on which they erected a trading house called Fort Aurania, or Orange, from whence did spring the great city of Albany. But I forbear to dwell on the various commercial and colonizing enterprises which took place; among which was that of Mynheer Adrian Block, who discovered and gave a name to Block Island, since famous for its cheese—and shall barely confine myself to that which gave birth to this renowned city.

It was some three or four years after the return of the immortal Hendrick, that a crew of honest, Low Dutch colonists set sail from the city of Amsterdam for the shores of America. It is an irreparable loss to history, and a great proof of the darkness of the age, and the lamentable neglect of the noble art of book-making, since so industriously cultivated by knowing sea-captains, and learned supercargoes, that an expedition so interesting and important in its results, should be passed over in utter silence. To my great-great-grandfather am I again indebted for the few facts I am enabled to give concerning it—he having once more embarked for this country, with a full determination, as he said, of ending his days here—and of begetting a race of Knickerbockers. that should rise to be great men in the land.

The ship in which these illustrious adventurers set sail was called the *Goede Vrouw*, or good woman, in compliment to the wife of the President of the West India Company, who was allowed by everybody (except her husband) to be a sweet-tempered lady—when not in liquor. It was in truth a most gallant vessel, of the most approved Dutch construction, and made by the ablest ship-carpenters of Amsterdam, who, it is well known, always model their ships after the fair forms of their country-women. Accordingly, it had one hundred feet in the beam, one hundred feet in the keel, and one hundred feet from the bottom of the stern-post to the tafferel. Like the beauteous model, who was declared to be the greatest belle in Amsterdam, it was full in the bows, with a pair of enormous cat-heads, a copper bottom, and, withal, a most prodigious poop!

The architect, who was somewhat of a religious man, far from decorating the ship with pagan idols, such as Jupiter, Neptune, or Hercules, (which heathenish abominations, I have no doubt, occasion the misfortunes and shipwreck of many a noble vessel,) he, I say, on the contrary, did laudably erect for a head, a goodly image of St. Nicholas, equipped with a low, broad-brimmed hat, a huge pair of Flemish trunk-hose, and a pipe that reached to the end of the bowsprit. Thus gallantly furnished, the stanch ship floated sideways, like a majestic goose, out of the harbor of the great city of Amsterdam, and all the bells, that were not otherwise engaged, rang a triple bobmajor on the joyful occasion.

My great-great-grandfather remarks, that the voyage was uncommonly prosperous, for, being under the especial care of the ever-revered St. Nicholas, the Goede Vrouw seemed to be endowed with qualities unknown to common vessels. Thus she made as much lee-way as head-way, could get along very nearly as fast with the wind a-head, as when it was a-poop—and was particularly great in a calm; in consequence of which singular advantages, she made out to accomplish her voyage in a very few months, and came to anchor at the mouth of the Hudson, a little to the east of Gibbet Island.

Here lifting up their eyes, they beheld, on what is at present called the Jersey shore, a small Indian village, pleasantly embowered in a grove of spreading elms, and the natives all collected on the beach, gazing in stupid admiration at the Goede Vrouw. A boat was immediately despatched to enter into a treaty with them, and approaching the shore, hailed them through a trumpet in the most friendly terms; but so horribly confounded were these poor savages at the tremendous and uncouth sound of the Low Dutch language, that they one and all took to their heels, and scampered over the Bergen hills; nor did they stop until they had buried themselves, head and ears, in the marshes on the other side, where they all miserably perished to a man—and their bones being collected and decently covered by the Tammany Society of that day, formed that singular mound called RATTLESNAKE HILL, which rises out of the centre of the salt marshes, a little to the east of the Newark Causeway.

Animated by this unlooked-for victory, our valiant heroes sprang ashore in triumph, took possession of the soil as conquerors in the name of their High Mightinesses, the Lords States General; and marching fearlessly forward, carried the village of COMMUNIPAW by storm, notwithstanding that it was vigorously defended by some half-a-score of old squaws and pappooses. On looking about them, they were so transported with the excellencies of the place, that they had very little doubt the blessed St. Nicholas had guided them thither, as the very spot whereon to settle their colony. The softness of the soil was wonderfully adapted to the driving of piles; the swamps and marshes around them afforded ample opportunities for the constructing of dikes and dams; the shallowness of the shore was peculiarly favorable to the building of docks—in a word, this spot abounded with all the requisites for the foundation of a great Dutch city. On making a faithful report, therefore, to the crew of the Goede Vrouw, they one and all determined that this was the destined end of their voyage. Accordingly they descended from the Goede Vrouw, men, women, and children, in goodly groups, as did the animals of yore from the ark, and formed themselves into a thriving settlement, which they called by the Indian name COMMUNIPAW.

As all the world is doubtless perfectly acquainted with Communipaw, it may seem somewhat superfluous to treat of it in the present work; but my readers will please to recollect, that notwithstanding it is my chief desire to satisfy the present age, yet I write likewise for posterity, and have to consult the understanding and curiosity of some half a score of centuries yet to come; by which time, perhaps, were it not for this invaluable history, the great Communipaw, like Babylon, Carthage, Nineveh, and other great cities, might be perfectly extinct—sunk and forgotten in its own mud—its inhabitants turned into oysters,[1] and even its situation a fertile subject of learned controversy and hard-headed investigation among indefatigable historians. Let me then piously rescue from oblivion the humble relics of a place which was the egg from whence was hatched the mighty city of New York!

Communipaw is at present but a small village pleasantly situated, among rural scenery, on that beauteous part of the Jersey shore which was known in ancient legends by the name of Pavonia,[2] and commands a grand prospect of the superb bay of New York. It is within but half an hour's sail of the latter place, provided you have a fair wind, and may be distinctly seen from the city. Nay, it is a well-known fact, which I can testify from my own experience, that on a clear still summer evening, you may hear, from the Battery of New York, the obstreperous peals of broad-mouthed laughter of the Dutch negroes at Communipaw, who, like most other negroes, are famous for their risible powers. This is peculiarly the case on Sunday evenings, when, it is remarked by an ingenious and observant philosopher, who has made great discoveries in the neighborhood of this city, that they always laugh loudest—

[1] Men by inaction degenerate into oysters.—*Kaimes*.

[2] Pavonia, in the ancient maps, is given to a tract of country extending from about Hoboken to Amboy.

which he attributes to the circumstance of their having their holiday clothes on.

These negroes, in fact, like the monks in the dark ages, engross all the knowledge of the place, and being infinitely more adventurous and more knowing than their masters, carry on all the foreign trade; making frequent voyages to town in canoes loaded with oysters, buttermilk, and cabbages. They are great astrologers, predicting the different changes of weather almost as accurately as an almanac—they are moreover exquisite performers on three-stringed fiddles: in whistling, they almost boast the far-famed powers of Orpheus's lyre, for not a horse or an ox in the place, when at the plough or before the wagon, will budge a foot until he hears the well-known whistle of his black driver and companion.—And from their amazing skill at casting up accounts upon their fingers, they are regarded with as much veneration as were the disciples of Pythagoras of yore, when initiated into the sacred quaternary of numbers.

As to the honest burghers of Communipaw, like wise men and sound philosophers, they never look beyond their pipes, nor trouble their heads about any affairs out of their immediate neighborhood; so that they live in profound and enviable ignorance of all the troubles, anxieties, and revolutions of this distracted planet. I am even told that many among them do verily believe that Holland, of which they have heard so much from tradition, is situated somewhere on Long Island—that *Spiking-devil* and *the Narrows* are the two ends of the world—that the country is still under the dominion of their High Mightinesses, and that the city of New York still goes by the name of Nieuw Amsterdam. They meet every Saturday afternoon at the only tavern in the place, which bears as a sign, a square-headed likeness of the Prince of Orange, where they smoke a silent pipe, by way of promoting social conviviality, and invariably drink a mug of cider to the success of Admiral Van Tromp, who they imagine is still sweeping the British channel, with a broom at his mast-head.

Communipaw, in short, is one of the numerous little villages in the vicinity of this most beautiful of cities, which are so many strong-holds and fastnesses, whither the primitive manners of our Dutch forefathers have retreated, and where they are cherished with devout and scrupulous strictness. The dress of the original settlers is handed down inviolate, from father to son—the identical broad-brimmed hat, broad-skirted coat, and broad-bottomed breeches continue from generation to generation; and several gigantic knee-buckles of massy silver are still in wear, that made gallant display in the days of the patriarchs of Communipaw. The language likewise continues unadulterated by barbarous innovations; and so critically correct is the village schoolmaster in his dialect, that his reading of a Low Dutch psalm has much the same effect on the nerves as the filing of a handsaw.

CHAPTER III.

In Which Is Set Forth the True Art of Making a Bargain—Together with the Miraculous Escape of a Great Metropolis in a
Fog—and the Biography of Certain Heroes of Communipaw.

Having, in the trifling digression which concluded the last chapter, discharged the filial duty which the city of New York owed to Communipaw, as being the mother settlement; and having given a faithful picture of it as it stands at present, I return with a soothing sentiment of self-approbation, to dwell upon its early history. The crew of the Goede Vrouw being soon reinforced by fresh importations from Holland, the settlement went jollily on, increasing in magnitude and prosperity. The neighboring Indians in a short time became accustomed to the uncouth sound of the Dutch language, and an intercourse gradually took place between them and the new comers. The Indians were much given to long talks, and the Dutch to long silence—in this particular, therefore, they accommodated each other completely. The chiefs would make long speeches about the big bull, the Wabash, and the Great Spirit, to which the others would listen very attentively, smoke their pipes, and grunt *yah, myn-her*—whereat the poor savages were wondrously delighted. They instructed the new settlers in the best art of curing and smoking tobacco, while the latter, in return, made them drunk with true Hollands—and then taught them the art of making bargains.

A brisk trade for furs was soon opened: the Dutch traders were scrupulously honest in their dealings, and purchased by weight, establishing it as an invariable table of avoirdupois, that the hand of a Dutchman weighed one pound, and his foot two pounds. It is true, the simple Indians were often puzzled by the great disproportion between bulk and weight, for let them place a bundle of furs, never so large, in one scale, and a Dutchman put his hand or foot in the other, the bundle was sure to kick the beam—never was a package of furs known to weigh more than two pounds in the market of Communipaw!

This is a singular fact—but I have it direct from my great-great-grandfather, who had risen to considerable importance in the colony, being promoted to the office of weigh-master, on account of the uncommon heaviness of his foot.

The Dutch possessions in this part of the globe began now to assume a very thriving appearance, and were comprehended under the general title of Nieuw Nederlandts, on account, as the sage Vander Donck observes, of their great resemblance to the Dutch Netherlands—which indeed was truly remarkable, excepting that the former were rugged and mountainous, and the latter level and marshy. About this time the tranquillity of the Dutch colonists was doomed to suffer a temporary interruption. In 1614, Captain Sir Samuel Argal, sailing under a commission from Dale, governor of Virginia, visited the Dutch settlements on Hudson River, and demanded their submission to the English crown and Virginian dominion. To this arrogant demand as they were in no condition to resist it, they submitted for the time, like discreet and reasonable men.

It does not appear that the valiant Argal molested the settlement of Communipaw; on the contrary, I am told that when his vessel first hove in sight, the worthy burghers were seized with such a panic, that they fell to smoking their pipes with astonishing vehemence; insomuch that they quickly raised a cloud, which, combining with the surrounding woods and marshes, completely enveloped and concealed their beloved village, and overhung the fair regions of Pavonia—so that the terrible Captain Argal passed on, totally unsuspicious that a sturdy little Dutch settlement lay snugly couched in the mud, under cover of all this pestilent vapor. In commemoration of this fortunate escape, the worthy inhabitants have continued to smoke, almost without intermission, unto this very day; which is said to be the cause of the remarkable fog which often hangs over Communipaw of a clear afternoon.

Upon the departure of the enemy, our worthy ancestors took full six months to recover their wind and get over the consternation into which they had been thrown. They then called a council of safety to smoke over the state of the province. At this council presided one Oloffe Van Kortlandt, a personage who was held in great reverence among the sages of Communipaw for the variety and darkness of his knowledge. He had originally been one of a set of peripatetic philosophers who passed much of their time sunning themselves on the side of the great canal of Amsterdam in Holland; enjoying, like Diogenes, a free and unencumbered estate in sunshine. His name Kortlandt (Shortland or Lackland) was supposed, like that of the illustrious Jean Sansterre, to indicate that he had *no land;* but he insisted, on the contrary, that he had great landed estates somewhere in Terra Incognita; and he had come out to the new world to look after them. He was the first great land speculator that we read of in these parts.

Like all land speculators, he was much given to dreaming. Never did anything extraordinary happen at Communipaw but he declared that he had previously dreamt it; being one of those infallible prophets who predict events after they have come to pass. This supernatural gift was as highly valued among the burghers of Pavonia as among the enlightened nations of antiquity. The wise Ulysses was more indebted to his sleeping than his waking moments for his most subtle achievements, and seldom undertook any great exploit without first soundly sleeping upon it; and the same may be said of Oloffe Van Kortlandt, who was thence aptly denominated Oloffe the Dreamer.

As yet his dreams and speculations had turned to little personal profit; and he was as much a lack-land as ever. Still he carried a high head in the community; if his sugar-loaf hat was rather the worse for wear, he set it off with a taller cock's-tail; if his shirt was none of the cleanest, he puffed it out the more at the bosom; and if the tail of it peeped out of a hole in his breeches, it at least proved that it really had a tail and was not mere ruffle.

The worthy Van Kortlandt, in the council in question, urged the policy of emerging from the swamps of Communipaw and seeking some more eligible site for the seat of empire. Such, he said, was the advice of the good St. Nicholas, who had appeared to him in a dream the night before; and whom he had known by his broad hat, his long pipe, and the resemblance which he bore to the figure on the bow of the Goede Vrouw.

Many have thought this dream was a mere invention of Oloffe Van Kortlandt; who, it is said, had ever regarded Communipaw with an evil eye because he had arrived there after all the land had been shared out, and who was anxious to change the seat of empire to some new place, where he might be present at the distribution of "town lots." But we must not give heed to such insinuations, which are too apt to be advanced against those worthy gentlemen engaged in laying out towns, and in other land speculations. For my own part, I am disposed to place the same implicit faith in the vision of Oloffe the Dreamer that was manifested by the honest burghers of Communipaw, who one and all agreed that an expedition should be forthwith fitted out to go on a voyage of discovery in quest of a new seat of empire.

This perilous enterprise was to be conducted by Oloffe himself; who chose as lieutenants or coadjutors Mynheers Abraham Hardenbroeck, Jacobus Van Zandt, and Winant Ten Broeck—three indubitably great men, but of whose history, although I have made diligent inquiry, I can learn but little previous to their leaving Holland. Nor need this occasion much surprise; for adventurers, like prophets, though they make great noise abroad, have seldom much celebrity in their own countries; but this much is certain, that the overflowings and offscourings of a country are invariably composed of the richest parts of the soil. And here I cannot help remarking how convenient it would be to many of our great men and great families of doubtful origin, could they have the privilege of the heroes of yore, who, whenever their origin was involved in obscurity, modestly announced themselves descended from a god—and who never visited a foreign country but what they told some cock and bull stories about their being kings and princes at home. This venal trespass on the truth, though it has been occasionally played off by some pseudo marquis, baronet, and other illustrious foreigner, in our land of good-natured credulity, has been completely discountenanced in this sceptical, matter of fact age—and I even question whether any tender virgin, who was accidentally and unaccountably enriched with a bantling, would save her character at parlor firesides and evening tea-parties by ascribing the phenomenon to a swan, a shower of gold, or a river god.

Had I the benefit of mythology and classic fable above alluded to, I should have furnished the first of the trio with a pedigree equal to that of the proudest hero of antiquity. His name Van Zandt, that is to say, *from the sand*, or in common parlance, from the dirt, gave reason to suppose that like Triptolemus, Themis, the Cyclops and the Titans, he had sprung from Dame Terra or the earth! This supposition is strongly corroborated by his size, for it is well known that all the progeny of mother earth were of a gigantic stature; and Van Zandt, we are told, was a tall, raw-boned man, above six feet high—with an astonishingly hard head. Nor is this origin of the illustrious Van Zandt a whit more improbable or repugnant to belief than what is related and universally admitted of certain of our greatest, or rather richest men; who, we are told with the utmost gravity, did originally spring from a dunghill!

Of the second of the trio, but faint accounts have reached to this time, which mention that he was a sturdy, obstinate, worrying, bustling little man; and, from being usually equipped in an old pair of buckskins, was familiarly dubbed Harden Broeck; that is to say, Hard in the Breech; or, as it was generally rendered, Tough Breeches.

Ten Broeck completed this junto of adventurers. It is a singular but ludicrous fact, which, were I not scrupulous in recording the whole truth, I should almost be tempted to pass over in silence as incompatible with the gravity and dignity of history; that this worthy gentleman should likewise have been nicknamed from what in modern times is considered the most ignoble part of the dress. But in truth the small clothes seems to have been a very dignified garment in the eyes of our venerated ancestors, in all probability from its covering that part of the body which has been pronounced "the seat of honor."

The name of Ten Broeck, or as it was sometimes spelled Tin Broeck, has been indifferently translated into Ten Breeches and Tin Breeches. Certain elegant and ingenious writers on the subject declare in favor of *Tin*, or rather *Thin* Breeches; whence they infer that the original bearer of it was a poor but merry rogue, whose galligaskins were none of the soundest, and who, peradventure, may have been the author of that truly philosophical stanza:—

> *"Then why should we quarrel for riches,*
> *Or any such glittering toy;*
> *A light heart and thin pair of breeches*
> *Will go thorough the world, my brave boys!"*

The more accurate commentators, however, declare in favor of the other reading, and affirm that the worthy in question was a burly, bulbous man, who, in sheer ostentation of his venerable progenitors, was the first to introduce into the settlement the ancient Dutch fashion of ten pair of breeches.

Such was the trio of coadjutors chosen by Oloffe the Dreamer, to accompany him in his voyage into unknown realms; as to the names of his crews they have not been handed down by history.

Having, as I before observed, passed much of his life in the open air, among the peripatetic philosophers of Amsterdam, Oloffe had become familiar with the aspect of the heavens, and could as accurately determine when a storm was brewing or a squall rising, as a dutiful husband can foresee, from the brow of his spouse, when a tempest is gathering about his ears. Having pitched upon a time for his voyage, when the skies appeared propitious he exhorted all his crews to take a good night's rest; wind up their family affairs and make their wills; precautions taken by our forefathers even in after times when they became more adventurous, and voyaged to Haverstraw, or Kaatskill, or Groodt Esopus, or any other far country, beyond the great waters of the Tappan Zee.

CHAPTER IV.

How the Heroes of Communipaw Voyaged to Hell-Gate, and How They Were Received There.

AND now the rosy blush of morn began to mantle in the east, and soon the rising sun, emerging from amidst golden and purple clouds, shed his blithesome rays on the tin weathercocks of Communipaw. It was that delicious season of the year, when nature, breaking from the chilling thraldom of old winter, like a blooming damsel from the tyranny of a sordid old father, threw herself, blushing with ten thousand charms, into the arms of youthful spring. Every tufted copse and blooming grove resounded with the notes of hymeneal love. The very insects, as they sipped the dew that gemmed the tender grass of the meadows, joined in the joyous epithalamium—the virgin bud timidly put forth its blushes, "the voice of the turtle was heard in the land," and the heart of man dissolved away in tenderness. Oh! sweet Theocritus! had I thine oaten reed, wherewith thou erst did charm the gay Sicilian plains.—Or, oh! gentle Bion! thy pastoral pipe, wherein the happy swains of the Lesbian isle so much delighted, then might I attempt to sing, in soft Bucolic or negligent Idyllium, the rural beauties of the scene—but having nothing, save this jaded goose-quill, wherewith to wing my flight, I must fain resign all poetic disportings of the fancy, and pursue my narrative in humble prose; comforting myself with the hope, that though it may not steal so sweetly upon the imagination of my reader, yet it may commend itself, with virgin modesty, to his better judgment, clothed in the chaste and simple garb of truth.

No sooner did the first rays of cheerful Phœbus dart into the windows of Communipaw, than the little settlement was all in motion. Forth issued from his castle the sage Van Kortlandt, and seizing a conch-shell, blew a far-resounding blast, that soon summoned all his lusty followers. Then did they trudge resolutely down to the water-side, escorted by a multitude of relatives and friends, who all went down, as the common phrase expresses it, "to see them off." And this shows the antiquity of those long family processions, often seen in our city, composed of all ages, sizes and sexes, laden, with bundles and band-boxes, escorting some bevy of country cousins about to depart for home in a market-boat.

The good Oloffe bestowed his forces in a squadron of three canoes, and hoisted his flag on board a little round Dutch boat, shaped not unlike a tub, which had formerly been the jolly-boat of the Goede Vrouw. And now all being embarked, they bade farewell to the gazing throng upon the beach, who continued shouting after them, even when out of hearing, wishing them a happy voyage, advising them to take good care of themselves, not to get drowned—with an abundance other of those sage and invaluable cautions, generally given by landsmen to such as go down to the sea in ships, and adventure upon the deep waters. In the meanwhile, the voyagers cheerily urged their course across the crystal bosom of the bay, and soon left behind them the green shores of ancient Pavonia.

And first they touched at two small islands which lie nearly opposite Communipaw, and which are said to have been brought into existence about the time of the great irruption of the Hudson, when it broke through the Highlands, and made its way to the ocean.[1] For in this tremendous uproar of the waters, we are told that many huge fragments of rock and land were rent from the mountains and swept down by this runaway river for sixty or seventy miles; where some of them ran aground on the shoals just opposite Communipaw, and formed the identical islands in question, while others drifted out to sea and were never heard of more. A sufficient proof of the fact is, that the rock which forms the bases of these islands is exactly similar to that of the Highlands, and, moreover, one of our philosophers, who has diligently compared the agreement of their respective surfaces, has even gone so far as to assure me, in confidence, that Gibbet Island was originally nothing more nor less than a wart on Anthony's Nose.[2]

Leaving these wonderful little isles, they next coasted by Governor's Island, since terrible from its frowning fortress and grinning batteries. They would by no means, however, land upon this island, since they doubted much it might be the abode of demons and spirits, which in those days did greatly abound throughout this savage and pagan country.

Just at this time a shoal of jolly porpoises came rolling and tumbling by, turning up their sleek sides to the sun, and spouting up the briny element in sparkling showers. No sooner did the sage Oloffe mark this, than he was greatly rejoiced. "This," exclaimed he, "if I mistake not, augurs well—the porpoise is a fat, well-conditioned fish—a burgomaster among fishes—his looks betoken ease, plenty, and prosperity—I greatly admire this round, fat fish, and doubt not but this is a happy omen of the success of our undertaking." So saying, he directed his squadron to steer in the track of these alderman fishes.

Turning, therefore, directly to the left, they swept up the strait vulgarly called the East River. And here the rapid tide which courses through this strait, seizing on the gallant tub in which Commodore Van Kortlandt had embarked, hurried it forward with a velocity unparalleled in a Dutch boat, navigated by Dutchmen; insomuch that the good commodore, who had all his life long been accustomed only to the drowsy navigation of canals, was more than ever con-

---

[1] It is a matter long since established by certain of our philosophers, that is to say, having been often advanced, and never contradicted, it has grown to be pretty nigh equal to a settled fact, that the Hudson was originally a lake, dammed up by the mountains of the Highlands. In process of time, however, becoming very mighty and obstreperous, and the mountains waxing pursy, dropsical, and weak in the back, by reason of their extreme old age, it suddenly rose upon them, and after a violent struggle effected its escape. This is said to have come to pass in very remote time; probably before that rivers had lost the art of running up hill. The foregoing is a theory in which I do not pretend to be skilled, notwithstanding that I do fully give it my belief.

[2] A promontory in the Highlands.

vinced that they were in the hands of some supernatural power, and that the jolly porpoises were towing them to some fair haven that was to fulfil all their wishes and expectations.

Thus borne away by the resistless current, they doubled that boisterous point of land since called Corlear's Hook,[3] and leaving to the right the rich winding cove of the Wallabout, they drifted into a magnificent expanse of water, surrounded by pleasant shores, whose verdure was exceedingly refreshing to the eye. While the voyagers were looking around them, on what they conceived to be a serene and sunny lake, they beheld at a distance a crew of painted savages, busily employed in fishing, who seemed more like the genii of this romantic region—their slender canoe lightly balanced like a feather on the undulating surface of the bay.

At sight of these, the hearts of the heroes of Communipaw were not a little troubled. But as good fortune would have it, at the bow of the commodore's boat was stationed a very valiant man, named Hendrick Kip, (which being interpreted, means *chicken*, a name given him in token of his courage). No sooner did he behold these varlet heathens than he trembled with excessive valor, and, although a good half mile distant, he seized a musketoon that lay at hand, and turning away his head, fired it most intrepidly in the face of the blessed sun. The blundering weapon recoiled and gave the valiant Kip an ignominious kick, which laid him prostrate with uplifted heels in the bottom of the boat. But such was the effect of this tremendous fire, that the wild men of the woods, struck with consternation, seized hastily upon their paddles, and shot away into one of the deep inlets of the Long Island shore.

This signal victory gave new spirits to the voyagers, and in honor of the achievement they gave the name of the valiant Kip to the surrounding bay, and it has continued to be called KIP'S BAY from that time to the present. The heart of the good Van Kortlandt—who, having no land of his own, was a great admirer of other people's—expanded to the full size of a peppercorn at the sumptuous prospect of rich, unsettled country around him, and falling into a delicious revery, he straightway began to riot in the possession of vast meadows of salt marsh and interminable patches of cabbages. From this delectable vision he was all at once awakened by the sudden turning of the tide, which would soon have hurried him from this land of promise, had not the discreet navigator given signal to steer for shore; where they accordingly landed hard by the rocky heights of Bellevue—that happy retreat, where our jolly aldermen eat for the good of the city, and fatten the turtle that are sacrificed on civic solemnities.

Here, seated on the greensward, by the side of a small stream that ran sparkling among the grass, they refreshed themselves after the toils of the seas, by feasting lustily on the ample stores which they had provided for this perilous voyage. Thus having well fortified their deliberative powers, they fell into an earnest consultation, what was farther to be done. This was the first council dinner ever eaten at Bellevue by Christian burghers, and here, as tradition

[3]Properly spelt *hoeck* (i.e., a point of land).

relates, did originate the great family feud between the Hardenbroecks and the Ten Broecks, which afterwards had a singular influence on the building of the city. The sturdy Hardenbroeck, whose eyes had been wondrously delighted with the salt marshes which spread their reeking bosoms along the coast, at the bottom of Kip's Bay, counselled by all means to return thither, and found the intended city. This was strenuously opposed by the unbending Ten Broeck, and many testy arguments passed between them. The particulars of this controversy have not reached us, which is ever to be lamented; this much is certain, that the sage Oloffe put an end to the dispute, by determining to explore still farther in the route which the mysterious porpoises had so clearly pointed out—whereupon the sturdy Tough Breeches abandoned the expedition, took possession of a neighboring hill, and in a fit of great wrath peopled all that tract of country, which has continued to be inhabited by the Hardenbroecks unto this very day.

By this time the jolly Phœbus, like some wanton urchin sporting on the side of a green hill, began to roll down the declivity of the heavens; and now, the tide having once more turned in their favor, the Pavonians again committed themselves to its discretion, and coasting along the western shores, were borne towards the straits of Blackwell's Island.

And here the capricious wanderings of the current occasioned not a little marvel and perplexity to these illustrious mariners. Now would they be caught by the wanton eddies, and, sweeping round a jutting point, would wind deep into some romantic little cove, that indented the fair island of Manna-hata; now were they hurried narrowly by the very bases of impending rocks, mantled with the flaunting grapevine, and crowned with groves which threw a broad shade on the waves beneath; and anon they were borne away into the mid-channel, and wafted along with a rapidity that very much discomposed the sage Van Kortlandt, who, as he saw the land swiftly receding on either side, began exceedingly to doubt that terra firma was giving them the slip.

Wherever the voyagers turned their eyes, a new creation seemed to bloom around. No signs of human thrift appeared to check the delicious wildness of nature, who here revelled in all her luxuriant variety. Those hills, now bristled, like the fretful porcupine, with rows of poplars, (vain upstart plants! minions of wealth and fashion!) were then adorned with the vigorous natives of the soil; the lordly oak, the generous chestnut, the graceful elm—while here and there the tulip-tree reared its majestic head, the giant of the forest. Where now are seen the gay retreats of luxury—villas half buried in twilight bowers, whence the amorous flute oft breathes the sighings of some city swain—there the fish-hawk built his solitary nest, on some dry tree that overlooked his watery domain. The timid deer fed undisturbed along those shores now hallowed by the lovers' moonlight walk, and printed by the slender foot of beauty; and a savage solitude extended over those happy regions where now are reared the stately towers of the Joneses, the Schermerhornos, and the Rhinelanders.

Thus gliding in silent wonder through these new and unknown scenes, the gallant squadron of Pavonia swept by the foot of a promontory which strutted forth boldly into the waves, and seemed to frown upon them as they brawled against its base. This is the bluff well known to modern mariners by the name of Gracie's point, from the fair castle which, like an elephant, it carries upon its back. And here broke upon their view a wild and varied prospect, where land and water were beauteously intermingled, as though they had combined to heighten and set off each other's charms. To their right lay the sedgy point of Blackwell's Island, drest in the fresh garniture of living green—beyond it stretched the pleasant coast of Sundswick, and the small harbor well known by the name of Hallet's Cove—a place infamous in latter days, by reason of its being the haunt of pirates who infest these seas, robbing orchards and watermelon patches, and insulting gentlemen navigators when voyaging in their pleasure-boats. To the left a deep bay, or rather creek, gracefully receded between shores fringed with forests, and forming a kind of vista, through which were beheld the sylvan regions of Haerlem, Morrisania, and East Chester. Here the eye reposed with delight on a richly wooded country, diversified by tufted knolls, shadowy intervals, and waving lines of upland swelling above each other; while over the whole the purple mists of spring diffused a hue of soft voluptuousness.

Just before them the grand course of the stream, making a sudden bend, wound among embowered promontories and shores of emerald verdure, that seemed to melt into the wave. A character of gentleness and mild fertility prevailed around. The sun had just descended, and the thin haze of twilight, like a transparent veil drawn over the bosom of virgin beauty, heightened the charms which it half concealed.

Ah! witching scenes of foul delusion! Ah! hapless voyagers gazing with simple wonder on these Circean shores! Such alas! are they, poor easy souls, who listen to the seductions of a wicked world—treacherous are its smiles! fatal its caresses! He who yields to its enticements launches upon a whelming tide, and trusts his feeble bark among the dimpling eddies of a whirlpool! And thus it fared with the worthies of Pavonia, who, little mistrusting the guileful scene before them, drifted quietly on, until they were aroused by an uncommon tossing and agitation of their vessels. For now the late dimpling current began to brawl around them, and the waves to boil and foam with horrific fury. Awakened as if from a dream, the astonished Oloffe bawled aloud to put about, but his words were lost amid the roaring of the waters. And now ensued a scene of direful consternation—at one time they were borne with dreadful velocity among tumultuous breakers; at another, hurried down boisterous rapids. Now they were nearly dashed upon the Hen and Chickens; (infamous rocks!—more voracious than Scylla and her whelps;) and anon they seemed sinking into yawning gulfs, that threatened to entomb them beneath the waves. All the elements combined to produce a hideous confusion. The waters raged —the winds howled—and as they were hurried along, several of the astonished mariners beheld the rocks and trees of the neighboring shores driving through the air!

At length the mighty tub of Commodore Van Kortlandt was drawn into the vortex of that tremendous whirlpool called the Pot, where it was whirled about in giddy mazes, until the senses of the good commander and his crew were overpowered by the horror of the scene and the strangeness of the revolution.

How the gallant squadron of Pavonia was snatched from the jaws of this modern Charybdis, has never been truly made known, for so many survived to tell the tale, and, what is still more wonderful, told it in so many different ways, that there has ever prevailed a great variety of opinions on the subject.

As to the commodore and his crew, when they came to their senses they found themself stranded on the Long Island shore. The worthy commodore, indeed, used to relate many and wonderful stories of his adventures in this time of peril; how that he saw spectres flying in the air, and heard the yelling of hobgoblins, and put his hand into the Pot when they were whirled round and found the water scalding hot, and beheld several uncouth-looking beings seated on rocks and skimming it with huge ladles—but particularly he declared, with great exultation, that he saw the losel porpoises, which had betrayed them into this peril, some broiling on the Gridiron and others hissing on the Frying-pan!

These, however, were considered by many as mere fantasies of the commodore while he lay in a trance; especially as he was known to be given to dreaming; and the truth of them has never been clearly ascertained. It is certain, however, that to the accounts of Oloffe and his followers may be traced the various traditions handed down of this marvellous strait—as how the devil has been seen there, sitting astride of the Hog's Back and playing on the fiddle—how he broils fish there before a storm; and many other stories, in which we must be cautious of putting too much faith. In consequence of all these terrific circumstances, the Pavonian commander gave this pass the name of *Helle-gat,* or as it has been interpreted, *Hell-Gate;*[4] which it continues to bear at the present day.

CHAPTER V.

How the Heroes of Communipaw Returned Somewhat Wiser Than They Went—and How the Sage Oloffe Dreamed a Dream —and the Dream That He Dreamed.

The darkness of night had closed upon this disastrous day, and a doleful night was it to the shipwrecked Pavonians, whose ears were incessantly assailed with the raging of the elements, and the howling of the hobgoblins that infested this perfidious strait. But when the morning dawned, the horrors of the preceding evening had passed away, rapids, breakers, and whirlpools had disappeared, the

[4]This is a narrow strait in the Sound, at the distance of six miles above New York. It is dangerous to shipping, unless under the care of skilful pilots, by reason of numerous rocks, shelves, and whirlpools. These have received sundry appellations, such as the Gridiron, Frying-pan, Hog's Back, Pot, etc., and are very violent and turbulent at certain times of tide. Certain mealy-mouthed men, of squeamish consciences, who are loth to give the Devil his due, have softened the above characteristic name into *Hurl*-gate forsooth! Let those take care how they venture into the

stream again ran smooth and dimpling, and having changed its tide, rolled gently back, towards the quarter where lay their much-regretted home.

The woebegone heroes of Communipaw eyed each other with rueful countenances; their squadron had been totally dispersed by the late disaster. Some were cast upon the western shore, where, headed by one Ruleff Hopper, they took possession of all the country lying about the six mile stone; which is held by the Hoppers at this present writing.

The Waldrons were driven by stress of weather to a distant coast, where, having with them a jug of genuine Hollands, they were enabled to conciliate the savages, setting up a kind of tavern; whence, it is said, did spring the fair town of Haerlem, in which their descendants have ever since continued to be reputable publicans. As to the Suydams, they were thrown upon the Long Island coast, and may still be found in those parts. But the most singular luck attended the great Ten Broeck, who, falling overboard, was miraculously preserved from sinking by the multitude of his nether garments. Thus buoyed up, he floated on the waves like a merman, or like an angler's dobber, until he landed safely on a rock, where he was found the next morning busily drying his many breeches in the sunshine.

I forbear to treat of the long consultation of Oloffe with his remaining followers, in which they determined that it would never do to found a city in so diabolical a neighborhood. Suffice it in simple brevity to say that they once more committed themselves, with fear and trembling, to the briny element, and steered their course back again through the scenes of their yesterday's voyage, determined no longer to roam in search of distant sites, but to settle themselves down in the marshy regions of Pavonia.

Scarce, however, had they gained a distant view of Communipaw when they were encountered by an obstinate eddy which opposed their homeward voyage. Weary and dispirited as they were, they yet tugged a feeble oar against the stream; until, as if to settle the strife, half a score of potent billows rolled the tub of Commodore Van Kortlandt high and dry on the long point of an island which divided the bosom of the bay.

Some pretend that these billows were sent by old Neptune to strand the expedition on a spot whereon was to be founded his stronghold in this western world: others more pious, attribute everything to the guardianship of the good St. Nicholas; and after events will be found to corroborate this opinion. Oloffe Van Kortlandt was a devout trencherman. Every repast was a kind of religious rite with him; and his first thought on finding himself once more on dry ground, was how he should contrive to celebrate his wonderful escape from Hell-gate and all its horrors by a solemn banquet. The stores which had been provided for the voyage by the good housewives of Communipaw were nearly

Gate, or they may be hurled into the Pot before they are aware of it. The name of this strait, as given by our author, is supported by the map in Vander Donck's history, published in 1656—by Ogilvie's history of America, 1671—as also by a journal still extant, written in the 16th century, and to be found in Hazard's State Papers. And an old MS., written in French, speaking of various alterations in names about this city, observes, "De *Helle-gat*, trou d'Enfer, ils ont fait *Hell-Gate*, Porte d'Enfer."

exhausted, but, in casting his eyes about, the commodore beheld that the shore abounded with oysters. A great store of these was instantly collected; a fire was made at the foot of a tree; all hands fell to roasting and broiling and stewing and frying, and a sumptuous repast was soon set forth. This is thought to be the origin of those civic feasts with which, to the present day, all our public affairs are celebrated, and in which the oyster is ever sure to play an important part.

On the present occasion the worthy Van Kortlandt was observed to be particularly zealous in his devotions to the trencher; for having the cares of the expedition especially committed to his care, he deemed it incumbent on him to eat profoundly for the public good. In proportion as he filled himself to the very brim with the dainty viands before him, did the heart of this excellent burgher rise up towards his throat, until he seemed crammed and almost choked with good eating and good nature. And at such times it is, when a man's heart is in his throat, that he may more truly be said to speak from it, and his speeches abound with kindness and good fellowship. Thus having swallowed the last possible morsel, and washed it down with a fervent potation, Oloffe felt his heart yearning, and his whole frame in a manner dilating with unbounded benevolence. Everything around him seemed excellent and delightful; and laying his hands on each side of his capacious periphery, and rolling his half closed eyes around on the beautiful diversity of land and water before him, he exclaimed, in a fat half smothered voice, "What a charming prospect!" The words died away in his throat—he seemed to ponder on the fair scene for a moment—his eyelids heavily closed over their orbs—his head drooped upon his bosom—he slowly sank upon the green turf, and a deep sleep stole gradually over him.

And the sage Oloffe dreamed a dream—and lo, the good St. Nicholas came riding over the tops of the trees, in that selfsame wagon wherein he brings his yearly presents to children, and he descended hard by where the heroes of Communipaw had made their late repast. And he lit his pipe by the fire, and sat himself down and smoked; and as he smoked the smoke from his pipe ascended into the air and spread like a cloud overhead. And Oloffe bethought him, and he hastened and climbed up to the top of one of the tallest trees, and saw that the smoke spread over a great extent of country—and as he considered it more attentively, he fancied that the great volume of smoke assumed a variety of marvellous forms, where in dim obscurity he saw shadowed out palaces and domes and lofty spires, all of which lasted but a moment, and then faded away, until the whole rolled off, and nothing but the green woods were left. And when St. Nicholas had smoked his pipe, he twisted it in his hat-band, and laying his finger beside his nose, gave the astonished Van Kortlandt a very significant look, then mounting his wagon, he returned over the tree-tops and disappeared.

And Van Kortlandt awoke from his sleep greatly instructed, and he aroused his companions, and related to them his dream, and interpreted it, that it was the will of St. Nicholas that they should settle down and build the city here. And that the smoke of the pipe was a type how vast would be the extent of the city; inasmuch as the volumes of its smoke would spread over a wide extent of country. And they all with one voice assented to this interpretation excepting Mynheer Ten Broeck, who declared the meaning to be that it would be a city wherein a little fire would occasion a great smoke, or in other words, a very vaporing little city—both which interpretations have strangely come to pass!

The great object of their perilous expedition, therefore, being thus happily accomplished, the voyagers returned merrily to Communipaw, where they were received with great rejoicings. And here calling a general meeting of all the wise men and the dignitaries of Pavonia, they related the whole history of their voyage, and of the dream of Oloffe Van Kortlandt. And the people lifted up their voices and blessed the good St. Nicholas, and from that time forth the sage Van Kortlandt was held in more honor than ever, for his great talent at dreaming, and was pronounced a most useful citizen and a right good man —when he was asleep.

CHAPTER VI.

Containing an Attempt at Etymology—and of the Founding of the Great City of New Amsterdam.

The original name of the island whereon the squadron of Communipaw was thus propitiously thrown, is a matter of some dispute, and has already undergone considerable vitiation—a melancholy proof of the instability of all sublunary things, and the vanity of all our hopes of lasting fame; for who can expect his name will live to posterity, when even the names of mighty islands are thus soon lost in contradiction and uncertainty!

The name most current at the present day, and which is likewise countenanced by the great historian Vander Donck, is Manhattan; which is said to have originated in a custom among the squaws, in the early settlement, of wearing men's hats, as is still done among many tribes. "Hence," as we are told by an old governor who was somewhat of a wag, and flourished almost a century since, and had paid a visit to the wits of Philadelphia, "hence arose the appellation of man-hat-on, first given to the Indians, and afterwards to the island"—a stupid joke!—but well enough for a governor.

Among the more venerable sources of information on this subject, is that valuable history of the American possessions, written by Master Richard Blome, in 1687, wherein it is called Manhadaes and Manahanent; nor must I forget the excellent little book, full of precious matter, of that authentic historian, John Josselyn, Gent., who expressly calls it Manadaes.

Another etymology still more ancient, and sanctioned by the countenance of our ever to be lamented Dutch ancestors, is that found in certain letters still extant;[1] which passed between the early governors and their neighboring powers, wherein it is called indifferently Monhattoes—Munhatos, and Manhat-

[1] *Vide* Hazard's Col. Stat. Pap.

toes, which are evidently unimportant variations of the same name; for our wise forefathers set little store by those niceties either in orthography or orthoëpy, which form the sole study and ambition of many learned men and women of this hypercritical age. This last name is said to be derived from the great Indian spirit Manetho; who was supposed to make this island his favorite abode, on account of its uncommon delights. For the Indian traditions affirm that the bay was once a translucid lake, filled with silver and golden fish, in the midst of which lay this beautiful island, covered with every variety of fruits and flowers; but that the sudden irruption of the Hudson laid waste these blissful scenes, and Manetho took his flight beyond the great waters of Ontario.

These, however, are very fabulous legends, to which very cautious credence must be given; and though I am willing to admit the last quoted orthography of the name as very fit for prose, yet is there another which I peculiarly delight in, as at once poetical, melodious, and significant—and which we have on the authority of Master Juet; who, in his account of the voyage of the great Hudson, calls this MANNA-HATA—that is to say, the island of manna—or, in other words, a land flowing with milk and honey.

Still my deference to the learned obliges me to notice the opinion of the worthy Dominie Heckwelder, which ascribes the name to a great drunken bout held on the island by the Dutch discoverers, whereat they made certain of the natives most ecstatically drunk for the first time in their lives; who, being delighted with their jovial entertainment, gave the place the name of Manna-hattanink; that is to say, The Island of Jolly Topers: a name which it continues to merit to the present day.[2]

CHAPTER VII.

How the People of Pavonia Migrated from Communipaw to the Island of Manna-hata—and How Oloffe the Dreamer Proved Himself a Great Land Speculator.

It having been solemnly resolved that the seat of empire should be removed from the green shores of Pavonia to the pleasant island of Manna-hata, everybody was anxious to embark under the standard of Oloffe the Dreamer, and to be among the first sharers of the promised land. A day was appointed for the grand migration, and on that day little Communipaw was in a buzz and a bustle like a hive in swarming time. Houses were turned inside out and stripped of the venerable furniture which had come from Holland; all the community, great and small, black and white, man, woman, and child, was in commotion, forming lines from the houses to the waterside, like lines of ants from an ant-hill; everybody laden with some article of household furniture; while busy housewives plied backwards and forwards along the lines, helping everything forward by the nimbleness of their tongues.

[2]MSS. of the Rev. John Heckwelder, in the archives of the New York Historical Society.

By degrees a fleet of boats and canoes were piled up with all kinds of household articles: ponderous tables; chests of drawers resplendent with brass ornaments; quaint corner cupboards; beds and bedsteads; with any quantity of pots, kettles, frying-pans, and Dutch ovens. In each boat embarked a whole family, from the robustious burgher down to the cats and dogs and little negroes. In this way they set off across the mouth of the Hudson, under the guidance of Oloffe the Dreamer, who hoisted his standard on the leading boat.

This memorable migration took place on the first of May, and was long cited in tradition as the *grand moving*. The anniversary of it was piously observed among the "sons of the pilgrims of Communipaw," by turning their houses topsy-turvy and carrying all the furniture through the streets, in emblem of the swarming of the parent hive; and this is the real origin of the universal agitation and "moving" by which this most restless of cities is literally turned out of doors on every May day.

As the little squadron from Communipaw drew near to the shores of Mannahata, a sachem, at the head of a band of warriors, appeared to oppose their landing. Some of the most zealous of the pilgrims were for chastising this insolence with powder and ball, according to the approved mode of discoverers; but the sage Oloffe gave them the significant sign of St. Nicholas, laying his finger beside his nose and winking hard with one eye; whereupon his followers perceived that there was something sagacious in the wind. He now addressed the Indians in the blandest terms; and made such tempting display of beads, hawks'-bells, and red blankets, that he was soon permitted to land, and a great land speculation ensued. And here let me give the true story of the original purchase of the site of this renowned city, about which so much has been said and written. Some affirm that the first cost was but sixty guilders. The learned Dominie Heckwelder records a tradition[1] that the Dutch discoverers bargained for only so much land as the hide of a bullock would cover; but that they cut the hide in strips no thicker than a child's finger, so as to take in a large portion of land, and to take in the Indians into the bargain. This, however, is an old fable which the worthy Dominie may have borrowed from antiquity. The true version is, that Oloffe Van Kortlandt bargained for just so much land as a man could cover with his nether garments. The terms being concluded, he produced his friend Mynheer Ten Broeck, as the man whose breeches were to be used in measurement. The simple savages, whose ideas of a man's nether garments had never expanded beyond the dimensions of a breech clout, stared with astonishment and dismay as they beheld this bulbous-bottomed burgher peeled like an onion, and breeches after breeches spread forth over the land until they covered the actual site of this venerable city.

This is the true history of the adroit bargain by which the island of Manhattan was bought for sixty guilders; and in corroboration of it I will add, that Mynheer Ten Breeches, for his services on this memorable occasion, was elevated to the office of land measurer; which he ever afterwards exercised in the colony.

[1]MSS. of the Rev. John Heckwelder; New York Historical Society.

CHAPTER VIII.

Of the Founding and Naming of the New City; of the City Arms; and of the Direful Feud Between Ten Breeches and Tough Breeches.

The land being thus fairly purchased of the Indians, a circumstance very unusual in the history of colonization, and strongly illustrative of the honesty of our Dutch progenitors, a stockade fort and trading house were forthwith erected on an eminence in front of the place where the good St. Nicholas had appeared in a vision to Oloffe the Dreamer; and which, as has already been observed, was the identical place at present known as the Bowling Green.

Around this fort a progeny of little Dutch-built houses, with tiled roofs and weathercocks, soon sprang up, nestling themselves under its walls for protection, as a brood of half-fledged chickens nestle under the wings of the mother hen. The whole was surrounded by an enclosure of strong palisadoes, to guard against any sudden irruption of the savages. Outside of these extended the corn-fields and cabbage-gardens of the community; with here and there an attempt at a tobacco plantation; all covering those tracts of country at present called Broadway, Wall-street, William-street and Pearl-street.

I must not omit to mention that in portioning out the land a goodly "bowerie" or farm was allotted to the sage Oloffe in consideration of the service he had rendered to the public by his talent at dreaming; and the site of his "bowerie" is known by the name of Kortlandt (or Courtlandt) street to the present day.

And now the infant settlement having advanced in age and stature, it was thought high time it should receive an honest Christian name. Hitherto it had gone by the original Indian name Manna-hata, or as some will have it, "The Manhattoes;" but this was now decried as savage and heathenish, and as tending to keep up the memory of the pagan brood that originally possessed it. Many were the consultations held upon the subject, without coming to a conclusion, for though everybody condemned the old name, nobody could invent a new one. At length, when the council was almost in despair, a burgher, remarkable for the size and squareness of his head, proposed that they should call it New Amsterdam. The proposition took everybody by surprise; it was so striking, so apposite, so ingenious. The name was adopted by acclamation, and New Amsterdam the metropolis was thenceforth called. Still, however, the early authors of the province continued to call it by the general appellation of "The Manhattoes," and the poets fondly clung to the euphonious name of Manna-hata; but those are a kind of folk whose tastes and notions should go for nothing in matters of this kind.

Having thus provided the embryo city with a name, the next was to give it an armorial bearing or device, as some cities have a rampant lion, others a soaring eagle; emblematical, no doubt, of the valiant and high-flying qualities of the inhabitants: so after mature deliberation a sleek beaver was emblazoned on the city standard as indicative of the amphibious origin, and patient, persevering habits of the New Amsterdammers.

The thriving state of the settlement and the rapid increase of houses soon made it necessary to arrange some plan upon which the city should be built; but at the very first consultation held on the subject, a violent discussion arose; and I mention it with much sorrowing as being the first altercation on record in the councils of New Amsterdam. It was, in fact, a breaking forth of the grudge and heart-burning that had existed between those two eminent burghers, Mynheers Ten Broeck and Hardenbroeck, ever since their unhappy dispute on the coast of Bellevue. The great Hardenbroeck had waxed very wealthy and powerful from his domains, which embraced the whole chain of Apulean mountains that stretched along the gulf of Kip's Bay, and from part of which his descendants have been expelled in latter ages by the powerful clans of the Joneses and the Schermerhorns.

An ingenious plan for the city was offered by Mynheer Hardenbroeck, who proposed that it should be cut up and intersected by canals, after the manner of the most admired cities in Holland. To this Mynheer Ten Broeck was diametrically opposed, suggesting in place thereof, that they should run out docks and wharves, by means of piles driven into the bottom of the river, on which the town should be built. "By these means," said he, triumphantly, "shall we rescue a considerable space of territory from these immense rivers, and build a city that shall rival Amsterdam, Venice, or any amphibious city in Europe." To this proposition, Hardenbroeck (or Tough Breeches) replied, with a look of as much scorn as he could possibly assume. He cast the utmost censure upon the plan of his antagonist, as being preposterous, and against the very order of things, as he would leave to every true Hollander. "For what," said he, "is a town without canals?—it is like a body without veins and arteries, and must perish for want of a free circulation of the vital fluid."—Ten Breeches, on the contrary, retorted with a sarcasm upon his antagonist, who was somewhat of an arid, dry-boned habit; he remarked, that as to the circulation of the blood being necessary to existence, Mynheer Tough Breeches was a living contradiction to his own assertion; for every body knew there had not a drop of blood circulated through his wind-dried carcass for good ten years, and yet there was not a greater busy-body in the whole colony. Personalities have seldom much effect in making converts in argument—nor have I ever seen a man convinced of error by being convicted of deformity. At least such was not the case at present. If Ten Breeches was very happy in sarcasm, Tough Breeches, who was a sturdy little man, and never gave up the last word, rejoined with increasing spirit—Ten Breeches had the advantage of the greatest volubility, but Tough Breeches had that invaluable coat of mail in argument called obstinacy—Ten Breeches had, therefore, the most mettle, but Tough Breeches the best bottom—so that though Ten Breeches made a dreadful clattering about his ears, and battered and belabored him with hard words and sound arguments, yet Tough Breeches hung on most resolutely to the last. They parted, therefore, as is usual in all arguments, where both parties are in the right, without coming to any conclusion—but they hated each other most heartily for ever after, and a similar breach with that between the houses of Capulet and Montague did ensue between the families of Ten Breeches and Tough Breeches.

I would not fatigue my reader with these dull matters of fact, but that my duty as a faithful historian requires that I should be particular—and in truth, as I am now treating of the critical period, when our city, like a young twig, first received the twists and turns which have since contributed to give it its present picturesque irregularity, I cannot be too minute in detailing their first causes.

After the unhappy altercation I have just mentioned, I do not find that anything farther was said on the subject worthy of being recorded. The council, consisting of the largest and oldest heads in the community, met regularly once a week, to ponder on this momentous subject; but, either they were deterred by the war of words they had witnessed, or they were naturally averse to the exercise of the tongue, and the consequent exercise of the brains—certain it is, the most profound silence was maintained—the question as usual lay on the table—the members quietly smoked their pipes, making but few laws, without ever enforcing any, and in the meantime the affairs of the settlement went on— as it pleased God.

As most of the council were but little skilled in the mystery of combining pot-hooks and hangers, they determined most judiciously not to puzzle either themselves or posterity with voluminous records. The secretary, however, kept the minutes of the council with tolerable precision, in a large vellum folio, fastened with massy brass clasps; the journal of each meeting consisted but of two lines, stating in Dutch, that "the council sat this day, and smoked twelve pipes, on the affairs of the colony."—By which it appears that the first settlers did not regulate their time by hours, but pipes, in the same manner as they measure distances in Holland at this very time; an admirably exact measurement, as a pipe in the mouth of a true-born Dutchman is never liable to those accidents and irregularities that are continually putting our clocks out of order.

In this manner did the profound council of NEW AMSTERDAM smoke, and doze, and ponder, from week to week, month to month, and year to year, in what manner they should construct their infant settlement—meanwhile, the town took care of itself, and like a sturdy brat which is suffered to run about wild, unshackled by clouts and bandages, and other abominations by which your notable nurses and sage old women cripple and disfigure the children of men, increased so rapidly in strength and magnitude, that before the honest burgomasters had determined upon a plan, it was too late to put it in execution —whereupon they wisely abandoned the subject altogether.

BOOK III.

IN WHICH IS RECORDED THE GOLDEN REIGN OF WOUTER VAN TWILLER.

CHAPTER I.

OF THE RENOWNED WOUTER VAN TWILLER, HIS UNPARALLELED VIR-
TUES—AS LIKEWISE HIS UNUTTERABLE WISDOM IN THE LAW CASE OF
WANDLE SCHOONHOVEN AND BARENT BLEECKER—AND THE GREAT
ADMIRATION OF THE PUBLIC THEREAT.

GRIEVOUS and very much to be commiserated is the task of the feeling historian, who writes the history of his native land. If it fall to his lot to be the recorder of calamity or crime, the mournful page is watered with his tears—nor can he recall the most prosperous and blissful era, without a melancholy sigh at the reflection, that it has passed away forever! I know not whether it be owing to an immoderate love for the simplicity of former times, or to that certain tenderness of heart incident to all sentimental historians; but I candidly confess that I cannot look back on the happier days of our city, which I now describe, without great dejection of spirits. With faltering hand do I withdraw the curtain of oblivion, that veils the modest merit of our venerable ancestors, and as their figures rise to my mental vision, humble myself before their mighty shades.

Such are my feelings when I revisit the family mansion of the Knickerbock-ers, and spend a lonely hour in the chamber where hang the portraits of my forefathers, shrouded in dust, like the forms they represent. With pious rev-erence do I gaze on the countenances of those renowned burghers, who have preceded me in the steady march of existence—whose sober and temperate blood now meanders through my veins, flowing slower and slower in its feeble conduits, until its current shall soon be stopped forever!

These, I say to myself, are but frail memorials of the mighty men who flourished in the days of the patriarchs; but who, alas, have long since mould-ered in the tomb, towards which my steps are insensibly and irresistibly hastening! As I pace the darkened chamber and lose myself in melancholy musings, the shadowy images around me almost seem to steal once more into existence—their countenances to assume the animation of life—their eyes to pur-sue me in every movement! Carried away by the delusions of fancy, I almost imagine myself surrounded by the shades of the departed, and holding sweet converse with the worthies of antiquity! Ah, hapless Diedrich! born in a degen-erate age, abandoned to the buffetings of fortune—a stranger and a weary pil-grim in thy native land—blest with no weeping wife, nor family of helpless children; but doomed to wander neglected through those crowded streets, and elbowed by foreign upstarts from those fair abodes where once thine ancestors held sovereign empire!

Let me not, however, lose the historian in the man, nor suffer the doting recollections of age to overcome me, while dwelling with fond garrulity on the virtuous days of the patriarchs—on those sweet days of simplicity and ease, which never more will dawn on the lovely island of Manna-hata.

These melancholy reflections have been forced from me by the growing wealth and importance of New Amsterdam, which, I plainly perceive, are to involve it in all kinds of perils and disasters. Already, as I observed at the close of my last book, they had awakened the attention of the mother country. The usual mark of protection shown by mother countries to wealthy colonies was forthwith manifested; a governor being sent out to rule over the province and squeeze out of it as much revenue as possible. The arrival of a governor of course put an end to the protectorate of Oloffe the Dreamer. He appears, however, to have dreamt to some purpose during his sway, as we find him afterwards living as a patroon on a great landed estate on the banks of the Hudson; having virtually forfeited all right to his ancient appellation of Kortlandt or Lackland.

It was in the year of our Lord 1629 that Mynheer Wouter Van Twiller was appointed governor of the province of Nieuw Nederlands, under the commission and control of their High Mightinesses the Lords States General and the United Netherlands, and the privileged West India Company.

This renowned old gentleman arrived at New Amsterdam in the merry month of June, the sweetest month in all the year; when dan Apollo seems to dance up the transparent firmament—when the robin, the thrush, and a thousand other wanton songsters make the woods to resound with amorous ditties, and the luxurious little boblincon revels among the clover blossoms of the meadows—all which happy coincidence persuaded the old dames of New Amsterdam, who were skilled in the art of foretelling events, that this was to be a happy and prosperous administration.

The renowned Wouter (or Walter) Van Twiller was descended from a long line of Dutch burgomasters, who had successively dozed away their lives, and grown fat upon the bench of magistracy in Rotterdam; and who had comported themselves with such singular wisdom and propriety, that they were never either heard or talked of—which, next to being universally applauded, should be the object of ambition of all magistrates and rulers. There are two opposite ways by which some men make a figure in the world; one by talking faster than they think; and the other by holding their tongues and not thinking at all. By the first many a smatterer acquires the reputation of a man of quick parts; by the other many a dunderpate, like the owl, the stupidest of birds, comes to be considered the very type of wisdom. This, by the way, is a casual remark, which I would not for the universe have it thought I apply to Governor Van Twiller. It is true he was a man shut up within himself, like an oyster, and rarely spoke except in monosyllables; but then it was allowed he seldom said a foolish thing. So invincible was this gravity that he was never known to laugh or even to smile through the whole course of a long and prosperous life. Nay if a joke were uttered in his presence, that set light-minded hearers in a roar, it was observed to throw him into a state of perplexity. Sometimes he would deign to inquire into the matter, and when, after much explanation, the joke was made as plain as a pike-staff, he would continue to smoke his pipe in silence, and at length, knocking out the ashes would exclaim, "Well! I see nothing in all that to laugh about."

With all his reflective habits, he never made up his mind on a subject. His adherents accounted for this by the astonishing magnitude of his ideas. He conceived every subject on so grand a scale that he had not room in his head to turn it over and examine both sides of it. Certain it is that if any matter were propounded to him on which ordinary mortals would rashly determine at first glance, he would put on a vague, mysterious look; shake his capacious head; smoke some time in profound silence, and at length observe that "he had his doubts about the matter," which gained him the reputation of a man slow of belief, and not easily imposed upon. What is more, it gained him a lasting name: for to this habit of the mind has been attributed his surname of Twiller; which is said to be a corruption of the original Twijfler, or, in plain English, *Doubter*.

The person of this illustrious old gentleman was formed and proportioned, as though it had been moulded by the hands of some cunning Dutch statuary, as a model of majesty and lordly grandeur. He was exactly five feet six inches in height, and six feet five inches in circumference. His head was a perfect sphere, and of such stupendous dimensions, that dame Nature with all her sex's ingenuity would have been puzzled to construct a neck capable of supporting it; wherefore she wisely declined the attempt, and settled it firmly on the top of his backbone, just between the shoulders. His body was oblong and particularly capacious at bottom; which was wisely ordered by Providence, seeing that he was a man of sedentary habits, and very averse to the idle labor of walking. His legs were short, but sturdy in proportion to the weight they had to sustain; so that when erect he had not a little the appearance of a beer barrel on skids. His face, that infallible index of the mind, presented a vast expanse, unfurrowed by any of those lines and angles which disfigure the human countenance with what is termed expression. Two small gray eyes twinkled feebly in the midst, like two stars of lesser magnitude in a hazy firmament; and his full-fed cheeks, which seemed to have taken toll of every thing that went into his mouth, were curiously mottled and streaked with dusky red, like a spitzenberg apple.

His habits were as regular as his person. He daily took his four stated meals, appropriating exactly an hour to each; he smoked and doubted eight hours, and he slept the remaining twelve of the four-and-twenty. Such was the renowned Wouter Van Twiller—a true philosopher, for his mind was either elevated above, or tranquilly settled below, the cares and perplexities of this world. He had lived in it for years, without feeling the least curiosity to know whether the sun revolved round it, or it round the sun; and he had watched, for at least half a century, the smoke curling from his pipe to the ceiling, without once troubling his head with any of those numerous theories, by which a philosopher would have perplexed his brain, in accounting for its rising above the surrounding atmosphere.

In his council he presided with great state and solemnity. He sat in a huge chair of solid oak, hewn in the celebrated forest of the Hague, fabricated by an experienced timmerman of Amsterdam, and curiously carved about the arms and feet, into exact imitations of gigantic eagle's claws. Instead of a sceptre he swayed a long Turkish pipe, wrought with jasmin and amber, which had been presented to a stadtholder of Holland, at the conclusion of a treaty with one of the petty Barbary powers. In this stately chair would he sit, and this magnificent pipe would he smoke, shaking his right knee with a constant motion, and fixing his eye for hours together upon a little print of Amsterdam, which hung in a black frame against the opposite wall of the council chamber. Nay, it has even been said, that when any deliberation of extraordinary length and intricacy was on the carpet, the renowned Wouter would shut his eyes for full two hours at a time, that he might not be disturbed by external objects —and at such times the internal commotion of his mind was evinced by certain regular guttural sounds, which his admirers declared were merely the noise of conflict, made by his contending doubts and opinions.

It is with infinite difficulty I have been enabled to collect these biographical anecdotes of the great man under consideration. The facts respecting him were so scattered and vague, and divers of them so questionable in point of authenticity, that I have had to give up the search after many, and decline the admission of still more, which would have tended to heighten the coloring of his portrait.

I have been the more anxious to delineate fully the person and habits of Wouter Van Twiller, from the consideration that he was not only the first, but also the best governor that ever presided over this ancient and respectable province; and so tranquil and benevolent was his reign, that I do not find throughout the whole of it, a single instance of any offender being brought to punishment—a most indubitable sign of a merciful governor, and a case unparalleled, excepting in the reign of the illustrious King Log, from whom, it is hinted, the renowned Van Twiller was a lineal descendant.

The very outset of the career of this excellent magistrate was distinguished by an example of legal acumen, that gave flattering presage of a wise and equitable administration. The morning after he had been installed in office, and at the moment that he was making his breakfast from a prodigious earthen dish, filled with milk and Indian pudding, he was interrupted by the appearance of Wandle Schoonhoven, a very important old burgher of New Amsterdam, who complained bitterly of one Barent Bleecker, inasmuch as he refused to come to a settlement of accounts, seeing that there was a heavy balance in favor of the said Wandle. Governor Van Twiller, as I have already observed, was a man of few words; he was likewise a mortal enemy to multiplying writings—or being disturbed at his breakfast. Having listened attentively to the statement of Wandle Schoonhoven, giving an occasional grunt, as he shovelled a spoonful of Indian pudding into his mouth—either as a sign that he relished the dish, or comprehended the story—he called unto him his constable, and pulling out of his breeches pocket a huge jackknife, despatched it after the defendant as a summons, accompanied by his tobacco-box as a warrant.

This summary process was as effectual in those simple days as was the seal ring of the great Haroun Alraschid among the true believers. The two parties being confronted before him, each produced a book of accounts, written in a language and character that would have puzzled any but a High Dutch commentator, or a learned decipherer of Egyptian obelisks. The sage Wouter took them one after the other, and having poised them in his hands, and attentively counted over the number of leaves, fell straightway into a very great doubt, and smoked for half an hour without saying a word; at length, laying his finger beside his nose, and shutting his eyes for a moment, with the air of a man who has just caught a subtle idea by the tail, he slowly took his pipe from his mouth, puffed forth a column of tobacco smoke, and with marvellous gravity and solemnity pronounced—that having carefully counted over the leaves and weighed the books, it was found, that one was just as thick and as heavy as the other—therefore it was the final opinion of the court that the accounts were equally balanced—therefore Wandle should give Barent a receipt, and Barent should give Wandle a receipt—and the constable should pay the costs.

This decision being straightway made known diffused general joy throughout New Amsterdam, for the people immediately perceived that they had a very wise and equitable magistrate to rule over them. But its happiest effect was, that not another lawsuit took place throughout the whole of his administration—and the office of constable fell into such decay, that there was not one of those losel scouts known in the province for many years. I am the more particular in dwelling on this transaction, not only because I deem it one of the most sage and righteous judgments on record, and well worthy the attention of modern magistrates; but because it was a miraculous event in the history of the renowned Wouter—being the only time he was ever known to come to a decision in the whole course of his life.

CHAPTER II.

Containing Some Account of the Grand Council of New Amsterdam, as Also Divers Especial Good Philosophical Reasons Why an Alderman Should Be Fat—with Other Particulars Touching the State of the Province.

In treating of the early governors of the province, I must caution my readers against confounding them, in point of dignity and power, with those worthy gentlemen, who are whimsically denominated governors in this enlightened republic—a set of unhappy victims of popularity, who are in fact the most dependent hen-pecked beings in the community: doomed to bear the secret goadings and corrections of their own party, and the sneers and revilings of the whole world beside. Set up, like geese at Christmas holidays, to be pelted and shot at by every whipster and vagabond in the land. On the contrary, the Dutch governors enjoyed that uncontrolled authority, vested in all commanders of distant colonies or territories. They were in a manner absolute despots in their little domains, lording it, if so disposed, over both law and gospel, and accountable to none but the mother country; which it is well known is astonishingly deaf to all complaints against its governors, provided they discharge the main duty of their station—squeezing out a good revenue. This hint will be of importance, to prevent my readers from being seized with doubt and incredulity, whenever, in the course of this authentic history, they encounter the uncommon circumstance of a governor acting with independence, and in opposition to the opinions of the multitude.

To assist the doubtful Wouter in the arduous business of legislation, a board of magistrates was appointed, which presided immediately over the police. This potent body consisted of a schout or bailiff, with powers between those of the present mayor and sheriff—five burgermeesters, who were equivalent to aldermen, and five schepens, who officiated as scrubs, subdevils, or bottle-holders to the burgermeesters, in the same manner as do assistant alderman to their principals at the present day; it being their duty to fill the pipes of the lordly burgermeesters—hunt the markets for delicacies for corporation dinners, and to discharge such other little offices of kindness as were occasionally required. It was, moreover, tacitly understood, though not specifically enjoined, that they should consider themselves as butts for the blunt wits of the burgermeesters, and should laugh most heartily at all their jokes; but this last was a duty as rarely called in action in those days as it is at present, and was shortly remitted, in consequence of the tragical death of a fat little schepen—who actually died of suffocation in an unsuccessful effort to force a laugh at one of burgermeester Van Zandt's best jokes.

In return for these humble services, they were permitted to say *yes* and *no* at the council-board, and to have that enviable privilege, the run of the public kitchen—being graciously permitted to eat, and drink, and smoke, at all those snug junketings and public gormandizings, for which the ancient magistrates were equally famous with their modern successors. The post of schepen, therefore, like that of assistant alderman, was eagerly coveted by all your burghers of a certain description, who have a huge relish for good feeding, and an humble ambition to be great men in a small way—who thirst after a little brief authority, that shall render them the terror of the alms-house and the bridewell —that shall enable them to lord it over obsequious poverty, vagrant vice, outcast prostitution, and hunger-driven dishonesty—that shall give to their beck a hound-like pack of catchpolls and bumbailiffs—tenfold greater rogues than the culprits they hunt down!—my readers will excuse this sudden warmth, which I confess is unbecoming of a grave historian—but I have a mortal antipathy to catchpolls, bumbailiffs, and little great men.

The ancient magistrates of this city corresponded with those of the present time no less in form, magnitude, and intellect, than in prerogative and privilege. The burgomasters, like our aldermen, were generally chosen by weight—and not only the weight of the body, but likewise the weight of the head. It is a maxim practically observed in all honest, plain-thinking, regular cities, that an alderman should be fat—and the wisdom of this can be proved to a certainty.

That the body is in some measure an image of the mind, or rather that the mind is moulded to the body, like melted lead to the clay in which it is cast, has been insisted on by many philosophers, who have made human nature their peculiar study—for as a learned gentleman of our own city observes, "there is a constant relation between the moral character of all intelligent creatures, and their physical constitution—between their habits and the structure of their bodies." Thus we see that a lean, spare, diminutive body is generally accompanied by a petulant, restless, meddling mind—either the mind wears down the body, by its continual motion; or else the body, not affording the mind sufficient house-room, keeps it continually in a state of fretfulness, tossing and worrying about from the uneasiness of its situation. Whereas your round, sleek, fat, unwieldy periphery is ever attended by a mind like itself, tranquil, torpid, and at ease; and we may always observe, that your well fed, robustious burghers are in general very tenacious of their ease and comfort; being great enemies to noise, discord, and disturbance—and surely none are more likely to study the public tranquillity than those who are so careful of their own. Who ever hears of fat men heading a riot, or herding together in turbulent mobs?—no—no—it is your lean, hungry men who are continually worrying society, and setting the whole community by the ears.

The divine Plato, whose doctrines are not sufficiently attended to by philosophers of the present age, allows to every man three souls—one immortal and rational, seated in the brain, that it may overlook and regulate the body—a second consisting of the surly and irascible passions which, like belligerent powers, lie encamped around the heart—a third mortal and sensual, destitute of reason, gross and brutal in its propensities, and enchained in the belly, that it may not disturb the divine soul by its ravenous howlings. Now, according to this excellent theory, what can be more clear, than that your fat alderman is most likely to have the most regular and well-conditioned mind. His head is like a huge spherical chamber, containing a prodigious mass of soft brains, whereon the rational soul lies softly and snugly couched, as on a feather bed; and the eyes, which are the windows of the bed-chamber, are usually half closed, that its slumberings may not be disturbed by external objects. A mind thus comfortably lodged, and protected from disturbance, is manifestly most likely to perform its functions with regularity and ease. By dint of good feeding moreover, the mortal and malignant soul, which is confined in the belly, and which, by its raging and roaring, puts the irritable soul in the neighborhood of the heart in an intolerable passion, and thus renders men crusty and quarrelsome when hungry, is completely pacified, silenced, and put to rest—whereupon a host of honest, good fellow qualities and kind-hearted affections, which had lain perdue, slyly peeping out of the loop-holes of the heart, finding this cerberus asleep, do pluck up their spirits, turn out one and all in their holiday suits, and gambol up and down the diaphragm—disposing their possessor to laughter, good humor, and a thousand friendly offices towards his fellow mortals.

As a board of magistrates, formed on this principle, think but very little, they are the less likely to differ and wrangle about favorite opinions—and as they generally transact business upon a hearty dinner, they are naturally disposed to be lenient and indulgent in the administration of their duties. Charlemagne was conscious of this, and therefore ordered in his cartularies, that no judge should hold a court of justice, except in the morning, on an empty stomach.—A pitiful rule, which I can never forgive, and which I warrant bore hard upon all the poor culprits in the kingdom. The more enlightened and humane generation of the present day have taken an opposite course, and have so managed, that the aldermen are the best fed men in the community; feasting lustily on the fat things of the land, and gorging so heartily on oysters and turtles, that in process of time they acquire the activity of the one, and the form, the waddle, and the green fat of the other. The consequence is, as I have just said, these luxurious feastings do produce such a dulcet equanimity and repose of the soul, rational and irrational, that their transactions are proverbial for unvarying monotony—and the profound laws which they enact in their dozing moments, amid the labors of digestion, are quietly suffered to remain as dead letters, and never enforced, when awake. In a word, your fair, round-bellied burgomaster, like a full-fed mastiff, dozes quietly at the house door, always at home, and always at hand to watch over its safety—but as to electing a lean, meddling candidate to the office, as has now and then been done, I would as lief put a greyhound to watch the house, or a race-horse to draw an ox wagon.

The burgomasters then, as I have already mentioned, were wisely chosen by weight, and the schepens, or assistant aldermen, were appointed to attend upon them, and help them eat; but the latter, in the course of time, when they had been fed and fattened into sufficient bulk of body and drowsiness of brain, became very eligible candidates for the burgomasters' chairs, having fairly eaten themselves into office, as a mouse eats his way into a comfortable lodgment in a goodly, blue-nosed, skimmed milk, New England cheese.

Nothing could equal the profound deliberations that took place between the renowned Wouter, and these his worthy compeers, unless it be the sage divans of some of our modern corporations. They would sit for hours smoking and dozing over public affairs, without speaking a word to interrupt that perfect stillness, so necessary to deep reflection. Under the sober sway of Wouter Van Twiller and these his worthy coadjutors, the infant settlement waxed vigorous apace, gradually emerging from the swamps and forests, and exhibiting that mingled appearance of town and country, customary in new cities, and which at this day may be witnessed in the city of Washington; that immense metropolis, which makes so glorious an appearance on paper.

It was a pleasing sight in those times, to behold the honest burgher, like a patriarch of yore, seated on the bench at the door of his whitewashed house, under the shade of some gigantic sycamore or overhanging willow. Here would he smoke his pipe of a sultry afternoon, enjoying the soft southern breeze, and listening with silent gratulation to the clucking of his hens, the cackling of his geese, and the sonorous grunting of his swine; that combination of farm-yard melody, which may truly be said to have a silver sound, inasmuch as it conveys a certain assurance of profitable marketing.

The modern spectator, who wanders through the streets of this populous city, can scarcely form an idea of the different appearance they presented in the primitive days of the Doubter. The busy hum of multitudes, the shouts of revelry, the rumbling equipages of fashion, the rattling of accursed carts, and all the spirit-grieving sounds of brawling commerce, were unknown in the settlement of New Amsterdam. The grass grew quietly in the highways—the bleating sheep and frolicsome calves sported about the verdant ridge, where now the Broadway loungers take their morning stroll—the cunning fox or ravenous wolf skulked in the woods, where now are to be seen the dens of Gomez and his righteous fraternity of money-brokers—and flocks of vociferous geese cackled about the fields, where now the great Tammany wigwam and the patriotic tavern of Martling echo with the wranglings of the mob.

In these good times did a true and enviable equality of rank and property prevail, equally removed from the arrogance of wealth, and the servility and heart-burnings of repining poverty—and what in my mind is still more conducive to tranquillity and harmony among friends, a happy equality of intellect was likewise to be seen. The minds of the good burghers of New Amsterdam seemed all to have been cast in one mould, and to be those honest, blunt minds, which, like certain manufactures, are made by the gross, and considered as exceedingly good for common use.

Thus it happens that your true dull minds are generally preferred for public employ, and especially promoted to city honors; your keen intellects, like razors, being considered too sharp for common service. I know that it is common to rail at the unequal distribution of riches, as the great source of jealousies, broils, and heart-breakings; whereas, for my part, I verily believe it is the sad inequality of intellect that prevails, that embroils communities more than anything else; and I have remarked that your knowing people, who are so much wiser than any body else, are eternally keeping society in a ferment. Happily for New Amsterdam, nothing of the kind was known within its walls—the very words of learning, education, taste, and talents were unheard of—a bright genius was an animal unknown, and a blue-stocking lady would have been regarded with as much wonder as a horned frog or a fiery dragon. No man in fact seemed to know more than his neighbor, nor any man to know more than an honest man ought to know, who has nobody's business to mind but his own; the parson and the council clerk were the only men that could read in the community, and the sage Van Twiller always signed his name with a cross.

Thrice happy and ever to be envied little Burgh! existing in all the security of harmless insignificance—unnoticed and unenvied by the world, without ambition, without vainglory, without riches, without learning, and all their train of carking cares—and as of yore, in the better days of man, the deities were wont to visit him on earth and bless his rural habitations, so we are told, in the sylvan days of New Amsterdam, the good St. Nicholas would often make his appearance in his beloved city, of a holiday afternoon, riding jollily among the tree-tops, or over the roofs of the houses, now and then drawing forth magnificent presents from his breeches pockets, and dropping them down the chimneys of his favorites. Whereas in these degenerate days of iron and brass he never shows us the light of his countenance, nor ever visits us, save one night in the year; when he rattles down the chimneys of the descendants of the patriarchs, confining his presents merely to the children, in token of the degeneracy of the parents.

Such are the comfortable and thriving effects of a fat government. The province of the New Netherlands, destitute of wealth, possessed a sweet tranquillity that wealth could never purchase. There were neither public commotions, nor private quarrels; neither parties, nor sects, nor schisms; neither persecutions, nor trials, nor punishments; nor were there counsellors, attorneys, catchpolls, or hangmen. Every man attended to what little business he was lucky enough to have, or neglected it if he pleased, without asking the opinion of his neighbor. In those days nobody meddled with concerns above his comprehension; nor thrust his nose into other people's affairs; nor neglected to correct his own conduct, and reform his own character, in his zeal to pull to pieces the characters of others—but in a word, every respectable citizen ate when he was not hungry, drank when he was not thirsty, and went regularly to bed when the sun set and the fowls went to roost, whether he were sleepy or not; all which tended so remarkably to the population of the settlement, that I am told every dutiful wife throughout New Amsterdam made a point of enriching her husband with at least one child a year, and very often a brace—this superabundance of good things clearly constituting the true luxury of life, according to the favorite Dutch maxim, that "more than enough constitutes a feast." Every thing, therefore, went on exactly as it should do, and in the usual words employed by historians to express the welfare of a country, "the profoundest *tranquillity* and *repose* reigned throughout the province."

CHAPTER III.

How the Town of New Amsterdam Arose out of Mud, and Came to Be Marvellously Polished and Polite—Together with a Picture of the Manners of Our Great-Great-Grandfather.

MANIFOLD are the tastes and dispositions of the enlightened literati, who turn over the pages of history. Some there be whose hearts are brimful of the yeast of courage, and whose bosoms do work, and swell, and foam, with untried valor, like a barrel of new cider, or a train-band captain, fresh from under the hands of his tailor. This doughty class of readers can be satisfied with nothing but bloody battles, and horrible encounters; they must be continually storming forts, sacking cities, springing mines, marching up to the muzzles of cannon, charging bayonet through every page, and revelling in gunpowder and carnage. Others, who are of a less martial, but equally ardent imagination, and who, withal, are a little given to the marvellous, will dwell with wondrous satisfaction on descriptions of prodigies, unheard-of events, hair-breadth escapes, hardy adventures, and all those astonishing narrations, which just amble along the boundary line of possibility. A third class, who, not to speak slightly of them, are of a lighter turn, and skim over the records of past times, as they do over the edifying pages of a novel, merely for relaxation and innocent amusement, do singularly delight in treasons, executions, Sabine rapes, Tarquin outrages, conflagrations, murders, and all the other catalogue of hideous crimes, which like cayenne in cookery, do give a pungency and flavor to the dull detail of history—while a fourth class, of more philosophic habits, do diligently pore over the musty chronicles of time, to investigate the operations of the human kind, and watch the gradual changes in men and manners, effected by the progress of knowledge, the vicissitudes of events, or the influence of situation.

If the three first classes find but little wherewithal to solace themselves in the tranquil reign of Wouter Van Twiller, I entreat them to exert their patience for a while, and bear with the tedious picture of happiness, prosperity, and peace, which my duty as a faithful historian obliges me to draw; and I promise them that as soon as I can possibly alight upon any thing horrible, uncommon, or impossible, it shall go hard but I will make it afford them entertainment. This being premised, I turn with great complacency to the fourth class of my readers, who are men, or, if possible, women after my own heart; grave, philosophical, and investigating; fond of analyzing characters, of taking a start from first causes, and so hunting a nation down, through all the mazes of innovation and improvement. Such will naturally be anxious to witness the first development of the newly hatched colony, and the primitive manners and customs prevalent among its inhabitants, during the halcyon reign of Van Twiller or the Doubter.

I will not grieve their patience, however, by describing minutely the increase and improvement of New Amsterdam. Their own imaginations will doubtless present to them the good burghers, like so many painstaking and persevering beavers, slowly and surely pursuing their labors—they will behold the prosperous transformation from the rude log hut to the stately Dutch mansion, with brick front, glazed windows, and tiled roof; from the tangled thicket to the luxuriant cabbage garden; and from the skulking Indian to the ponderous burgomaster. In a word, they will picture to themselves the steady, silent, and undeviating march of prosperity, incident to a city destitute of pride or ambition, cherished by a fat government, and whose citizens do nothing in a hurry.

The sage council, as has been mentioned in a preceding chapter, not being able to determine upon any plan for the building of their city—the cows, in a laudable fit of patriotism, took it under their peculiar charge, and as they went to and from pasture, established paths through the bushes, on each side of which the good folks built their houses; which is one cause of the rambling and picturesque turns and labyrinths, which distinguish certain streets of New York at this very day.

The houses of the higher class were generally constructed of wood, excepting the gable end, which was of small black and yellow Dutch bricks, and always faced on the street, as our ancestors, like their descendants, were very much given to outward show, and were noted for putting the best leg foremost. The house was always furnished with abundance of large doors and small windows on every floor, the date of its erection was curiously designated by iron figures on the front, and on the top of the roof was perched a fierce little weathercock, to let the family into the important secret, which way the wind blew. These, like the weathercocks on the tops of our steeples, pointed so many different ways, that every man could have a wind to his mind;—the most stanch and loyal citizens, however, always went according to the weathercock on the top of the governor's house, which was certainly the most correct, as he had a trusty servant employed every morning to climb up and set it to the right quarter.

In those good days of simplicity and sunshine, a passion for cleanliness was the leading principle in domestic economy, and the universal test of an able housewife—a character which formed the utmost ambition of our unenlightened grandmothers. The front door was never opened except on marriages, funerals, New Year's days, the festival of St. Nicholas, or some such great occasion. It was ornamented with a gorgeous brass knocker, curiously wrought, sometimes in the device of a dog, and sometimes of a lion's head, and was daily burnished with such religious zeal, that it was ofttimes worn out by the very precautions taken for its preservation. The whole house was constantly in a state of inundation, under the discipline of mops and brooms and scrubbing brushes; and the good housewives of those days were a kind of amphibious animal, delighting exceedingly to be dabbling in water—insomuch that an historian of the day gravely tells us, that many of his townswomen grew to have webbed fingers like unto a duck; and some of them, he had little doubt, could the matter be examined into, would be found to have the tails of mermaids—but this I look upon to be a mere sport of fancy, or what is worse, a wilful misrepresentation.

The grand parlor was the sanctum sanctorum, where the passion for cleaning was indulged without control. In this sacred apartment no one was permitted to enter, excepting the mistress and her confidential maid, who visited it once a week, for the purpose of giving it a thorough cleaning, and putting things to rights—always taking the precaution of leaving their shoes at the door, and entering devoutly on their stocking feet. After scrubbing the floor, sprinkling it with fine white sand, which was curiously stroked into angles, and curves, and rhomboids with a broom—after washing the windows, rubbing and polishing the furniture, and putting a new bunch of evergreens in the fireplace—the window shutters were again closed to keep out the flies, and the room carefully locked up until the revolution of time brought round the weekly cleaning day.

As to the family, they always entered in at the gate, and most generally lived in the kitchen. To have seen a numerous household assembled round the fire, one would have imagined that he was transported back to those happy days of primeval simplicity, which float before our imaginations like golden visions. The fireplaces were of a truly patriarchal magnitude, where the whole family, old and young, master and servant, black and white, nay, even the very cat and dog, enjoyed a community of privilege, and had each a right to a corner. Here the old burgher would sit in perfect silence, puffing his pipe, looking in the fire with half shut eyes, and thinking of nothing for hours together; the goede vrouw on the opposite side would employ herself diligently in spinning yarn, or knitting stockings. The young folks would crowd around the hearth, listening with breathless attention to some old crone of a negro, who was the oracle of the family, and who, perched like a raven in a corner of the chimney, would croak forth for a long winter afternoon a string of incredible stories about New England witches—grisly ghosts, horses without heads—and hairbreadth escapes and bloody encounters among the Indians.

In those happy days a well regulated family always rose with the dawn, dined at eleven, and went to bed at sunset. Dinner was invariably a private meal, and the fat old burghers showed incontestable signs of disapprobation and uneasiness at being surprised by a visit from a neighbor on such occasions. But though our worthy ancestors were thus singularly averse to giving dinners, yet they kept up the social bands of intimacy by occasional banquetings, called tea-parties.

These fashionable parties were generally confined to the higher classes, or noblesse, that is to say, such as kept their own cows, and drove their own wagons. The company commonly assembled at three o'clock, and went away about six, unless it was in winter time, when the fashionable hours were a little earlier, that the ladies might get home before dark. The tea-table was crowned with a huge earthen dish, well stored with slices of fat pork, fried brown, cut up into morsels, and swimming in gravy. The company being seated round the genial board, and each furnished with a fork, evinced their dexterity in launching at the fattest pieces in this mighty dish—in much the same manner as sailors harpoon porpoises at sea, or our Indians spear salmon in the lakes. Sometimes the table was graced with immense apple pies, or saucers full of preserved peaches and pears; but it was always sure to boast an enormous dish of balls of sweetened dough, fried in hog's fat, and called doughnuts, or olykoeks—a delicious kind of cake, at present scarce known in this city, except in genuine Dutch families.

The tea was served out of a majestic delft tea-pot, ornamented with paintings of fat little Dutch shepherds and shepherdesses tending pigs—with boats sailing in the air, and houses built in the clouds, and sundry other ingenious Dutch fantasies. The beaux distinguished themselves by their adroitness in replenishing this pot from a huge copper tea-kettle, which would have made the pygmy macaronies of these degenerate days sweat merely to look at it. To sweeten the beverage, a lump of sugar was laid beside each cup—and the company alternately nibbled and sipped with great decorum, until an improvement was introduced by a shrewd and economic old lady, which was to suspend a large lump directly over the tea-table, by a string from the ceiling, so that it could be swung from mouth to mouth—an ingenious expedient, which is still kept up by some families in Albany; but which prevails without exception in Communipaw, Bergen, Flatbush, and all our uncontaminated Dutch villages.

At these primitive tea-parties the utmost propriety and dignity of deportment prevailed. No flirting nor coquetting—no gambling of old ladies nor hoyden chattering and romping of young ones—no self-satisfied struttings of wealthy gentlemen, with their brains in their pockets—nor amusing conceits, and monkey divertisements, of smart young gentlemen, with no brains at all. On the contrary, the young ladies seated themselves demurely in their rush-bottomed chairs, and knit their own woollen stockings; nor ever opened their lips excepting to say *yah Mynheer*, or *yah ya Vrouw*, to any question that was asked them; behaving, in all things, like decent, well-educated damsels. As to the gentlemen, each of them tranquilly smoked his pipe, and seemed lost in contemplation of the blue and white tiles with which the fireplaces were decorated; wherein sundry passages of Scripture were piously portrayed—Tobit and his dog figured to great advantage; Haman swung conspicuously on his gibbet, and Jonah appeared most manfully bouncing out of the whale, like Harlequin through a barrel of fire.

The parties broke up without noise and without confusion. They were carried home by their own carriages, that is to say, by the vehicles nature had provided them, excepting such of the wealthy as could afford to keep a wagon. The gentlemen gallantly attended their fair ones to their respective abodes, and took leave of them with a hearty smack at the door; which, as it was an established piece of etiquette, done in perfect simplicity and honesty of heart, occasioned no scandal at that time, nor should it at the present—if our great-grandfathers approved of the custom, it would argue a great want of reverence in their descendants to say a word against it.

CHAPTER IV.

Containing Further Particulars of the Golden Age, and What Constituted a Fine Lady and Gentleman in the Days of Walter the Doubter.

In this dulcet period of my history, when the beauteous island of Manna-hata presented a scene, the very counterpart of those glowing pictures drawn of the golden reign of Saturn, there was, as I have before observed, a happy ignorance, an honest simplicity prevalent among its inhabitants, which, were I even able to depict, would be but little understood by the degenerate age for which I am doomed to write. Even the female sex, those arch innovators upon the tranquillity, the honesty, and gray-beard customs of society, seemed for a while to conduct themselves with incredible sobriety and comeliness.

Their hair, untortured by the abominations of art, was scrupulously pomatumed back from their foreheads with a candle, and covered with a little cap of quilted calico, which fitted exactly to their heads. Their petticoats of linsey-woolsey were striped with a variety of gorgeous dyes—though I must confess these gallant garments were rather short, scarce reaching below the knee; but then they made up in the number, which generally equalled that of the gentlemen's small clothes; and what is still more praiseworthy, they were all of their own manufacture—of which circumstance, as may well be supposed, they were not a little vain.

These were the honest days, in which every woman staid at home, read the

Bible, and wore pockets—ay, and that too of a goodly size, fashioned with patchwork into many curious devices, and ostentatiously worn on the outside. These, in fact, were convenient receptacles, where all good housewives carefully stored away such things as they wished to have at hand; by which means they often came to be incredibly crammed—and I remember there was a story current when I was a boy, that the lady of Wouter Van Twiller once had occasion to empty her right pocket in search of a wooden ladle, when the contents filled a couple of corn baskets, and the utensil was discovered lying among some rubbish in one corner—but we must not give too much faith to all these stories; the anecdotes of those remote periods being very subject to exaggeration.

Besides these notable pockets, they likewise wore scissors and pincushions suspended from their girdles by red ribands, or among the more opulent and showy classes, by brass, and even silver chains—indubitable tokens of thrifty housewives and industrious spinsters. I cannot say much in vindication of the shortness of the petticoats; it doubtless was introduced for the purpose of giving the stockings a chance to be seen, which were generally of blue worsted with magnificent red clocks—or perhaps to display a well-turned ankle, and a neat, though serviceable foot, set off by a high-heeled leathern shoe, with a large and splendid silver buckle. Thus we find that the gentle sex in all ages have shown the same disposition to infringe a little upon the laws of decorum, in order to betray a lurking beauty, or gratify an innocent love of finery.

From the sketch here given, it will be seen that our good grandmothers differed considerably in their ideas of a fine figure from their scantily dressed descendants of the present day. A fine lady, in those times, waddled under more clothes, even on a fair summer's day, than would have clad the whole bevy of a modern ballroom. Nor were they the less admired by the gentlemen in consequence thereof. On the contrary, the greatness of a lover's passion seemed to increase in proportion to the magnitude of its object—and a voluminous damsel, arrayed in a dozen of petticoats, was declared by a Low Dutch sonneteer of the province to be radiant as a sunflower, and luxuriant as a fullblown cabbage. Certain it is, that in those days the heart of a lover could not contain more than one lady at a time; whereas the heart of a modern gallant has often room enough to accommodate half a dozen. The reason of which I conclude to be, that either the hearts of the gentlemen have grown larger, or the persons of the ladies smaller—this, however, is a question for physiologists to determine.

But there was a secret charm in these petticoats, which, no doubt, entered into the consideration of the prudent gallants. The wardrobe of a lady was in those days her only fortune; and she who had a good stock of petticoats and stockings, was as absolutely an heiress as is a Kamschatka damsel with a store of bear skins, or a Lapland belle with a plenty of reindeer. The ladies, therefore, were very anxious to display these powerful attractions to the greatest advantage; and the best rooms in the house, instead of being adorned with caricatures of dame Nature, in water-colors and needle-work, were always hung round with abundance of homespun garments, the manufacture and the property of the females—a piece of laudable ostentation that still prevails among the heiresses of our Dutch villages.

The gentlemen, in fact, who figured in the circles of the gay world in these ancient times, corresponded, in most particulars, with the beauteous damsels whose smiles they were ambitious to deserve. True it is, their merits would make but a very inconsiderable impression upon the heart of a modern fair; they neither drove their curricles nor sported their tandems, for as yet those gaudy vehicles were not even dreamt of—neither did they distinguish themselves by their brilliancy at the table, and their consequent rencontres with watchmen, for our forefathers were of too pacific a disposition to need those guardians of the night, every soul throughout the town being sound asleep before nine o'clock. Neither did they establish their claims to gentility at the expense of their tailors—for as yet those offenders against the pockets of society, and the tranquillity of all aspiring young gentlemen, were unknown in New Amsterdam; every good housewife made the clothes of her husband and family, and even the goede vrouw of Van Twiller himself thought it no disparagement to cut out her husband's linsey-woolsey galligaskins.

Not but what there were some two or three youngsters who manifested the first dawning of what is called fire and spirit; who held all labor in contempt; skulked about docks and market places; loitered in the sunshine; squandered what little money they could procure at hustle-cap and chuck-farthing; swore, boxed, fought cocks, and raced their neighbor's horses—in short, who promised to be the wonder, the talk, and abomination of the town, had not their stylish career been unfortunately cut short by an affair of honor with a whipping-post.

Far other, however, was the truly fashionable gentleman of those days—his dress, which served for both morning and evening, street and drawing-room, was a linsey-woolsey coat, made, perhaps, by the fair hands of the mistress of his affections, and gallantly bedecked with abundance of large brass buttons—half a score of breeches heightened the proportions of his figure—his shoes were decorated by enormous copper buckles—a low-crowned broad-brimmed hat overshadowed his burly visage, and his hair dangled down his back in a prodigious queue of eelskin.

Thus equipped, he would manfully sally forth with pipe in mouth to besiege some fair damsel's obdurate heart—not such a pipe, good reader, as that which Acis did sweetly tune in praise of his Galatea, but one of true Delft manufacture, and furnished with a charge of fragrant tobacco. With this would he resolutely set himself down before the fortress, and rarely failed, in the process of time, to smoke the fair enemy into a surrender, upon honorable terms.

Such was the happy reign of Wouter Van Twiller, celebrated in many a long forgotten song as the real golden age, the rest being nothing but counterfeit copper-washed coin. In that delightful period, a sweet and holy calm reigned over the whole province. The burgomaster smoked his pipe in peace—the substantial solace of his domestic cares, after her daily toils were done, sat soberly at the door, with her arms crossed over her apron of snowy white, without being insulted by ribald street-walkers or vagabond boys—those unlucky urchins, who do so infest our streets, displaying under the roses of youth the thorns and briers of iniquity. Then it was that the lover with ten breeches, and the damsel with petticoats of half a score, indulged in all the innocent endearments of virtuous love without fear and without reproach; for what had that virtue to fear, which was defended by a shield of good linsey-woolseys, equal at least to the seven bull-hides of the invincible Ajax?

Ah blissful, and never to be forgotten age! when everything was better than it has ever been since, or ever will be again—when Buttermilk Channel was quite dry at low water—when the shad in the Hudson were all salmon, and when the moon shone with a pure and resplendent whiteness, instead of that melancholy yellow light which is the consequence of her sickening at the abominations she every night witnesses in this degenerate city!

Happy would it have been for New Amsterdam could it always have existed in this state of blissful ignorance and lowly simplicity, but alas! the days of childhood are too sweet to last! Cities, like men, grow out of them in time, and are doomed alike to grow into the bustle, the cares, and miseries of the world. Let no man congratulate himself, when he beholds the child of his bosom or the city of his birth increasing in magnitude and importance—let the history of his own life teach him the dangers of the one, and this excellent little history of Manna-hata convince him of the calamities of the other.

CHAPTER V.

Of the Founding of Fort Aurania—of the Mysteries of the Hudson—of the Arrival of the Patroon Killian Van Rensellaer; His Lordly Descent upon the Earth, and His Introduction of Club-Law.

It has already been mentioned that, in the early times of Oloffe the Dreamer, a frontier post, or trading-house, called Fort Aurania, had been established on the upper waters of the Hudson, precisely on the site of the present venerable city of Albany; which was at that time considered at the very end of the habitable world. It was, indeed, a remote possession with which, for a long time, New Amsterdam held but little intercourse. Now and then the "Company's Yacht," as it was called, was sent to the Fort with supplies, and to bring away the peltries which had been purchased of the Indians. It was like an expedition to the Indias, or the North Pole, and always made great talk in the settlement. Sometimes an adventurous burgher would accompany the expedition, to the great uneasiness of his friends; but, on his return, had so many stories to tell of storms and tempests on the Tappan Zee; of hobgoblins in the Highlands and at the Devils Dans Kammer, and of all the other wonders and perils with which the river abounded in those early days, that he deterred the less adventurous inhabitants from following his example.

Matters were in this state, when, one day, as Walter the Doubter and his burgermeesters were smoking and pondering over the affairs of the province, they were roused by the report of a cannon. Sallying forth, they beheld a strange vessel at anchor in the bay. It was unquestionably of Dutch build; broad-bottomed and high pooped, and bore the flag of their High Mightinesses at the mast-head.

After a while a boat put off for land, and a stranger stepped on shore, a lofty, lordly kind of man, tall and dry, with a meagre face, furnished with huge moustaches. He was clad in Flemish doublet and hose, and an insufferably tall hat, with a cocktail feather. Such was the patroon Killian Van Rensellaer, who had come out from Holland to found a colony or patroonship on a great tract of wild land, granted to him by their High Mightinesses the Lords States General, in the upper regions of the Hudson.

Killian Van Rensellaer was a nine days' wonder in New Amsterdam; for he carried a high head, looked down upon the portly, short-legged burgomasters, and owned no allegiance to the governor himself; boasting that he held his patroonship directly from the Lords States General.

He tarried but a short time in New Amsterdam; merely to beat up recruits for his colony. Few, however, ventured to enlist for those remote and savage regions; and when they embarked, their friends took leave of them as if they should never see them more; and stood gazing with tearful eye as the stout, round-sterned little vessel ploughed and splashed its way up the Hudson, with great noise and little progress, taking nearly a day to get out of sight of the city.

And now, from time to time, floated down tidings to the Manhattoes of the growing importance of this new colony. Every account represented Killian Van Rensellaer as rising in importance and becoming a mighty patroon in the land. He had received more recruits from Holland. His patroonship of Rensellaerwick lay immediately below Fort Aurania, and extended for several miles on each side of the Hudson, beside embracing the mountainous region of the Helderberg. Over all this he claimed to hold separate jurisdiction independent of the colonial authorities at New Amsterdam.

All these assumptions of authority were duly reported to Governor Van Twiller and his council, by despatches from Fort Aurania; at each new report the governor and his counsellors looked at each other, raised their eyebrows, gave an extra puff or two of smoke, and then relapsed into their usual tranquillity.

At length tidings came that the patroon of Rensellaerwick had extended his usurpations along the river, beyond the limits granted him by their High Mightinesses; and that he had even seized upon a rocky island in the Hudson, commonly known by the name of Bearn or Bear's Island; where he was erecting a fortress called by the lordly name of Rensellaerstein.

Wouter Van Twiller was roused by this intelligence. After consulting with his burgomasters, he despatched a letter to the patroon of Rensellaerwick, demanding by what right he had seized upon this island, which lay beyond the bounds of his patroonship. The answer of Killian Van Rensellaer was in his own lordly style, *"By wapen recht!"* that is to say, by the right of arms, or, in common parlance, by club-law. This answer plunged the worthy Wouter in one of the deepest doubts he had in the whole course of his administration; in the meantime, while Wouter doubted, the lordly Killian went on to finish his fortress of Rensellaerstein, about which I foresee I shall have something to record in a future chapter of this most eventful history.

CHAPTER VI.

In Which the Reader Is Beguiled into a Delectable Walk, Which Ends Very Differently from What It Commenced.

In the year of our Lord one thousand eight hundred and four, on a fine afternoon in the glowing month of September, I took my customary walk upon the battery, which is at once the pride and bulwark of this ancient and impregnable city of New York. The ground on which I trod was hallowed by recollections of the past, and as I slowly wandered through the long alley of poplars, which, like so many birch brooms standing on end, diffused a melancholy and lugubrious shade, my imagination drew a contrast between the surrounding scenery, and what it was in the classic days of our forefathers. Where the government house by name, but the custom house by occupation, proudly reared its brick walls and wooden pillars, there whilom stood the low, but substantial, red-tiled mansion of the renowned Wouter Van Twiller. Around it the mighty bulwarks of Fort Amsterdam frowned defiance to every absent foe; but, like many a whiskered warrior and gallant militia captain, confined their martial deeds to frowns alone. The mud breastworks had long been levelled with the earth, and their site converted into the green lawns and leafy alleys of the battery; where the gay apprentice sported his Sunday coat, and the laborious mechanic, relieved from the dirt and drudgery of the week, poured his weekly tale of love into the half averted ear of the sentimental chambermaid. The capacious bay still presented the same expansive sheet of water, studded with islands, sprinkled with fishing boats, and bounded by shores of picturesque beauty. But the dark forests which once clothed those shores had been violated by the savage hand of cultivation, and their tangled mazes, and impenetrable thickets, had degenerated into teeming orchards and waving fields of grain. Even Governor's Island, once a smiling garden, appertaining to the sovereigns of the province, was now covered with fortifications, enclosing a tremendous block-house—so that this once peaceful island resembled a fierce little warrior in a big cocked hat, breathing gun powder and defiance to the world!

For some time did I indulge in a pensive train of thought; contrasting, in sober sadness, the present day with the hallowed years behind the mountains; lamenting the melancholy progress of improvement, and praising the zeal with which our worthy burghers endeavor to preserve the wrecks of venerable customs, prejudices, and errors, from the overwhelming tide of modern innovation—when by degrees my ideas took a different turn, and I insensibly awakened to an enjoyment of the beauties around me.

It was one of those rich autumnal days which heaven particularly bestows upon the beauteous island of Manna-hata and its vicinity—not a floating cloud obscured the azure firmament—the sun, rolling in glorious splendor through his ethereal course, seemed to expand his honest Dutch countenance into an unusual expression of benevolence, as he smiled his evening salutation upon a city which he delights to visit with his most bounteous beams—the very winds seemed to hold in their breaths in mute attention, lest they should ruffle the tranquillity of the hour—and the waveless bosom of the bay presented a polished mirror, in which nature beheld herself and smiled. The standard of our city, reserved like a choice handkerchief, for days of gala, hung motionless on the flag-staff, which forms the handle of a gigantic churn; and even the tremulous leaves of the poplar and the aspen ceased to vibrate to the breath of heaven. Everything seemed to acquiesce in the profound repose of nature. The formidable eighteen-pounders slept in the embrazures of the wooden batteries, seemingly gathering fresh strength to fight the battles of their country on the next fourth of July—the solitary drums on Governor's Island forgot to call the garrison to their *shovels*—the evening gun had not yet sounded its signal for all the regular well-meaning poultry throughout the country to go to roost; and the fleet of canoes at anchor between Gibbet Island and Communipaw slumbered on their rakes, and suffered the innocent oysters to lie for a while unmolested in the soft mud of their native banks!—My own feelings sympathized with the contagious tranquillity, and I should infallibly have dozed upon one of those fragments of benches, which our benevolent magistrates have provided for the benefit of convalescent loungers, had not the extraordinary inconvenience of the couch set all repose at defiance.

In the midst of this slumber of the soul, my attention was attracted to a black speck, peering above the western horizon, just in the rear of Bergen steeple—gradually it augments and overhangs the would-be cities of Jersey, Harsimus, and Hoboken, which, like three jockies, are starting on the course of existence, and jostling each other at the commencement of the race. Now, it skirts the long shore of ancient Pavonia, spreading its wide shadows from the high settlements of Weehawk quite to the lazaretto and quarantine, erected by the sagacity of our police, for the embarrassment of commerce—now it climbs the serene vault of heaven, cloud rolling over cloud, shrouding the orb of day, darkening the vast expanse, and bearing thunder and hail and tempest in its bosom. The earth seems agitated at the confusion of the heavens—the late waveless mirror is lashed into furious waves that roll in hollow murmurs to the shore—the oyster boats that erst sported in the placid vicinity of Gibbet Island now hurry affrighted to the land—the poplar writhes and twists and whistles in the blast—torrents of drenching rain and sounding hail deluge the battery walks—the gates are thronged by apprentices, servant maids, and little Frenchmen, with pocket handkerchiefs over their hats, scampering from the storm—the late beauteous prospect presents one scene of anarchy and wild uproar, as though old Chaos had resumed his reign, and was hurling back into one vast turmoil the conflicting elements of nature.

Whether I fled from the fury of the storm, or remained boldly at my post, as our gallant train-band captains, who march their soldiers through the rain without flinching, are points which I leave to the conjecture of the reader. It is possible he may be a little perplexed also to know the reason why I introduced this tremendous tempest to disturb the serenity of my work. On this latter point I will gratuitously instruct his ignorance. The panorama view of the battery was given merely to gratify the reader with a correct description of that celebrated place, and the parts adjacent—secondly, the storm was played off partly to give a little bustle and life to this tranquil part of my work, and to keep my drowsy readers from falling asleep—and partly to serve as an overture to the tempestuous times which are about to assail the pacific province of Nieuw Nederlands—and which overhang the slumbrous administration of the renowned Wouter Van Twiller. It is thus the experienced playwright puts all the fiddles, the French-horns, the kettle-drums, and trumpets of his orchestra in requisition, to usher in one of those horrible and brimstone uproars called Melodrames—and it is thus he discharges his thunder, his lightning, his rosin, and saltpetre, preparatory to the rising of a ghost, or the murdering of a hero.—We will now proceed with our history.

Whatever may be advanced by philosophers to the contrary, I am of opinion that, as to nations, the old maxim, that "honesty is the best policy," is a sheer and ruinous mistake. It might have answered well enough in the honest times when it was made; but in these degenerate days, if a nation pretends to rely merely upon the justice of its dealings, it will fare something like the honest man who fell among thieves, and found his honesty a poor protection against bad company. Such, at least, was the case with the guileless government of the New Netherlands; which, like a worthy unsuspicious old burgher, quietly settled itself down in the city of New Amsterdam, as into a snug elbow chair—and fell into a comfortable nap—while, in the meantime, its cunning neighbors stepped in and picked its pockets. In a word, we may ascribe the commencement of all the woes of this great province, and its magnificent metropolis, to the tranquil security, or, to speak more accurately, to the unfortunate honesty of its government. But as I dislike to begin an important part of my history towards the end of a chapter; and as my readers, like myself, must doubtless be exceedingly fatigued with the long walk we have taken, and the tempest we have sustained—I hold it meet we shut up the book, smoke a pipe, and having thus refreshed our spirits, take a fair start in a new chapter.

CHAPTER VII.

FAITHFULLY DESCRIBING THE INGENIOUS PEOPLE OF CONNECTICUT AND THEREABOUTS—SHOWING, MOREOVER, THE TRUE MEANING OF LIBERTY OF CONSCIENCE, AND A CURIOUS DEVICE AMONG THESE STURDY BARBARIANS, TO KEEP UP A HARMONY OF INTERCOURSE, AND PROMOTE POPULATION.

THAT my readers may the more fully comprehend the extent of the calamity, at this very moment impending over the honest, unsuspecting province of

Nieuw Nederlands, and its dubious governor, it is necessary that I should give some account of a horde of strange barbarians, bordering upon the eastern frontier.

Now so it came to pass, that many years previous to the time of which we are treating, the sage cabinet of England had adopted a certain national creed, a kind of public walk of faith, or rather a religious turnpike, in which every loyal subject was directed to travel to Zion—taking care to pay the *toll-gatherers* by the way.

Albeit a certain shrewd race of men, being very much given to indulge their own opinions on all manner of subjects (a propensity exceedingly offensive to your free governments of Europe), did most presumptuously dare to think for themselves in matters of religion, exercising what they considered a natural and unextinguishable right—the liberty of conscience.

As, however, they possessed that ingenious habit of mind which always thinks aloud; which rides cock-a-hoop on the tongue, and is forever galloping into other people's ears, it naturally followed that their liberty of conscience like-wise implied *liberty of speech*, which being freely indulged, soon put the country in a hubbub, and aroused the pious indignation of the vigilant fathers of the church.

The usual methods were adopted to reclaim them, which in those days were considered efficacious in bringing back stray sheep to the fold; that is to say, they were coaxed, they were admonished, they were menaced, they were buffeted—line upon line, precept upon precept, lash upon lash, here a little and there a great deal, were exhausted without mercy, and without success; until the worthy pastors of the church, wearied out by their unparalleled stubbornness, were driven in the excess of their tender mercy, to adopt the Scripture text, and literally to "heap live embers on their heads."

Nothing, however, could subdue that independence of the tongue which has ever distinguished this singular race, so that, rather than subject that heroic member to further tyranny, they one and all embarked for the wilderness of America, to enjoy, unmolested, the inestimable right of talking. And, in fact, no sooner did they land upon the shore of this free-spoken country, than they all lifted up their voices, and made such a clamor of tongues, that we are told they frightened every bird and beast out of the neighborhood, and struck such mute terror into certain fish, that they have been called *dumb-fish* ever since.

This may appear marvellous, but it is nevertheless true, in proof of which I would observe, that the dumb-fish has ever since become an object of super-stitious reverence, and forms the Saturday's dinner of every true Yankee.

The simple aborigines of the land for a while contemplated these strange folk in utter astonishment, but discovering that they wielded harmless, though noisy weapons, and were a lively, ingenious, good-humored race of men, they became very friendly and sociable, and gave them the name of *Yanokies*, which in the Mais-Tchusaeg (or Massachusett) language signifies *silent men*— a waggish appellation, since shortened into the familar epithet of YANKEES, which they retain unto the present day.

True it is, and my fidelity as a historian will not allow me to pass over the fact, that having served a regular apprenticeship in the school of persecution, these ingenious people soon showed that they had become masters of the art. The great majority were of one particular mode of thinking in matters of religion; but to their great surprise and indignation, they found that divers papists, quakers and anabaptists were springing up among them, and all claiming to use the liberty of speech. This was at once pronounced a daring abuse of the liberty of conscience; which they now insisted was nothing more than the liberty to think as one pleased in matters of religion—provided one thought right; for otherwise it would be giving a latitude to damnable heresies. Now as they, the majority, were convinced that they alone thought right, it consequently followed, that whoever thought different from them thought wrong —and whoever thought wrong, and obstinately persisted in not being convinced and converted, was a flagrant violator of the inestimable liberty of conscience, and a corrupt and infectious member of the body politic, and deserved to be lopped off and cast into the fire. The consequence of all which was a fiery persecution of divers sects, and especially of quakers.

Now I'll warrant there are hosts of my readers ready at once to lift up their hands and eyes, with that virtuous indignation with which we contemplate the faults and errors of our neighbors, and to exclaim at the preposterous idea of convincing the mind by tormenting the body, and establishing the doctrine of charity and forbearance by intolerant persecution. But in simple truth, what are we doing at this very day, and in this very enlightened nation, but acting upon the very same principle in our political controversies? Have we not within but a few years released ourselves from the shackles of a government which cruelly denied us the privilege of governing ourselves, and using in full latitude that invaluable member, the tongue? and are we not at this very moment striving our best to tyrannize over the opinions, tie up the tongues, and ruin the fortunes of one another? What are our great political societies, but mere political inquisitions—our pothouse committees but little tribunals of denunciation—our newspapers but mere whipping-posts and pillories, where unfortunate individuals are pelted with rotten eggs—and our council of appointment, but a grand *auto da fe*, where culprits are annually sacrificed for their political heresies?

Where then is the difference in principle between our measures and those you are so ready to condemn among the people I am treating of? There is none; the difference is merely circumstantial.—Thus we *denounce*, instead of banishing—we *libel*, instead of scourging—we *turn out of office*, instead of hanging— and where they burnt an offender in proper person, we either tar and feather or *burn him in effigy*—this political persecution being, somehow or other, the grand palladium of our liberties, and an incontrovertible proof that this is *a free country!*

But notwithstanding the fervent zeal with which this holy war was prosecuted against the whole race of unbelievers, we do not find that the population of this new colony was in anywise hindered thereby; on the contrary, they multiplied to a degree which would be incredible to any man unacquainted with the marvellous fecundity of this growing country.

This amazing increase may, indeed, be partly ascribed to a singular custom prevalent among them, commonly known by the name of *bundling*—a superstitious rite observed by the young people of both sexes, with which they usually terminated their festivities; and which was kept up with religious strictness by the more bigoted part of the community. This ceremony was likewise, in those primitive times, considered as an indispensable preliminary to matrimony; their courtships commencing where ours usually finish—by which means they acquired that intimate acquaintance with each others' good qualities before marriage, which has been pronounced by philosophers the sure basis of a happy union. Thus early did this cunning and ingenious people display a shrewdness of making a bargain, which has ever since distinguished them—and a strict adherence to the good old vulgar maxim about "buying a pig in a poke."

To this sagacious custom, therefore, do I chiefly attribute the unparalleled increase of the Yanokie or Yankee race; for it is a certain fact, well authenticated by court records and parish registers, that wherever the practice of bundling prevailed, there was an amazing number of sturdy brats annually born unto the State, without the license or the law, or the benefit of clergy. Neither did the irregularity of their birth operate in the least to their disparagement. On the contrary, they grew up a long-sided, raw-boned, hardy race of whoreson whalers, wood-cutters, fishermen, and pedlers, and strapping corn-fed wenches; who by their united efforts tended marvellously towards peopling those notable tracts of country called Nantucket, Piscataway, and Cape Cod.

CHAPTER VIII.

How These Singular Barbarians Turned out to Be Notorious Squatters—How They Built Air Castles, and Attempted to Initiate the Nederlanders into the Mystery of Bundling.

In the last chapter I have given a faithful and unprejudiced account of the origin of that singular race of people, inhabiting the country eastward of the Nieuw Nederlands; but I have yet to mention certain peculiar habits which rendered them exceedingly annoying to our ever honored Dutch ancestors.

The most prominent of these was a certain rambling propensity, with which, like the sons of Ishmael, they seem to have been gifted by heaven, and which continually goads them on, to shift their residence from place to place, so that a Yankee farmer is in a constant state of migration; *tarrying* occasionally here and there; clearing lands for other people to enjoy, building houses for others to inhabit, and in a manner may be considered the wandering Arab of America.

His first thought, on coming to the years of manhood, is to *settle* himself in the world—which means nothing more nor less than to begin his rambles. To this end he takes unto himself for a wife some buxom country heiress, passing rich in red ribands, glass beads, and mock tortoise-shell combs, with a white gown and morocco shoes for Sunday, and deeply skilled in the mystery of making apple sweetmeats, long sauce, and pumpkin pie.

Having thus provided himself, like a pedler with a heavy knapsack, wherewith to regale his shoulders through the journey of life, he literally sets out on the peregrination. His whole family, household furniture, and farming utensils, are hoisted into a covered cart; his own and his wife's wardrobe packed up in a firkin—which done, he shoulders his axe, takes staff in hand, whistles "yankee doodle," and trudges off to the woods, as confident of the protection of Providence, and relying as cheerfully upon his own resources, as did ever a patriarch of yore, when he journeyed into a strange country of the Gentiles. Having buried himself in the wilderness, he builds himself a log hut, clears away a cornfield and potato patch, and Providence smiling upon his labors, is soon surrounded by a snug farm and some half a score of flaxen-headed urchins, who, by their size, seem to have sprung all at once out of the earth, like a crop of toadstools.

But it is not the nature of this most indefatigable of speculators to rest contented with any state of sublunary enjoyment—*improvement* is his darling passion, and having thus improved his lands, the next care is to provide a mansion worthy the residence of a landholder. A huge palace of pine boards immediately springs up in the midst of the wilderness, large enough for a parish church, and furnished with windows of all dimensions, but so rickety and flimsy withal, that every blast gives it a fit of the ague.

By the time the outside of this mighty air castle is completed, either the funds or the zeal of our adventurer are exhausted, so that he barely manages to half finish one room within, where the whole family burrow together—while the rest of the house is devoted to the curing of pumpkins, or storing of carrots and potatoes, and is decorated with fanciful festoons of dried apples and peaches. The outside, remaining unpainted, grows venerably black with time; the family wardrobe is laid under contribution for old hats, petticoats, and breeches, to stuff into the broken windows, while the four winds of heaven keep up a whistling and howling about this aerial palace, and play as many unruly gambols as they did of yore in the cave of old Æolus.

The humble log hut, which whilom nestled this *improving* family snugly within its narrow but comfortable walls, stands hard by, in ignominious contrast, degraded into a cow-house or pigsty; and the whole scene reminds one forcibly of a fable, which I am surprised has never been recorded, of an aspiring snail, who abandoned his humble habitation, which he had long filled with great respectability, to crawl into the empty shell of a lobster—where he would no doubt have resided with great style and splendor, the envy and the hate of all the painstaking snails in the neighborhood, had he not perished with cold, in one corner of his stupendous mansion.

Being thus completely settled, and, to use his own words, "to rights," one would imagine that he would begin to enjoy the comforts of his situation, to read newspapers, talk politics, neglect his own business, and attend to the affairs of the nation, like a useful and patriotic citizen; but now it is that his wayward disposition begins again to operate. He soon grows tired of a spot where there is no longer any room for improvement—sells his farm, air castle, petticoat windows and all, reloads his cart, shoulders his axe, puts himself at the head of his family, and wanders away in search of new lands—again to fell trees—again to clear cornfields—again to build a shingle palace, and again to sell off and wander.

Such were the people of Connecticut, who bordered upon the eastern frontier of New Netherlands, and my readers may easily imagine what uncomfortable neighbors this light-hearted but restless tribe must have been to our tranquil progenitors. If they cannot, I would ask them if they have ever known one of our regular, well-organized Dutch families, whom it hath pleased heaven to afflict with the neighborhood of a French boarding-house? The honest old burgher cannot take his afternoon's pipe on the bench before his door, but he is persecuted with the scraping of fiddles, the chattering of women, and the squalling of children—he cannot sleep at night for the horrible melodies of some amateur, who chooses to serenade the moon, and display his terrible proficiency in *execution*, on the clarionet, hautboy, or some other soft-toned instrument—nor can he leave the street door open, but his house is defiled by the unsavory visits of a troop of pup dogs, who even sometimes carry their loathsome ravages into the sanctum sanctorum, the parlor!

If my readers have ever witnessed the sufferings of such a family, so situated, they may form some idea how our worthy ancestors were distressed by their mercurial neighbors of Connecticut.

Gangs of these marauders, we are told, penetrated into the New Netherland settlements, and threw whole villages into consternation by their unparalleled volubility, and their intolerable inquisitiveness—two evil habits hitherto unknown in those parts, or only known to be abhorred; for our ancestors were noted as being men of truly Spartan taciturnity, and who neither knew nor cared aught about any body's concerns but their own. Many enormities were committed on the highways, where several unoffending burghers were brought to a stand, and tortured with questions and guesses, which outrages occasioned as much vexation and heart-burning as does the modern right of search on the high seas.

Great jealousy did they likewise stir up, by their intermeddling and successes among the divine sex; for being a race of brisk, likely, pleasant-tongued varlets, they soon seduced the light affections of the simple damsels from their ponderous Dutch gallants. Among other hideous customs, they attempted to introduce among them that of *bundling*, which the Dutch lasses of the Nederlandts, with that eager passion for novelty and foreign fashions natural to their sex, seemed very well inclined to follow, but that their mothers, being more experienced in the world, and better acquainted with men and things, strenuously discountenanced all such outlandish innovations.

But what chiefly operated to embroil our ancestors with these strange folk was an unwarrantable liberty which they occasionally took of entering in hordes into the territories of the New Netherlands, and settling themselves down, without leave or license, to *improve* the land, in the manner I have before noticed. This unceremonious mode of taking possession of *new land* was technically termed *squatting*, and hence is derived the appellation of *squatters;* a name odious in the ears of all great landholders, and which is given to those enterprising worthies who seize upon land first and take their chance to make good their title to it afterwards.

All these grievances, and many others which were constantly accumulating, tended to form that dark and portentous cloud, which, as I observed in a former chapter, was slowly gathering over the tranquil province of New Netherlands. The pacific cabinet of Van Twiller, however, as will be perceived in the sequel, bore them all with a magnanimity that redounds to their immortal credit—becoming by passive endurance inured to this increasing mass of wrongs; like that mighty man of old, who by dint of carrying about a calf from the time it was born, continued to carry it without difficulty when it had grown to be an ox.

CHAPTER IX.

How the Fort Goed Hoop Was Fearfully Beleaguered—How the Renowned Wouter Fell into a Profound Doubt, and How He Finally Evaporated.

By this time my readers must fully perceive what an arduous task I have undertaken—exploring a little kind of Herculaneum of history, which had lain nearly for ages buried under the rubbish of years, and almost totally forgotten—raking up the limbs and fragments of disjointed facts, and endeavoring to put them scrupulously together, so as to restore them to their original form and connection—now lugging forth the character of an almost forgotten hero, like a mutilated statue—now deciphering a half defaced inscription, and now lighting upon a mouldering manuscript, which, after painful study, scarce repays the trouble of perusal.

In such case how much has the reader to depend upon the honor and probity of his author, lest, like a cunning antiquarian, he either impose upon him some spurious fabrication of his own, for a precious relic from antiquity —or else dress up the dismembered fragment with such false trappings, that it is scarcely possible to distinguish the truth from the fiction with which it is enveloped. This is a grievance which I have more than once had to lament, in the course of my wearisome researches among the works of my fellow historians, who have strangely disguised and distorted the facts respecting this country; and particularly respecting the great province of New Netherlands; as will be perceived by any who will take the trouble to compare their romantic effusions, tricked out in the meretricious gauds of fable, with this authentic history.

I have had more vexations of the kind to encounter, in those parts of my history which treat of the transactions on the eastern border, than in any other, in consequence of the troops of historians who have infested those quarters, and have shown the honest people of Nieuw Nederlands no mercy in their works. Among the rest, Mr. Benjamin Trumbull arrogantly declares, that "the Dutch were always mere intruders."—Now to this I shall make no other reply, than to proceed in the steady narration of my history, which will contain not only proofs that the Dutch had clear title and possession in the fair valleys of the Connecticut, and that they were wrongfully dispossessed thereof—but likewise, that they have been scandalously maltreated ever since, by the misrepresentations of the crafty historians of New England. And in this I shall be guided by a spirit of truth and impartiality, and a regard to immortal fame—for I would not wittingly dishonor my work by a single falsehood, misrepresentation, or prejudice, though it should gain our forefathers the whole country of New England.

I have already noticed in a former chapter of my history that the territories of the Nieuw Nederlands extended on the east, quite to the Varshe or fresh, or Connecticut river. Here, at an early period, had been established a frontier post on the bank of the river, and called Fort Goed Hoop, not far from the site of the present fair city of Hartford. It was placed under the command of Jacobus Van Curlet, or Curlis, as some historians will have it; a doughty soldier, of that stomachful class famous for eating all they kill. He was long in the body and short in the limb, as though a tall man's body had been mounted on a little man's legs. He made up for this turnspit construction by striding to such an extent, that you would have sworn he had on the seven-leagued boots of Jack the Giant-killer; and so high did he tread on parade, that his soldiers were sometimes alarmed lest he should trample himself under foot.

But notwithstanding the erection of this fort and the appointment of this ugly little man of war as commander, the Yankees continued the interlopings hinted at in my last chapter, and at length had the audacity to *squat* themselves down within the jurisdiction of Fort Goed Hoop.

The long-bodied Van Curlet protested with great spirit against these unwarrantable encroachments, couching his protest in Low Dutch, by way of inspiring more terror, and forthwith despatched a copy of the protest to the governor at New Amsterdam, together with a long and bitter account of the aggressions of the enemy. This done, he ordered his men, one and all, to be of good cheer—shut the gate of the fort, smoked three pipes, went to bed, and awaited the result with a resolute and intrepid tranquillity, that greatly animated his adherents, and no doubt struck sore dismay and affright into the hearts of the enemy.

Now it came to pass, that about this time, the renowned Wouter Van Twiller, full of years and honors, and council dinners, had reached that period of life and faculty which, according to the great Gulliver, entitles a man to admission into the ancient order of Struldbrugs. He employed his time in smoking his Turkish pipe, amid an assemblage of sages, equally enlightened, and nearly as venerable as himself, and who, for their silence, their gravity, their wisdom, and their cautious averseness to coming to any conclusion in business, are only to be equalled by certain profound corporations which I have known in my time. Upon reading the protest of the gallant Jacobus Van Curlet, therefore, his excellency fell straightway into one of the deepest doubts that ever he was known to encounter; his capacious head gradually drooped on his chest, he closed his eyes, and inclined his ear to one side, as if listening with great attention to the discussion that was going on in his belly; and which all who knew him declared to be the huge court-house or council-chamber of his thoughts; forming to his head what the house of representatives does to the senate. An inarticulate sound, very much resembling a snore, occasionally escaped him—but the nature of this internal cogitation was never known, as he never opened his lips on the subject to man, woman, or child. In the meantime, the protest of Van Curlet laid quietly on the table, where it served to light the pipes of the venerable sages assembled in council; and in the great smoke which they raised, the gallant Jacobus, his protest, and his mighty fort Goed Hoop, were soon as completely beclouded and forgotten, as is a question of emergency swallowed up in the speeches and resolutions of a modern session of Congress.

There are certain emergencies when your profound legislators and sage deliberative councils are mightily in the way of a nation; and when an ounce of hair-brained decision is worth a pound of sage doubt and cautious discussion. Such, at least, was the case at present; for while the renowned Wouter Van Twiller was daily battling with his doubts, and his resolution growing weaker and weaker in the contest, the enemy pushed farther and farther into his territories, and assumed a most formidable appearance in the neighborhood of fort Goed Hoop. Here they founded the mighty town of *Pyquag,* or, as it has since been called, *Weathersfield,* a place which, if we may credit the assertions of that worthy historian, John Josselyn, Gent., "hath been infamous by reason of the witches therein."—And so daring did these men of Pyquag become, that they extended those plantations of onions, for which their town is illustrious, under the very noses of the garrison of fort Goed Hoop—insomuch that the honest Dutchmen could not look toward that quarter without tears in their eyes.

This crying injustice was regarded with proper indignation by the gallant Jacobus Van Curlet. He absolutely trembled with the violence of his choler and the exacerbations of his valor; which were the more turbulent in their workings, from the length of the body in which they were agitated. He forthwith proceeded to strengthen his redoubts, heighten his breastworks, deepen his fosse, and fortify his position with a double row of abatis; after which he despatched a fresh courier with accounts of his perilous situation.

The courier chosen to bear the despatches was a fat oily little man, as being less liable to be worn out, or to lose leather on the journey; and to insure his speed, he was mounted on the fleetest wagon horse in the garrison, remarkable for length of limb, largeness of bone, and hardness of trot; and so tall, that the little messenger was obliged to climb on his back by means of his tail and crupper. Such extraordinary speed did he make, that he arrived at fort Amsterdam in a little less than a month, though the distance was full two hundred pipes, or about one hundred and twenty miles.

With an appearance of great hurry and business, and smoking a short travelling-pipe, he proceeded on a long swing trot through the muddy lanes of the metropolis, demolishing whole batches of dirt pies, which the little Dutch children were making in the road; and for which kind of pastry the children of this city have ever been famous. On arriving at the governor's house, he climbed down from his steed; roused the gray-headed door-keeper, old Skaats, who, like his lineal descendant and faithful representative, the venerable crier of our court, was nodding at his post—rattled at the door of the council chamber, and startled the members as they were dozing over a plan for establishing a public market.

At that very moment a gentle grunt, or rather a deep-drawn snore, was heard from the chair of the governor; a whiff of smoke was at the same instant observed to escape from his lips, and a light cloud to ascend from the bowl of his pipe. The council, of course, supposed him engaged in deep sleep for the good of the community, and, according to custom in all such cases established, every man bawled out silence, when, of a sudden, the door flew open, and the little courier straddled into the apartment, cased to the middle in a pair of Hessian boots, which he had got into for the sake of expedition. In his right hand he held forth the ominous despatches, and with his left he grasped firmly the waistband of his galligaskins, which had unfortunately given way, in the exertion of descending from his horse. He stumped resolutely up to the governor, and with more hurry than perspicuity, delivered his message. But fortunately his ill tidings came too late to ruffle the tranquillity of this most tranquil of rulers. His venerable excellency had just breathed and smoked his last—his lungs and his pipe having been exhausted together, and his peaceful soul having escaped in the last whiff that curled from his tobacco pipe. In a word, the renowned Walter the Doubter, who had so often slumbered with his contemporaries, now slept with his fathers, and Wilhelmus Kieft governed in his stead.

BOOK IV.

CONTAINING THE CHRONICLES OF THE REIGN OF WILLIAM THE TESTY.

CHAPTER I.

SHOWING THE NATURE OF HISTORY IN GENERAL; CONTAINING FURTHERMORE THE UNIVERSAL ACQUIREMENTS OF WILLIAM THE TESTY, AND HOW A MAN MAY LEARN SO MUCH AS TO RENDER HIMSELF GOOD FOR NOTHING.

WHEN the lofty Thucydides is about to enter upon his description of the plague that desolated Athens, one of his modern commentators assures the reader, that the history is now going to be exceeding solemn, serious, and pathetic; and hints, with that air of chuckling gratulation with which a good dame draws forth a choice morsel from a cupboard to regale a favorite, that this plague will give his history a most agreeable variety.

In like manner did my heart leap within me, when I came to the dolorous dilemma of Fort Good Hope, which I at once perceived to be the forerunner of a series of great events and entertaining disasters. Such are the true subjects for the historic pen. For what is history, in fact, but a kind of Newgate calendar, a register of the crimes and miseries that man has inflicted on his fellow man? It is a huge libel on human nature, to which we industriously add page after page, volume after volume, as if we were building up a monument to the honor, rather than the infamy of our species. If we turn over the pages of these chronicles that man has written of himself, what are the characters dignified by the appellation of great, and held up to the admiration of posterity? Tyrants, robbers, conquerors, renowned only for the magnitude of their misdeeds, and the stupendous wrongs and miseries they have inflicted on mankind—warriors, who have hired themselves to the trade of blood, not from motives of virtuous patriotism, or to protect the injured and defenceless, but merely to gain the vaunted glory of being adroit and successful in massacring their fellow-beings! What are the great events that constitute a glorious era?—The fall of empires—the desolation of happy countries—splendid cities smoking in their ruins—the proudest works of art tumbled in the dust—the shrieks and groans of whole nations ascending unto heaven!

It is thus the historian may be said to thrive on the miseries of mankind, like birds of prey which hover over the field of battle, to fatten on the mighty dead. It was observed by a great projector of inland lock navigation, that rivers, lakes, and oceans, were only formed to feed canals.—In like manner I am tempted to believe, that plots, conspiracies, wars, victories, and massacres, are ordained by Providence only as food for the historian.

It is a source of great delight to the philosopher, in studying the wonderful economy of nature, to trace the mutual dependencies of things, how they are created reciprocally for each other, and how the most noxious and apparently unnecessary animal has its uses. Thus those swarms of flies, which are so often execrated as useless vermin, are created for the sustenance of spiders—and spiders, on the other hand, are evidently made to devour flies. So those heroes who have been such scourges to the world, were bounteously provided as themes for the poet and historian, while the poet and the historian were destined to record the achievements of heroes!

These, and many similar reflections, naturally arose in my mind, as I took up my pen to commence the reign of William Kieft: for now the stream of our history, which hitherto has rolled in a tranquil current, is about to depart forever from its peaceful haunts, and brawl through many a turbulent and rugged scene.

As some sleek ox, sunk in the rich repose of a clover-field, dozing and chewing the cud, will bear repeated blows before it raises itself; so the province of Nieuw Nederlands, having waxed fat under the drowsy reign of the Doubter, needed cuffs and kicks to rouse it into action. The reader will now witness the manner in which a peaceful community advances towards a state of war; which is apt to be like the approach of a horse to a drum, with much prancing and little progress, and too often with the wrong end foremost.

Wilhelmus Kieft, who, in 1634, ascended the gubernatorial chair (to borrow a favorite though clumsy appellation of modern phraseologists), was of a lofty descent, his father being inspector of windmills in the ancient town of Saardam; and our hero, we are told, when a boy, made very curious investigations into the nature and operation of these machines, which was one reason why he afterwards came to be so ingenious a governor. His name, according to the most authentic etymologists, was a corruption of Kyver; that is to say, a *wrangler* or *scolder;* and expressed the characteristic of his family, which, for nearly two centuries, had kept the windy town of Saardam in hot water, and produced more tartars and brimstones than any ten families in the place; and so truly did he inherit this family peculiarity, that he had not been a year in the government of the province, before he was universally denominated William the Testy. His appearance answered to his name. He was a brisk, wiry, waspish little old gentleman; such a one as may now and then be seen stumping about our city in a broad-skirted coat with huge buttons, a cocked hat stuck on the back of his head, and a cane as high as his chin. His face was broad, but his features were sharp; his cheeks were scorched into a dusky red, by two fiery little gray eyes; his nose turned up, and the corners of his mouth turned down, pretty much like the muzzle of an irritable pug-dog.

I have heard it observed by a profound adept in human physiology, that if a woman waxes fat with the progress of years, her tenure of life is somewhat precarious, but if haply she withers as she grows old, she lives forever. Such promised to be the case with William the Testy, who grew tough in proportion as he dried. He had withered, in fact, not through the process of years, but through the tropical fervor of his soul, which burnt like a vehement rushlight in his bosom; inciting him to incessant broils and bickerings. Ancient traditions speak much of his learning, and of the gallant inroads he had made into the dead languages in which he had made captive a host of Greek nouns and Latin verbs; and brought off rich booty in ancient saws and apothegms; which he was wont to parade in his public harangues, as a triumphant general of yore, his *spolia opima.* Of metaphysics he knew enough to confound all hearers and himself into the bargain. In logic, he knew the whole family of syllogisms and dilemmas, and was so proud of his skill that he never suffered even a self-evident fact to pass unargued. It was observed, however, that he seldom got into an argument without getting into a perplexity, and then into a passion with his adversary for not being convinced gratis.

He had, moreover, skirmished smartly on the frontiers of several of the sciences, was fond of experimental philosophy, and prided himself upon inventions of all kinds. His abode, which he had fixed at a Bowerie or country-seat at a short distance from the city, just at what is now called Dutch-street, soon abounded with proofs of his ingenuity: patent smoke-jacks that required a horse to work them; Dutch ovens that roasted meat without fire; carts that went before the horses; weather-cocks that turned against the wind; and other wrong-headed contrivances that astonished and confounded all beholders. The house, too, was beset with paralytic cats and dogs, the subjects of his experimental philosophy; and the yelling and yelping of the latter unhappy victims of science, while aiding in the pursuit of knowledge, soon gained for the place the name of "Dog's Misery," by which it continues to be known even at the present day.

It is in knowledge as in swimming; he who flounders and splashes on the surface, makes more noise, and attracts more attention, than the pearl-diver who quietly dives in quest of treasures to the bottom. The vast acquirements of the new governor were the theme of marvel among the simple burghers of New Amsterdam; he figured about the place as learned a man as a Bonze at Pekin, who has mastered one-half of the Chinese alphabet: and was unanimously pronounced a "universal genius!"

I have known in my time many a genius of this stamp; but, to speak my mind freely, I never knew one who, for the ordinary purposes of life, was worth his weight in straw. In this respect, a little sound judgment and plain common sense is worth all the sparkling genius that ever wrote poetry or invented theories. Let us see how the universal acquirements of William the Testy aided him in the affairs of government.

CHAPTER II.

How William the Testy Undertook to Conquer by Proclamation—How He Was a Great Man Abroad, but a Little Man in his Own House.

No sooner had this bustling little potentate been blown by a whiff of fortune into the seat of government than he called his council together to make them a speech on the state of affairs.

Caius Gracchus, it is said, when he harangued the Roman populace, modulated his tone by an oratorical flute or pitch-pipe; Wilhelmus Kieft, not having such an instrument at hand, availed himself of that musical organ or trump which nature has implanted in the midst of a man's face; in other words, he preluded his address by a sonorous blast of the nose; a preliminary flourish much in vogue among public orators.

He then commenced by expressing his humble sense of his utter unworthiness of the high post to which he had been appointed; which made some of the simple burghers wonder why he undertook it, not knowing that it is a point of etiquette with a public orator never to enter upon office without declaring himself unworthy to cross the threshold. He then proceeded in a manner highly classic and erudite to speak of government generally, and of the governments of ancient Greece in particular; together with the wars of Rome and Carthage; and the rise and fall of sundry outlandish empires which the worthy burghers had never read nor heard of. Having thus, after the manner of your learned orators, treated of things in general, he came by a natural, roundabout transition, to the matter in hand, namely, the daring aggressions of the Yankees.

As my readers are well aware of the advantage a potentate has of handling his enemies as he pleases in his speeches and bulletins, where he has the talk all on his own side, they may rest assured that William the Testy did not let such an opportunity escape of giving the Yankees what is called "a taste of his quality." In speaking of their inroads into the territories of their High Mightinesses, he compared them to the Gauls who desolated Rome; the Goths and Vandals who overran the fairest plains of Europe; but when he came to speak of the unparalleled audacity with which they of Weathersfield had advanced their patches up to the walls of Fort Goed Hoop, and threatened to smother the garrison in onions, tears of rage started into his eyes, as though he nosed the very offence in question.

Having thus wrought up his tale to a climax, he assumed a most belligerent look, and assured the council that he had devised an instrument, potent in its effects, and which he trusted would soon drive the Yankees from the land. So saying, he thrust his hand into one of the deep pockets of his broad-skirted coat and drew forth, not an infernal machine, but an instrument in writing, which he laid with great emphasis upon the table.

The burghers gazed at it for a time in silent awe, as a wary housewife does at a gun, fearful it may go off half-cocked. The document in question had a sinister look, it is true; it was crabbed in text, and from a broad red ribbon dangled the great seal of the province, about the size of a buckwheat pancake. Still, after all, it was but an instrument in writing. Herein, however, existed the wonder of the invention. The document in question was a PROCLAMATION, ordering the Yankees to depart instantly from the territories of their High Mightinesses under pain of suffering all the forfeitures and punishments in such case made and provided. It was on the moral effect of this formidable instrument that Wilhelmus Kieft calculated; pledging his valor as a governor that, once fulminated against the Yankees, it would, in less than two months, drive every mother's son of them across the borders.

The council broke up in perfect wonder, and nothing was talked of for some time among the old men and women of New Amsterdam but the vast genius of the governor, and his new and cheap mode of fighting by proclamation.

As to Wilhelmus Kieft, having despatched his proclamation to the frontiers, he put on his cocked hat and corduroy small-clothes, and mounting a tall rawboned charger, trotted out to his rural retreat of Dog's Misery. Here, like the good Numa, he reposed from the toils of state, taking lessons in government, not from the nymph Egeria, but from the honored wife of his bosom; who was one of that class of females sent upon the earth a little after the flood, as a punishment for the sins of mankind, and commonly known by the appellation of *knowing women*. In fact, my duty as an historian obliges me to make known a circumstance which was a great secret at the time, and consequently was not a subject of scandal at more than half the tea-tables in New Amsterdam, but which, like many other great secrets, has leaked out in the lapse of years—and this was, that Wilhelmus the Testy, though one of the most potent little men that ever breathed, yet submitted at home to a species of government, neither laid down in Aristotle nor Plato;

in short, it partook of the nature of a pure, unmixed tyranny, and is familiarly denominated *petticoat government.*—An absolute sway, which, although exceedingly common in these modern days, was very rare among the ancients, if we may judge from the rout made about the domestic economy of honest Socrates; which is the only ancient case on record.

The great Kieft, however, warded off all the sneers and sarcasms of his particular friends, who are ever ready to joke with a man on sore points of the kind, by alleging that it was a government of his own election, to which he submitted through choice; adding at the same time a profound maxim which he had found in an ancient author, that "he who would aspire to *govern* should first learn to *obey*."

CHAPTER III.

In Which Are Recorded the Sage Projects of a Ruler of Universal Genius—the Art of Fighting by Proclamation—and How That the Valiant Jacobus Van Curlet Came to Be Foully Dishonored at Fort Goed Hoop.

Never was a more comprehensive, a more expeditious, or, what is still better, a more economical measure devised, than this of defeating the Yankees by proclamation—an expedient, likewise, so gentle and humane, there were ten chances to one in favor of its succeeding,—but then there was one chance to ten that it would not succeed—as the ill-natured fates would have it, that single chance carried the day! The proclamation was perfect in all its parts, well constructed, well written, well sealed, and well published—all that was wanting to insure its effect was, that the Yankees should stand in awe of it; but, provoking to relate, they treated it with the most absolute contempt, applied it to an unseemly purpose, and thus did the first warlike proclamation come to a shameful end—a fate which I am credibly informed has befallen but too many of its successors.

So far from abandoning the country, those varlets continued their encroachments, squatting along the green banks of the Varsche river, and founding Hartford, Stamford, New Haven, and other border towns. I have already shown how the onion patches of Pyquag were an eyesore to Jacobus Van Curlet and his garrison; but now these moss-troopers increased in their atrocities, kidnapping hogs, impounding horses, and sometimes grievously rib-roasting their owners. Our worthy forefathers could scarcely stir abroad without danger of being outjockied in horseflesh, or taken in in bargaining; while, in their absence, some daring Yankee pedler would penetrate to their household, and nearly ruin the good housewives with tin-ware and wooden bowls.[1]

[1]The following cases in point appear in Hazard's Collection of State Papers.
"In the meantime, they of Hartford have not onely usurped and taken in the lande of Connecticott, although unrighteously and against the laws of nations, but have hindered our nation in sowing theire own purchased broken up lands, but have also

I am well aware of the perils which environ me in this part of my history. While raking, with curious hand but pious heart, among the mouldering remains of former days, anxious to draw therefrom the honey of wisdom, I may fare somewhat like that valiant worthy, Samson, who, in meddling with the carcass of a dead lion, drew a swarm of bees about his ears. Thus, while narrating the many misdeeds of the Yanokie or Yankee race, it is ten chances to one but I offend the morbid sensibilities of certain of their unreasonable descendants, who may fly out and raise such a buzzing about this unlucky head of mine, that I shall need the tough hide of an Achilles, or an Orlando Furioso, to protect me from their stings.

Should such be the case, I should deeply and sincerely lament—not my misfortune in giving offence—but the wrong-headed perverseness of an ill-natured generation, in taking offence at any thing I say. That their ancestors did use my ancestors ill is true, and I am very sorry for it. I would, with all my heart, the fact were otherwise; but as I am recording the sacred events of history, I'd not bate one nail's breadth of the honest truth, though I were sure the whole edition of my work would be bought up and burnt by the common hangman of Connecticut. And in sooth, now that these testy gentlemen have drawn me out, I will make bold to go farther, and observe that this is one of the grand purposes for which we impartial historians are sent into the world—to redress wrongs and render justice on the heads of the guilty. So that, though a powerful nation may wrong its neighbors with temporary impunity, yet sooner or later an historian springs up, who wreaks ample chastisement on it in return.

Thus these moss-troopers of the East little thought, I'll warrant it, while they were harassing the inoffensive province of Nieuw Nederlands, and driving its unhappy governor to his wit's end, that an historian would ever arise, and give them their own, with interest. Since, then, I am but performing my bounden duty as an historian, in avenging the wrongs of our revered ancestors, I shall make no further apology, and, indeed, when it is considered that I have all these ancient borderers of the east in my power, and at the mercy of my pen, I trust that it will be admitted I conduct myself with great humanity and moderation.

It was long before William the Testy could be persuaded that his much vaunted war measure was ineffectual; on the contrary, he flew in a passion

sowed them with corne in the night, which the Nederlanders had broken up and intended to sowe: and have beaten the servants of the high and mighty the honored companie, which were laboring upon theire master's lands, from theire lands, with sticks and plow staves in hostile manner laming, and among the rest, struck Ever Duckings [Evert Duyckink] a hole in his head, with a stick, so that the bloode ran downe very strongly downe upon his body."

"Those of Hartford sold a hogg, that belonged to the honored companie, under pretence that it had eaten of theire grounde grass, when they had not any foot of inheritance. They proffered the hogg for 5s. if the commissioners would have given 5s for damage; which the commissioners denied, because noe man's own hogg (as men used to say) can trespass upon his owne master's grounde."

whenever it was doubted, swearing that though slow in operating, yet when it once began to work, it would soon purge the land of these invaders. When convinced, at length, of the truth, like a shrewd physician he attributed the failure to the quantity, not the quality of the medicine, and resolved to double the dose. He fulminated, therefore, a second proclamation more vehement than the first, forbidding all intercourse with these Yankee intruders; ordering the Dutch burghers on the frontiers to buy none of their pacing horses, measly pork, apple sweetmeats, Weathersfield onions, or wooden bowls, and to furnish them with no supplies of gin, gingerbread, or sourkrout.

Another interval elapsed, during which the last proclamation was as little regarded as the first, and the nonintercourse was especially set at naught by the young folks of both sexes, if we may judge by the active bundling which took place along the borders.

At length one day the inhabitants of New Amsterdam were aroused by a furious barking of dogs, great and small, and beheld, to their surprise, the whole garrison of Fort Good Hope straggling into town all tattered and wayworn, with Jacobus Van Curlet at their head, bringing the melancholy intelligence of the capture of Fort Good Hope by the Yankees.

The fate of this important fortress is an impressive warning to all military commanders. It was neither carried by storm nor famine; nor was it undermined; nor bombarded; nor set on fire by red-hot shot; but was taken by a stratagem no less singular than effectual, and which can never fail of success, whenever an opportunity occurs of putting it in practice.

It seems that the Yankees had received intelligence that the garrison of Jacobus Van Curlet had been reduced nearly one-eighth by the death of two of his most corpulent soldiers, who had overeaten themselves on fat salmon caught in the Varsche river. A secret expedition was immediately set on foot to surprise the fortress. The crafty enemy knowing the habits of the garrison to sleep soundly after they had eaten their dinners and smoked their pipes, stole upon them at the noontide of a sultry summer's day, and surprised them in the midst of their slumbers.

In an instant the flag of their High Mightinesses was lowered, and the Yankee standard elevated in its stead, being a dried codfish, by way of a spread eagle. A strong garrison was appointed, of long-sided, hard-fisted Yankees, with Weathersfield onions for cockades and feathers. As to Jacobus Van Curlet and his men, they were seized by the nape of the neck, conducted to the gate, and one by one dismissed with a kick in the crupper, as Charles XIIth dismissed the heavy-bottomed Russians at the battle of Narva; Jacobus Van Curlet receiving two kicks in consideration of his official dignity.

CHAPTER IV.

CONTAINING THE FEARFUL WRATH OF WILLIAM THE TESTY, AND THE
ALARM OF NEW AMSTERDAM—HOW THE GOVERNOR DID STRONGLY
FORTIFY THE CITY—OF THE RISE OF ANTONY THE TRUMPETER, AND
THE WINDY ADDITION TO THE ARMORIAL BEARINGS OF
NEW AMSTERDAM.

LANGUAGE cannot express the awful ire of William the Testy on hearing of
the catastrophe at Fort Goed Hoop. For three good hours his rage was too
great for words, or rather the words were too great for him, (being a very
small man,) and he was nearly choked by the misshapen, nine-cornered Dutch
oaths and epithets which crowded at once into his gullet. At length his words
found vent, and for three days he kept up a constant discharge, anathematizing
the Yankees, man, woman, and child, for a set of dieven, schobbejacken,
deugenieten, twistzoekeren, blaes-kaken, loosen-schalken, kakken-bedden, and
a thousand other names, of which, unfortunately for posterity, history does
not make mention. Finally, he swore that he would have nothing more to do
with such a squatting, bundling, guessing, questioning, swapping, pumpkin-
eating, molasses-daubing, shingle-splitting, cider-watering, horse-jockeying,
notion-peddling crew—that they might stay at Fort Goed Hoop and rot,
before he would dirty his hands by attempting to drive them away; in proof
of which he ordered the new-raised troops to be marched forthwith into
winter quarters, although it was not as yet quite midsummer. Great despondency now fell upon the city of New Amsterdam. It was feared that the
conquerors of Fort Goed Hoop, flushed with victory and apple-brandy, might
march on to the capital, take it by storm, and annex the whole province to
Connecticut. The name of Yankee became as terrible among the Nieuw
Nederlanders as was that of Gaul among the ancient Romans; insomuch that the
good wives of the Manhattoes used it as a bugbear wherewith to frighten their
unruly children.

Everybody clamored around the governor, imploring him to put the city
in a complete posture of defence, and he listened to their clamors. Nobody
could accuse William the Testy of being idle in time of danger, or at any
other time. He was never idle, but then he was often busy to very little
purpose. When a youngling he had been impressed with the words of
Solomon, "Go to the ant, thou sluggard, observe her ways and be wise,"
in conformity to which he had ever been of a restless, antlike turn; hurrying
hither and thither, nobody knew why or wherefore, busying himself about
small matters with an air of great importance and anxiety, and toiling at a grain
of mustard-seed in the full conviction that he was moving a mountain. In
the present instance, he called in all his inventive powers to his aid, and was
continually pondering over plans, making diagrams, and worrying about with
a troop of workmen and projectors at his heels. At length, after a world of

consultation and contrivance, his plans of defence ended in rearing a great flag-staff in the centre of the fort, and perching a windmill on each bastion.

These warlike preparations in some measure allayed the public alarm, especially after an additional means of securing the safety of the city had been suggested by the governor's lady. It had already been hinted in this most authentic history, that in the domestic establishment of William the Testy "the gray mare was the better horse;" in other words, that his wife "ruled the roast," and, in governing the governor, governed the province, which might thus be said to be under petticoat government.

Now it came to pass, that about this time there lived in the Manhattoes a jolly, robustious trumpeter, named Antony Van Corlear, famous for his long wind; and who, as the story goes, could twang so potently upon his instrument, that the effect upon all within hearing was like that ascribed to the Scotch bagpipe when it sings right lustily i' the nose.

This sounder of brass was moreover a lusty bachelor, with a pleasant, burly visage, a long nose, and huge whiskers. He had his little *bowerie*, or retreat in the country, where he led a roystering life, giving dances to the wives and daughters of the burghers of the Manhattoes, insomuch that he became a prodigious favorite with all the women, young and old. He is said to have been the first to collect that famous toll levied on the fair sex at Kissing Bridge, on the highway to Hell-gate.[1]

To this sturdy bachelor the eyes of all the women were turned in this time of darkness and peril, as the very man to second and carry out the plans of defence of the governor. A kind of petticoat council was forthwith held at the government house, at which the governor's lady presided; and this lady, as has been hinted, being all potent with the governor, the result of these councils was the elevation of Antony the Trumpeter to the post of commandant of windmills and champion of New Amsterdam.

The city being thus fortified and garrisoned, it would have done one's heart good to see the governor snapping his fingers and fidgeting with delight, as the trumpeter strutted up and down the ramparts twanging defiance to the whole Yankee race, as does a modern editor to all the principalities and powers on the other side of the Atlantic. In the hands of Antony Van Corlear this windy instrument appeared to him as potent as the horn of the paladin Astolpho, or even the more classic horn of Alecto; nay, he had almost the temerity to compare it with the ram's horn celebrated in holy writ, at the very sound of which the walls of Jericho fell down.

Be all this as it may, the apprehensions of hostilities from the east gradually died away. The Yankees made no further invasion; nay, they declared they had only taken possession of Fort Goed Hoop as being erected within their territories. So far from manifesting hostility, they continued to throng to New Amsterdam with the most innocent countenances imaginable, filling the market with their notions, being as ready to trade with the Nederlanders

[1]The bridge here mentioned by Mr. Knickerbocker still exists; but it is said that the toll is seldom collected now-a-days excepting on sleighing parties, by the descendants of the patriarchs, who still preserve the traditions of the city.

as ever—and not a whit more prone to get to the windward of them in a bargain.

The old wives of the Manhattoes who took tea with the governor's lady attributed all this affected moderation to the awe inspired by the military preparations of the governor, and the windy prowess of Antony the Trumpeter.

There were not wanting illiberal minds, however, who sneered at the governor for thinking to defend his city as he governed it, by mere wind; but William Kieft was not to be jeered out of his windmills—he had seen them perched upon the ramparts of his native city of Saardam, and was persuaded they were connected with the great science of defence; nay, so much piqued was he by having them made a matter of ridicule, that he introduced them into the arms of the city, where they remain to this day, quartered with the ancient beaver of the Manhattoes, an emblem and memento of his policy.

I must not omit to mention that certain wise old burghers of the Manhattoes, skilful in expounding signs and mysteries, after events have come to pass, consider this early intrusion of the windmill into the escutcheon of our city, which before had been wholly occupied by the beaver, as portentous of its after fortune, when the quiet Dutchman would be elbowed aside by the enterprising Yankee, and patient industry overtopped by windy speculation.

CHAPTER V.

Of the Jurisprudence of William the Testy, and His Admirable Expedients for the Suppression of Poverty.

Among the wrecks and fragments of exalted wisdom which have floated down the stream of time from venerable antiquity, and been picked up by those humble, but industrious wights who ply along the shores of literature, we find a shrewd ordinance of Charondas the Locrian legislator. Anxious to preserve the judicial code of the State from the additions and amendments of country members and seekers of popularity, he ordained that, whoever proposed a new law should do it with a halter about his neck; whereby, in case his proposition were rejected, they just hung him up—and there the matter ended.

The effect was, that for more than two hundred years there was but one trifling alteration in the judicial code; and legal matters were so clear and simple that the whole race of lawyers starved to death for want of employment. The Locrians, too, being freed from all incitement to litigation, lived very lovingly together, and were so happy a people that they make scarce any figure in history; it being only your litigious, quarrelsome, rantipole nations who make much noise in the world.

I have been reminded of these historical facts in coming to treat of the internal policy of William the Testy. Well would it have been for him had he in the course of his universal acquirements tumbled upon the precaution of the good Charondas; or had he looked nearer home at the protectorate of Oloffe the Dreamer, when the community was governed without laws. Such legislation, however, was not suited to the busy, meddling mind of William the Testy. On the contrary, he conceived that the true wisdom of legislation consisted in the multiplicity of laws. He accordingly had great punishments for great crimes, and little punishments for little offences. By degrees the whole surface of society was cut up by ditches and fences, and quickset hedges of the law, and even the sequestered paths of private life so beset by petty rules and ordinances, too numerous to be remembered, that one could scarce walk at large without the risk of letting off a spring-gun or falling into a man-trap.

In a little while the blessings of innumerable laws became apparent—a class of men arose to expound and confound them. Petty courts were instituted to take cognizance of petty offences, pettifoggers began to abound; and the community was soon set together by the ears.

Let me not be thought as intending any thing derogatory to the profession of the law, or to the distinguished members of that illustrious order. Well am I aware that we have in this ancient city innumerable worthy gentlemen, the knights-errants of modern days, who go about redressing wrongs and defending the defenceless, not for the love of filthy lucre, nor the selfish cravings of renown, but merely for the pleasure of doing good. Sooner would I throw this trusty pen into the flames, and cork up my ink-bottle for ever, than infringe even for a nail's breadth upon the dignity of these truly benevolent champions of the distressed. On the contrary I allude merely to those caitiff scouts who, in these latter days of evil, infest the skirts of the profession, as did the recreant Cornish knights of yore, the honorable order of chivalry; who, under its auspices, commit flagrant wrongs; who thrive by quibbles, by quirks and chicanery, and like vermin increase the corruption in which they are engendered.

Nothing so soon awakens the malevolent passions as the facility of gratification. The courts of law would never be so crowded with petty, vexatious and disgraceful suits, were it not for the herds of pettifoggers. These tamper with the passions of the poorer and more ignorant classes; who, as if poverty were not a sufficient misery in itself, are ever ready to embitter it by litigation. These, like quacks in medicine, excite the malady to profit by the cure, and retard the cure to augment the fees. As the quack exhausts the constitution, the pettifogger exhausts the purse; and as he who has once been under the hands of a quack, is forever after prone to dabble in drugs, and poison himself with infallible prescriptions; so the client of the pettifogger is ever after prone to embroil himself with his neighbors, and impoverish himself with successful lawsuits. My readers will excuse this digression into which I have been unwarily betrayed; but I could not avoid giving a cool and unprejudiced account of an abomination too prevalent in this excellent city, and with the effects of which I am ruefully acquainted: having been nearly ruined by a lawsuit which was decided against me; and my ruin having been completed by another, which was decided in my favor.

To return to our theme. There was nothing in the whole range of moral offences against which the jurisprudence of William the Testy was more strenuously directed, than the crying sin of poverty. He pronounced it the root of all evil, and determined to cut it up root and branch, and extirpate it from the land. He had been struck, in the course of his travels in the old countries of Europe, with the wisdom of those notices posted up in country towns, that "any vagrant found begging there would be put in the stocks," and he observed, that no beggars were to be seen in these neighborhoods; having doubtless thrown off their rags and their poverty and become rich under the terror of the law. He determined to improve upon this hint. In a little while a new machine of his own invention, was erected hard by Dog's Misery. This was nothing more nor less than a gibbet, of a very strange, uncouth, and unmatchable construction, far more efficacious, as he boasted, than the stocks, for the punishment of poverty. It was for altitude not a whit inferior to that of Haman, so renowned in Bible history; but the marvel of the contrivance was, that the culprit, instead of being suspended by the neck according to venerable custom, was hoisted by the waistband, and kept dangling and sprawling between heaven and earth for an hour or two at a time—to the infinite entertainment and edification of the respectable citizens who usually attend exhibitions of the kind.

It is incredible how the little governor chuckled at beholding caitiff vagrants and sturdy beggars thus swinging by the crupper, and cutting antic gambols in the air. He had a thousand pleasantries, and mirthful conceits to utter upon these occasions. He called them his dandle-lions—his wild-fowl—his high-fliers—his spread-eagles—his goshawks—his scare-crows—and finally, his *gallows-birds;* which ingenious appellation, though originally confined to worthies who had taken the air in this strange manner, has since grown to be a cant-name given to all candidates for legal elevation. This punishment, moreover, if we may credit the assertions of certain grave etymologists, gave the first hint for a kind of harnessing, or strapping, by which our forefathers braced up their multifarious breeches, and which has of late years been revived, and continues to be worn at the present day.

Such was the punishment of all petty delinquents, vagrants and beggars and others detected in being guilty of poverty in a small way; as to those who had offended on a great scale, who had been guilty of flagrant misfortunes and enormous backslidings of the purse, and who stood convicted of large debts, which they were unable to pay, William Kieft had them straightway enclosed within the stone walls of a prison, there to remain until they should reform and grow rich. This notable expedient, however, does not appear to have been more efficacious under William the Testy than in more modern days: it being found that the longer a poor devil was kept in prison the poorer he grew.

CHAPTER VI.

PROJECTS OF WILLIAM THE TESTY FOR INCREASING THE CURRENCY—
HE IS OUTWITTED BY THE YANKEES—THE GREAT OYSTER WAR.

NEXT TO his projects for the suppression of poverty, may be classed those of William the Testy, for increasing the wealth of New Amsterdam. Solomon, ot whose character for wisdom the little governor was somewhat emulous, had made gold and silver as plenty as the stones in the streets of Jerusalem. William Kieft could not pretend to vie with him as to the precious metals, but he determined, as an equivalent, to flood the streets of New Amsterdam with Indian money. This was nothing more nor less than strings of beads wrought out of clams, periwinkles, and other shell-fish, and called seawant or wampum. These had formed a native currency among the simple savages; who were content to take them of the Dutchmen in exchange for peltries. In an unlucky moment, William the Testy, seeing this money of easy production, conceived the project of making it the current coin of the province. It is true it had an intrinsic value among the Indians, who used it to ornament their robes and moccasins, but among the honest burghers it had no more intrinsic value than those rags which form the paper currency of modern days. This consideration, however, had no weight with William Kieft. He began by paying all the servants of the company, and all the debts of government, in strings of wampum. He sent emissaries to sweep the shores of Long Island, which was the Ophir of this modern Solomon, and abounded in shell-fish. These were transported in loads to New Amsterdam, coined into Indian money, and launched into circulation.

And now, for a time, affairs went on swimmingly; money became as plentiful as in the modern days of paper currency, and, to use the popular phrase, "a wonderful impulse was given to public prosperity." Yankee traders poured into the province, buying everything they could lay their hands on, and paying the worthy Dutchmen their own price—in Indian money. If the latter, however, attempted to pay the Yankees in the same coin for their tinware and wooden bowls, the case was altered; nothing would do but Dutch guilders and such like "metallic currency." What was worse, the Yankees introduced an inferior kind of wampum made of oyster-shells, with which they deluged the province, carrying off in exchange all the silver and gold, the Dutch herrings, and Dutch cheeses: thus early did the knowing men of the East manifest their skill in bargaining the New Amsterdammers out of the oyster, and leaving them the shell.[1]

It was a long time before William the Testy was made sensible how completely his grand project of finance was turned against him by his Eastern

[1]In a manuscript record of the province, dated 1659, Library of the New York Historical Society, is the following mention of Indian money.

Seawant alias wampum. Beads manufactured from the *Quahaug* or *wilk*, a shell-fish formerly abounding on our coasts, but lately of more rare occurrence, of two colors, black and white; the former twice the value of the latter. Six beads of the white and three of the black for an English penny. The seawant depreciates from time to time. The New England people make use of it as a means of barter, not only to carry away the best cargoes which we send thither but to accumulate a large quantity of beavers and other furs; by which the company is defrauded of her revenues, and the merchants disappointed in making returns with that speed with which they might wish to meet their engagements: while their commissioners and the inhabitants remain overstocked with seawant—a sort of currency of no value except with the New Netherland savages, etc.

neighbors; nor would he probably have ever found it out, had not tidings been brought him that the Yankees had made a descent upon Long Island, and had established a kind of mint at Oyster Bay, where they were coining up all the oyster banks.

Now this was making a vital attack upon the province in a double sense, financial and gastronomical. Ever since the council dinner of Oloffe the Dreamer at the founding of New Amsterdam, at which banquet the oyster figured so conspicuously, this divine shell-fish has been held in a kind of superstitious reverence at the Manhattoes; as witness the temples erected to its cult in every street and lane and alley. In fact it is the standard luxury of the place, as is the terrapin at Philadelphia, the soft crab at Baltimore, or the canvas-back at Washington.

The seizure of Oyster Bay, therefore, was an outrage not merely on the pockets, but the larders of the New Amsterdammers; the whole community was aroused, and an oyster crusade was immediately set on foot against the Yankees. Every stout trencherman hastened to the standard; nay, some of the most corpulent Burgomasters and Schepens joined the expedition as a *corps de reserve*, only to be called into action when the sacking commenced.

The conduct of the expedition was intrusted to a valiant Dutchman, who for size and weight might have matched with Colbrand the Danish champion, slain by Guy of Warwick. He was famous throughout the province for strength of arm and skill at quarter-staff, and hence was named Stoffel Brinkerhoff; or rather, Brinkerhoofd; that is to stay, Stoffel the head-breaker.

This sturdy commander, who was a man of few words but vigorous deeds, led his troops resolutely on through Nineveh, and Babylon, and Jericho, and Patch-hog, and other Long Island towns, without encountering any difficulty of note; though it is said that some of the burgomasters gave out at Hard-scramble Hill and Hungry Hollow; and that others lost heart and turned back at Puss-panick. With the rest he made good his march until he arrived in the neighborhood of Oyster Bay.

Here he was encountered by a host of Yankee warriors headed by Preserved Fish, and Habakkuk Nutter, and Return Strong, and Zerubbabel Fisk, and Determined Cock! at the sound of whose names Stoffel Brinkerhoff verily believed the whole parliament of Praise-God Barebones had been let loose upon him. He soon found, however, that they were merely the "selectmen" of the settlement, armed with no weapon but the tongue, and disposed only to meet him on the field of argument. Stoffel had but one mode of arguing; that was, with the cudgel; but he used it with such effect that he routed his antagonists, broke up the settlement, and would have driven the inhabitants into the sea if they had not managed to escape across the Sound to the mainland by the Devil's stepping-stones, which remain to this day monuments of this great Dutch victory over the Yankees.

Stoffel Brinkerhoff made great spoil of oysters and clams, coined and uncoined, and then set out on his return to the Manhattoes. A grand triumph, after the manner of the ancients, was prepared for him by William the Testy. He entered New Amsterdam as a conqueror, mounted on a Narraganset pacer.

Five dried codfish on poles, standards taken from the enemy, were borne before him, and an immense store of oysters and clams, Weathersfield onions, and Yankee "notions" formed the spolia opima; while several coiners of oyster-shells were led captive to grace the hero's triumph.

The procession was accompanied by a full band of boys and negroes performing on the popular instruments of rattle-bones and clam-shells, while Antony Van Corlear sounded his trumpet from the ramparts.

A great banquet was served up in the stadthouse from the clams and oysters taken from the enemy; while the governor sent the shells privately to the mint and had them coined into Indian money, with which he paid his troops.

It is moreover said that the governor, calling to mind the practice among the ancients to honor their victorious general with public statues, passed a magnanimous decree, by which every tavern-keeper was permitted to paint the head of Stoffel Brinkerhoff upon his sign!

CHAPTER VII.

GROWING DISCONTENTS OF NEW AMSTERDAM UNDER THE GOVERNMENT OF WILLIAM THE TESTY.

IT HAS BEEN REMARKED by the observant writer of the Stuyvesant manuscript, that under the administration of William Kieft the disposition of the inhabitants of New Amsterdam experienced an essential change, so that they became very meddlesome and factious. The unfortunate propensity of the little governor to experiment and innovation, and the frequent exacerbations of his temper, kept his council in a continual worry; and the council being to the people at large what yeast or leaven is to a batch, they threw the whole community in a ferment; and the people at large being to the city what the mind is to the body, the unhappy commotions they underwent operated most disastrously upon New Amsterdam—insomuch that, in certain of their paroxysms of consternation and perplexity, they begat several of the most crooked, distorted, and abominable streets, lanes, and alleys, with which this metropolis is disfigured.

The fact was, that about this time the community, like Balaam's ass, began to grow more enlightened than its rider, and to show a disposition for what is called "self-government." This restive propensity was first evinced in certain popular meetings, in which the burghers of New Amsterdam met to talk and smoke over the complicated affairs of the province, gradually obfuscating themselves with politics and tobacco smoke. Hither resorted those idlers and squires of low degree who hang loose on society and are blown about by every wind of doctrine. Cobblers abandoned their stalls to give lessons on political economy; blacksmiths suffered their fires to go out while they stirred up the fires of faction; and even tailors, though said to be the ninth parts of humanity, neglected their own measures to criticise the measures of government.

Strange! that the science of government, which seems to be so generally understood, should invariably be denied to the only one called upon to exercise it. Not one of the politicians in question, but, take his word for it, could have administered affairs ten times better than William the Testy.

Under the instructions of these political oracles the good people of New Amsterdam soon became exceedingly enlightened; and as a matter of course, exceedingly discontented. They gradually found out the fearful error in which they had indulged, of thinking themselves the happiest people in creation; and were convinced that, all circumstances to the contrary notwithstanding, they were a very unhappy, deluded, and consequently ruined people!

We are naturally prone to discontent, and avaricious after imaginary causes of lamentation. Like lubberly monks we belabor our own shoulders, and take a vast satisfaction in the music of our own groans. Nor is this said by way of paradox; daily experience shows the truth of these observations. It is almost impossible to elevate the spirits of a man groaning under ideal calamities; but nothing is easier than to render him wretched, though on the pinnacle of felicity; as it would be an Herculean task to hoist a man to the top of a steeple, though the merest child could topple him off thence.

I must not omit to mention that these popular meetings were generally held at some noted tavern; these public edifices possessing what in modern times are thought the true fountains of political inspiration. The ancient Germans deliberated upon a matter when drunk, and reconsidered it when sober. Mob politicians in modern times dislike to have two minds upon a subject; so they both deliberate and act when drunk; by this means a world of delay is spared; and as it is universally allowed that a man when drunk sees double, it follows conclusively that he sees twice as well as his sober neighbors.

CHAPTER VIII.

Of the Edict of William the Testy against Tobacco—of the Pipe Plot, and the Rise of Feuds and Parties.

WILHELMUS KIEFT, as has already been observed, was a great legislator on a small scale, and had a microscopic eye in public affairs. He had been greatly annoyed by the factious meetings of the good people of New Amsterdam, but, observing that on these occasions the pipe was ever in their mouth, he began to think that the pipe was at the bottom of the affair, and that there was some mysterious affinity between politics and tobacco smoke. Determined to strike at the root of the evil, he began, forthwith, to rail at tobacco, as a noxious, nauseous weed; filthy in all its uses; and as to smoking he denounced it as a heavy tax upon the public pocket; a vast consumer of time, a great encourager of idleness, and a deadly bane to the prosperity and morals of the people. Finally he issued an edict, prohibiting the smoking of tobacco throughout the New Netherlands. Ill-fated Kieft! Had he lived in the present age and attempted to check the unbounded license of the press, he could not have struck more sorely upon the sensibilities of the million. The pipe, in fact, was the great organ of reflection and deliberation of the New Netherlander. It was his constant companion and solace—was he gay, he smoked; was he sad, he smoked; his pipe was never out of his mouth; it was a part of his physiognomy; without it his best friends would not know him. Take away his pipe? You might as well take away his nose!

The immediate effect of the edict of William the Testy was a popular commotion. A vast multitude armed with pipes and tobacco-boxes, and an immense supply of ammunition, sat themselves down before the governor's house, and fell to smoking with tremendous violence. The testy William issued forth like a wrathful spider, demanding the reason of this lawless fumigation. The sturdy rioters replied by lolling back in their seats, and puffing away with redoubled fury; raising such a murky cloud that the governor was fain to take refuge in the interior of his castle.

A long negotiation ensued through the medium of Antony the Trumpeter. The governor was at first wrathful and unyielding, but was gradually smoked into terms. He concluded by permitting the smoking of tobacco, but he abolished the fair long pipes used in the days of Wouter Van Twiller, denoting ease, tranquillity, and sobriety of deportment; these he condemned as incompatible with the despatch of business, in place whereof he substituted little captious short pipes, two inches in length, which, he observed, could be stuck in one corner of the mouth, or twisted in the hat-band; and would never be in the way. Thus ended this alarming insurrection, which was long known by the name of The Pipe Plot, and which, it has been somewhat quaintly observed, did end, like most plots and seditions, in mere smoke.

But mark, oh, reader! the deplorable evils which did afterwards result. The smoke of these villainous little pipes, continually ascending in a cloud about the nose, penetrated into and befogged the cerebellum; dried up all the kindly moisture of the brain, and rendered the people who used them as vaporish and testy as the governor himself. Nay, what is worse, from being goodly, burly, sleek-conditioned men, they became, like our Dutch yeomanry who smoke short pipes, a lantern-jawed, smoke-dried, leathern-hided race.

Nor was this all. From this fatal schism in tobacco pipes we may date the rise of parties in the Nieuw Nederlands. The rich and self-important burghers who had made their fortunes, and could afford to be lazy, adhered to the ancient fashion, and formed a kind of aristocracy known as the *Long Pipes;* while the lower order, adopting the reform of William Kieft as more convenient in their handicraft employments, were branded with the plebeian name of *Short Pipes.*

A third party sprang up, headed by the descendants of Robert Chewit, the companion of the great Hudson. These discarded pipes altogether and took to chewing tobacco; hence they were called *Quids;* an appellation since given to those political mongrels, which sometimes spring up between two great parties, as a mule is produced between a horse and an ass.

And here I would note the great benefit of party distinctions in saving the people at large the trouble of thinking. Hesiod divides mankind into three classes, those who think for themselves, those who think as others think, and those who do not think at all. The second class comprises the great mass of society; for most people require a set creed and a file-leader. Hence the origin of party: which means a large body of people, some few of whom think, and all the rest talk. The former take the lead and discipline the latter; prescribing what they must say; what they must approve; what they must hoot at; whom they must support; but, above all, whom they must hate; for no one can be a right good partisan, who is not a thorough-going hater.

The enlightened inhabitants of the Manhattoes, therefore, being divided into parties, were enabled to hate each other with great accuracy. And now the great business of politics went bravely on, the long pipes and short pipes assembling in separate beer-houses, and smoking at each other with implacable vehemence, to the great support of the State and profit of the tavern-keepers. Some, indeed, went so far as to bespatter their adversaries with those odoriferous little words which smell so strong in the Dutch language; believing, like true politicians, that they served their party, and glorified themselves in proportion as they bewrayed their neighbors. But, however they might differ among themselves, all parties agreed in abusing the governor; seeing that he was not a governor of their choice, but appointed by others to rule over them.

Unhappy William Kieft! exclaims the sage writer of the Stuyvesant manuscript, doomed to contend with enemies too knowing to be entrapped, and to reign over a people too wise to be governed. All his foreign expeditions were baffled and set at naught by the all-pervading Yankees; all his home measures were canvassed and condemned by "numerous and respectable meetings" of pot-house politicians.

In the multitude of counsellors, we are told, there is safety; but the multitude of counsellors was a continual source of perplexity to William Kieft. With a temperament as hot as an old radish, and a mind subject to perpetual whirlwinds and tornadoes, he never failed to get into a passion with every one who undertook to advise him. I have observed, however, that your passionate little men, like small boats with large sails, are easily upset or blown out of their course; so was it with William the Testy, who was prone to be carried away by the last piece of advice blown into his ear. The consequence was, that, though a projector of the first class, yet, by continually changing his projects, he gave none a fair trial; and by endeavoring to do everything, he in sober truth did nothing.

In the meantime, the sovereign people having got into the saddle, showed themselves, as usual, unmerciful riders; spurring on the little governor with harangues and petitions, and thwarting him with memorials and reproaches in much the same way as holiday apprentices manage an unlucky devil of a hack-horse—so that Wilhelmus Kieft was kept at a worry or a gallop throughout the whole of his administration.

BOOK V.

CONTAINING THE FIRST PART OF THE REIGN OF PETER STUYVESANT, AND HIS
TROUBLES WITH THE AMPHICTYONIC COUNCIL.

CHAPTER I.

IN WHICH THE DEATH OF A GREAT MAN IS SHOWN TO BE NO VERY
INCONSOLABLE MATTER OF SORROW—AND HOW PETER STUYVESANT
ACQUIRED A GREAT NAME FROM THE UNCOMMON STRENGTH OF HIS
HEAD.

TO A PROFOUND PHILOSOPHER like myself, who am apt to see clear through a
subject, where the penetration of ordinary people extends but half way, there
is no fact more simple and manifest than that the death of a great man is a
matter of very little importance. Much as we may think of ourselves, and much
as we may excite the empty plaudits of the million, it is certain that the greatest
among us do actually fill but an exceeding small space in the world; and it is
equally certain, that even that small space is quickly supplied when we leave
it vacant. "Of what consequence is it," said Pliny, "that individuals appear,
or make their exit? the world is a theatre whose scenes and actors are continually changing." Never did philosopher speak more correctly, and I only wonder
that so wise a remark could have existed so many ages, and mankind not have
laid it more to heart. Sage follows on in the footsteps of sage; one hero just
steps out of his triumphal car, to make way for the hero who comes after him;
and of the proudest monarch it is merely said that, "he slept with his fathers,
and his successor reigned in his stead."

The world, to tell the private truth, cares but little for their loss, and if left
to itself would soon forget to grieve, and though a nation has often been
figuratively drowned in tears on the death of a great man, yet it is ten to one
if an individual tear has been shed on the occasion, excepting from the forlorn
pen of some hungry author. It is the historian, the biographer, and the poet,
who have the whole burden of grief to sustain; who—kind souls!—like under-
takers in England, act the part of chief mourners—who inflate a nation with
sighs it never heaved, and deluge it with tears it never dreamt of shedding.
Thus, while the patriotic author is weeping and howling, in prose, in blank
verse, and in rhyme, and collecting the drops of public sorrow into his volume,
as into a lachrymal vase, it is more than probable his fellow-citizens are eating
and drinking, fiddling and dancing, as utterly ignorant of the bitter lamentations made in their name, as are those men of straw, John Doe and Richard
Roe, of the plaintiffs for whom they are generously pleased to become sureties.

The most glorious hero that ever desolated nations might have mouldered
into oblivion among the rubbish of his own monument, did not some historian

take him into favor, and benevolently transmit his name to posterity—and much as the valiant William Kieft worried, and bustled, and turmoiled, while he had the destinies of a whole colony in his hand, I question seriously whether he will not be obliged to this authentic history for all his future celebrity.

His exit occasioned no convulsion in the city of New Amsterdam nor its vicinity: the earth trembled not, neither did any stars shoot from their spheres —the heavens were not shrouded in black, as poets would fain persuade us they have been, on the death of a hero—the rocks (hard-hearted varlets!) melted not into tears, nor did the trees hang their heads in silent sorrow; and as to the sun, he lay a-bed the next night just as long, and showed as jolly a face when he rose, as he ever did on the same day of the month in any year, either before or since. The good people of New Amsterdam, one and all, declared that he had been a very busy, active, bustling little governor; that he was "the father of his country"—that he was "the noblest work of God"—that "he was a man, take him for all in all, they ne'er should look upon his like again"—together with sundry other civil and affectionate speeches regularly said on the death of all great men; after which they smoked their pipes, thought no more about him, and Peter Stuyvesant succeeded to his station.

Peter Stuyvesant was the last, and, like the renowned Wouter Van Twiller, the best of our ancient Dutch governors. Wouter having surpassed all who preceded him, and Pieter or Piet, as he was sociably called by the old Dutch burghers, who were ever prone to familiarize names, having never been equalled by any successor. He was in fact the very man fitted by nature to retrieve the desperate fortunes of her beloved province, had not the fates, those most potent and unrelenting of all ancient spinsters, destined them to inextricable confusion.

To say merely that he was a hero would be doing him great injustice—he was in truth a combination of heroes—for he was of a sturdy, rawboned make like Ajax Telamon, with a pair of round shoulders that Hercules would have given his hide for (meaning his lion's hide) when he undertook to ease old Atlas of his load. He was, moreover, as Plutarch describes Coriolanus, not only terrible for the force of his arm, but likewise of his voice, which sounded as though it came out of a barrel; and, like the self-same warrior, he possessed a sovereign contempt for the sovereign people, and an iron aspect, which was enough of itself to make the very bowels of his adversaries quake with terror and dismay. All this martial excellency of appearance was inexpressibly heightened by an accidental advantage, with which I am surprised that neither Homer nor Virgil has graced any of their heroes. This was nothing less than a wooden leg, which was the only prize he had gained in bravely fighting the battles of his country, but of which he was so proud, that he was often heard to declare he valued it more than all his other limbs put together; indeed so highly did he esteem it, that he had it gallantly enchased and relieved with silver devices, which caused it to be related in divers histories and legends that he wore a silver leg.[1]

[1]See the histories of Masters Josselyn and Blome.

Like that choleric warrior Achilles, he was somewhat subject to extempore bursts of passion, which was rather unpleasant to his favorites and attendants, whose perceptions he was apt to quicken, after the manner of his illustrious imitator, Peter the Great, by anointing their shoulders with his walking-staff.

Though I cannot find that he had read Plato, or Aristotle, or Hobbes, or Bacon, or Algernon Sidney, or Tom Paine, yet did he sometimes manifest a shrewdness and sagacity in his measures, that one would hardly expect from a man who did not know Greek, and had never studied the ancients. True it is, and I confess it with sorrow, that he had an unreasonable aversion to experiments, and was fond of governing his province after the simplest manner—but then he contrived to keep it in better order than did the erudite Kieft, though he had all the philosophers, ancient and modern, to assist and perplex him. I must likewise own that he made but very few laws, but then again he took care that those few were rigidly and impartially enforced—and I do not know but justice on the whole was as well administered as if there had been volumes of sage acts and statutes yearly made, and daily neglected and forgotten.

He was, in fact, the very reverse of his predecessors, being neither tranquil and inert, like Walter the Doubter, nor restless and fidgeting, like William the Testy; but a man, or rather a governor, of such uncommon activity and decision of mind, that he never sought nor accepted the advice of others; depending bravely upon his single head as would a hero of yore upon his single arm, to carry him through all difficulties and dangers. To tell the simple truth he wanted nothing more to complete him as a statesman than to think always right, for no one can say but that he always acted as he thought. He was never a man to flinch when he found himself in a scrape; but to dash forward through thick and thin, trusting, by hook or by crook, to make all things straight in the end. In a word, he possessed in an eminent degree that great quality in a statesman, called perseverance by the polite, but nicknamed obstinacy by the vulgar. A wonderful salve for official blunders; since he who perseveres in error without flinching, gets the credit of boldness and consistency, while he who wavers in seeking to do what is right gets stigmatized as a trimmer. This much is certain; and it is a maxim well worthy the attention of all legislators great and small, who stand shaking in the wind, irresolute which way to steer, that a ruler who follows his own will pleases himself, while he who seeks to satisfy the wishes and whims of others runs great risk of pleasing nobody. There is nothing too like putting down one's foot resolutely, when in doubt; and letting things take their course. The clock that stands still points right twice in the four and twenty hours: while others may keep going continually and be continually going wrong.

Nor did this magnanimous quality escape the discernment of the good people of Nieuw Nederlands; on the contrary, so much were they struck with the independent will and vigorous resolution displayed on all occasions by their new governor, that they universally called him Hard-Koppig Piet; or Peter the Headstrong—a great compliment to the strength of his understanding.

If, from all that I have said, thou dost not gather, worthy reader, that Peter Stuyvesant was a tough, sturdy, valiant, weather-beaten, mettlesome, obstinate, leathern-sided, lion-hearted, generous-spirited old governor, either I have written to but little purpose, or thou art very dull at drawing conclusions.

This most excellent governor commenced his administration on the 29th of May, 1647; a remarkably stormy day, distinguished in all the almanacs of the time which have come down to us by the name of *Windy Friday*. As he was very jealous of his personal and official dignity, he was inaugurated into office with great ceremony; the goodly oaken chair of the renowned Wouter Van Twiller being carefully preserved for such occasions, in like manner as the chair and stone were reverentially preserved at Scone, in Scotland, for the coronation of the Caledonian monarchs.

I must not omit to mention, that the tempestuous state of the elements, together with its being that unlucky day of the week termed "hanging day," did not fail to excite much grave speculation and divers very reasonable apprehensions among the more ancient and enlightened inhabitants; and several of the sager sex, who were reputed to be not a little skilled in the mysteries of astrology and fortune-telling, did declare outright that they were omens of a disastrous administration—an event that came to be lamentably verified, and which proves, beyond dispute, the wisdom of attending to those preternatural intimations furnished by dreams and visions, the flying of birds, falling of stones, and cackling of geese, on which the sages and rulers of ancient times placed such reliance—or to those shootings of stars, eclipses of the moon, howlings of dogs, and flarings of candles, carefully noted and interpreted by the oracular sybils of our day; who, in my humble opinion, are the legitimate inheritors and preservers of the ancient science of divination. This much is certain, that Governor Stuyvesant succeeded to the chair of state at a turbulent period; when foes thronged and threatened from without; when anarchy and stiff-necked opposition reigned rampant within; when the authority of their High Mightinesses the Lords States-General, though supported by economy, and defended by speeches, protests and proclamations, yet tottered to its very centre; and when the great city of New Amsterdam, though fortified by flag-staffs, trumpeters, and windmills, seemed, like some fair lady of easy virtue, to lie open to attack, and ready to yield to the first invader.

CHAPTER II.

Showing How Peter the Headstrong Bestirred Himself among the Rats and Cobwebs on Entering into Office; His Interview with Antony the Trumpeter, and His Perilous Meddling with the Currency.

The very first movements of the great Peter, on taking the reins of government, displayed his magnanimity, though they occasioned not a little marvel and uneasiness among the people of the Manhattoes. Finding himself constantly interrupted by the opposition, and annoyed by the advice of his privy council, the members of which had acquired the unreasonable habit of thinking and speaking for themselves during the preceding reign, he determined at once to put a stop to such grievous abominations. Scarcely, therefore, had he entered upon his authority, then he turned out of office all the meddlesome spirits of the factious cabinet of William the Testy; in place of whom he chose unto himself counsellors from those fat, somniferous, respectable burghers who had flourished and slumbered under the easy reign of Walter the Doubter. All these he caused to be furnished with abundance of fair long pipes, and to be regaled with frequent corporation dinners, admonishing them to smoke, and eat, and sleep, for the good of the nation, while he took the burden of government upon his own shoulders—an arrangement to which they all gave hearty acquiescence.

Nor did he stop here, but made a hideous rout among the inventions and expedients of his learned predecessor—rooting up his patent gallows, where caitiff vagabonds were suspended by the waistband—demolishing his flag-staffs and windmills, which, like mighty giants, guarded the ramparts of New Amsterdam—pitching to the duyvel whole batteries of quaker guns—and, in a word, turning topsy-turvy the whole philosophic, economic, and windmill system of the immortal sage of Saardam.

The honest folk of New Amsterdam began to quake now for the fate of their matchless champion, Antony the Trumpeter, who had acquired prodigious favor in the eyes of the women, by means of his whiskers and his trumpet. Him did Peter the Headstrong cause to be brought into his presence, and eying him for a moment from head to foot, with a countenance that would have appalled anything else than a sounder of brass—"Pr'ythee, who and what art thou?" said he. "Sire," replied the other, in no wise dismayed, "for my name, it is Antony Van Corlear—for my parentage, I am the son of my mother—for my profession, I am champion and garrison of this great city of New Amsterdam." "I doubt me much," said Peter Stuyvesant, "that thou art some scurvy costard-monger knave:—how didst thou acquire this paramount honor and dignity?" "Marry, sir," replied the other, "like many a great man before me, simply *by sounding my own trumpet*." "Ay, is it so?" quoth the governor; "why then let us have a relish of thy art." Whereupon the good Antony put his instrument to his lips, and sounded a charge with such a tremendous outset, such a delectable quaver, and such a triumphant cadence, that it was enough to make one's heart leap out of one's mouth only to be within a mile of it. Like as a warworn charger, grazing in peaceful plains, starts at a strain of martial music, pricks up his ears, and snorts, and paws, and kindles at the noise, so did the heroic Peter joy to hear the clangor of the trumpet; for of him might truly be said, what was recorded of the renowned St. George of England, "there was nothing in all the world that more rejoiced his heart than to hear the pleasant sound of war, and see the soldiers brandish forth their steeled weapons." Casting his eye more kindly, therefore, upon the sturdy Van Corlear, and finding him to be a jovial varlet, shrewd in his discourse, yet of great discretion and immeasurable wind, he straightway conceived a vast kindness for him, and discharging him from the troublesome duty of garrisoning, defending, and alarming the city, ever after retained him about his person, as his chief favorite, confidential envoy, and trusty squire. Instead of disturbing the city with disastrous notes, he was instructed to play so as to delight the governor while at his repasts, as did the minstrels of yore in the days of glorious chivalry—and on all public occasions to rejoice the ears of the people with warlike melody—thereby keeping alive a noble and martial spirit.

But the measure of the valiant Peter which produced the greatest agitation in the community, was his laying his hand upon the currency. He had old-fashioned notions in favor of gold and silver, which he considered the true standards of wealth and mediums of commerce, and one of his first edicts was, that all duties to government should be paid in those precious metals, and that seawant, or wampum, should no longer be a legal tender.

Here was a blow at public prosperity! All those who speculated on the rise and fall of this fluctuating currency, found their calling at an end: those, too, who had hoarded Indian money by barrels full, found their capital shrunk in amount; but, above all, the Yankee traders, who were accustomed to flood the market with newly-coined oyster-shells, and to abstract Dutch merchandise in exchange, were loud-mouthed in decrying this "tampering with the currency." It was clipping the wings of commerce; it was checking the development of public prosperity; trade would be at and end; goods would moulder on the shelves; grain would rot in the granaries; grass would grow in the market-place. In a word, no one who has not heard the outcries and howlings of a modern Tarshish, at any check upon "paper money," can have any idea of the clamor against Peter the Headstrong, for checking the circulation of oyster-shells.

In fact, trade did shrink into narrower channels; but then the stream was deep as it was broad; the honest Dutchmen sold less goods; but then they got the worth of them, either in silver and gold, or in codfish, tin-ware, apple-brandy, Weathersfield onions, wooden bowls, and other articles of Yankee barter. The ingenious people of the East, however, indemnified themselves in another way for having to abandon the coinage of oyster-shells, for about this time we are told that wooden nutmegs made their first appearance in New Amsterdam, to the great annoyance of the Dutch housewives.

NOTE.—*From a manuscript record of the province; Lib. N. Y. Hist. Society.*—We have been unable to render your inhabitants wiser and prevent their being further imposed upon than to declare absolutely and peremptorily that henceforward seawant shall be bullion—not longer admissible in trade, without any value, as it is indeed. So that every one may be upon his guard to barter no longer away his wares and merchandises for these bubbles—at least not to accept them at a higher rate or in a larger quantity than as they may want them in their trade with the savages.

In this way your English [Yankee] neighbors shall no longer be enabled to draw the best wares and merchandises from our country for nothing—the beavers and furs not excepted. This has indeed long since been insufferable, although it ought chiefly to be imputed to the imprudent penuriousness of our own merchants and inhabitants, who, it is to be hoped, shall through the abolition of this seawant become wiser and more prudent.

27th January, 1662.

Seawant falls into disrepute—duties to be paid in silver coin.

CHAPTER III.

How the Yankee League Waxed More and More Potent, and How It Outwitted the Good Peter in Treaty-Making.

Now it came to pass, that while Peter Stuyvesant was busy regulating the internal affairs of his domain, the great Yankee league, which had caused such tribulation to William the Testy, continued to increase in extent and power. The grand Amphictyonic council of the league was held at Boston, where it spun a web, which threatened to link within it all the mighty principalities and powers of the East. The object proposed by this formidable combination was mutual protection and defence against their savage neighbors; but all the world knows the real aim was to form a grand crusade against the Nieuw Nederlands and to get possession of the city of the Manhattoes—as devout an object of enterprise and ambition to the Yankees as was ever the capture of Jerusalem to ancient crusaders.

In the very year following the inauguration of Governor Stuyvesant, a grand deputation departed from the city of Providence (famous for its dusty streets and beauteous women) in behalf of the plantation of Rhode Island, praying to be admitted into the league.

The following minute of this deputation appears in the ancient records of the council.[1]

"Mr. Will. Cottington and Captain Partridg of Rhoode Island presented this inewing request to the commissioners in wrighting—

"Our request and motions is in behalfe of Rhoode Iland, that wee the Ilanders of Roode-Iland may be rescauied into combination with all the united colonyes of New England in a firme and perpetual league of friendship and amity of ofence and defence, mutuall advice and succor upon all just occasions for our mutuall safety and wellfaire, etc.

"Will Cottington,
"Alicxsander Partridg."

There was certainly something in the very physiognomy of this document that might well inspire apprehension. The name of Alexander, however misspelt, has been warlike in every age, and though its fierceness is in some measure softened by being coupled with the gentle cognomen of Partridge, still, like the color of scarlet, it bears an exceeding great resemblance to the sound of a trumpet. From the style of the letter, moreover, and the soldierlike ignorance of orthography displayed by the noble captain Alicxsander Partridg in spelling his own name, we may picture to ourselves this mighty man of Rhodes, strong in arms, potent in the field, and as great a scholar as though he had been educated among that learned people of Thrace, who, Aristotle assures us, could not count beyond the number four.

[1]Haz. Col. Stat. Pap.

The result of this great Yankee league was augmented audacity on the part of the moss-troopers of Connecticut—pushing their encroachments farther and farther into the territories of their High Mightinesses, so that even the inhabitants of New Amsterdam began to draw short breath and to find themselves exceedingly cramped for elbow-room.

Peter Stuyvesant was not a man to submit quietly to such intrusions; his first impulse was to march at once to the frontier and kick these squatting Yankees out of the country; but, bethinking himself in time that he was now a governor and legislator, the policy of the statesman for once cooled the fire of the old soldier, and he determined to try his hand at negotiation. A correspondence accordingly ensued between him and the grand council of the league, and it was agreed that commissioners from either side should meet at Hartford, to settle boundaries, adjust grievances, and establish a "perpetual and happy peace."

The commissioners on the part of the Manhattoes were chosen, according to immemorial usage of that venerable metropolis, from among the "wisest and weightiest" men of the community; that is to say, men with the oldest heads and heaviest pockets. Among these sages the veteran navigator, Hans Reinier Oothout, who had made such extensive discoveries during the time of Oloffe the Dreamer, was looked up to as an oracle in all matters of the kind; and he was ready to produce the very spy-glass with which he first spied the mouth of the Connecticut River from his masthead, and all the world knows that the discovery of the mouth of a river gives prior right to all the lands drained by its waters.

It was with feelings of pride and exultation that the good people of the Manhattoes saw two of the richest and most ponderous burghers departing on this embassy; men whose word on 'change was oracular, and in whose presence no poor man ventured to appear without taking off his hat: when it was seen, too, that the veteran Reinier Oothout accompanied them with his spy-glass under his arm, all the old men and old women predicted that men of such weight, with such evidence, would leave the Yankees no alternative but to pack up their tin kettles and wooden wares; put wife and children in a cart, and abandon all the lands of their High Mightinesses, on which they had squatted.

In truth, the commissioners sent to Hartford by the league, seemed in nowise calculated to compete with men of such capacity. They were two lean Yankee lawyers, litigious-looking varlets, and evidently men of no substance, since they had no rotundity in the belt, and there was no jingling of money in their pockets; it is true they had longer heads than the Dutchmen; but if the heads of the latter were flat on top, they were broad at bottom, and what was wanting in height of forehead, was made up by a double chin.

The negotiation turned as usual upon the good old cornerstone of original discovery; according to the principle that he who first sees a new country, has an unquestionable right to it. This being admitted, the veteran Oothout, at a concerted signal, stepped forth in the assembly with the identical tarpauling spy-glass in his hand, with which he had discovered the mouth of the Connecticut, while the worthy Dutch commissioners lolled back in their chairs, secretly chuckling at the idea of having for once got the weather-gage of the Yankees; but what was their dismay when the latter produced a Nantucket whaler with a spy-glass, twice as long, with which he discovered the whole coast, quite down to the Manhattoes; and so crooked that he had spied with it up the whole course of the Connecticut River. This principle pushed home, therefore, the Yankees had a right to the whole country bordering on the Sound; nay, the city of New Amsterdam was a mere Dutch squatting-place on their territories.

I forbear to dwell upon the confusion of the worthy Dutch commissioners at finding their main pillar of proof thus knocked from under them; neither will I pretend to describe the consternation of the wise men at the Manhattoes when they learnt how their commissioner had been out-trumped by the Yankees, and how the latter pretended to claim to the very gates of New Amsterdam.

Long was the negotiation protracted, and long was the public mind kept in a state of anxiety. There are two modes of settling boundary questions when the claims of the opposite parties are irreconcilable. One is by an appeal to arms, in which case the weakest party is apt to lose its right, and get a broken head into the bargain; the other mode is by compromise, or mutual concession; that is to say, one party cedes half of its claims, and the other party half of its rights; he who grasps most gets most, and the whole is pronounced an equitable division, "perfectly honorable to both parties."

The latter mode was adopted in the present instance. The Yankees gave up claims to vast tracts of the Nieuw Nederlands which they had never seen, and all right to the island of Manna-hata and the city of New Amsterdam, to which they had no right at all; while the Dutch, in return, agreed that the Yankees should retain possession of the frontier places where they had squatted, and of both sides of the Connecticut river.

When the news of this treaty arrived at New Amsterdam, the whole city was in an uproar of exultation. The old women rejoiced that there was to be no war, the old men that their cabbage-gardens were safe from invasion; while the political sages pronounced the treaty a great triumph over the Yankees, considering how much they had claimed, and how little they had been "fobbed off with."

And now my worthy reader is, doubtless, like the great and good Peter, congratulating himself with the idea, that his feelings will no longer be harassed by afflicting details of stolen horses, broken heads, impounded hogs, and all the other catalogue of heart-rending cruelties that disgraced these border wars. But if he should indulge in such expectations, it is proof that he is but little versed in the paradoxical ways of cabinets; to convince him of which, I solicit his serious attention to my next chapter, wherein I will show that Peter Stuyvesant has already committed a great error in politics; and by effecting a peace, has materially hazarded the tranquillity of the province.

CHAPTER IV.

Containing Divers Speculations on War and Negotiations—
Showing That a Treaty of Peace Is a Great National Evil.

It was the opinion of that poetical philosopher, Lucretius, that war was the original state of man, whom he described as being primitively a savage beast of prey, engaged in a constant state of hostility with his own species, and that this ferocious spirit was tamed and ameliorated by society. The same opinion has been advocated by Hobbes,[1] nor have there been wanting many other philosophers to admit and defend it.

For my part, though prodigiously fond of these valuable speculations, so complimentary to human nature, yet, in this instance, I am inclined to take the proposition by halves, believing with Horace,[2] that though war may have been originally the favorite amusement and industrious employment of our progenitors, yet, like many other excellent habits, so far from being ameliorated, it has been cultivated and confirmed by refinement and civilization, and increases in exact proportion as we approach towards that state of perfection, which is the *ne plus ultra* of modern philosophy.

The first conflict between man and man was the mere exertion of physical force, unaided by auxiliary weapons—his arm was his buckler, his fist was his mace, and a broken head the catastrophe of his encounters. The battle of unassisted strength was succeeded by the more rugged one of stones and clubs, and war assumed a sanguinary aspect. As man advanced in refinement, as his faculties expanded, and as his sensibilities became more exquisite, he grew rapidly more ingenious and experienced in the art of murdering his fellow-beings. He invented a thousand devices to defend and to assault—the helmet, the cuirass, and the buckler, the sword, the dart, and the javelin, prepared him to elude the wound as well as to launch the blow. Still urging on, in the career of philanthropic invention, he enlarges and heightens his powers of defence and injury: —The Aries, the Scorpio, the Balista, and the Catapulta, give a horror and sublimity to war, and magnify its glory, by increasing its desolation. Still insatiable, though armed with machinery that seemed to reach the limits of destructive invention, and to yield a power of injury commensurate even with the desires of revenge—still deeper researches must be made in the diabolical arcana. With furious zeal he dives into the bowels of the earth; he toils midst poisonous minerals and deadly salts—the sublime discovery of gunpowder blazes upon the

[1]Hobbes's Leviathan. Part i. ch. 13.

[2]Quum prorepserunt primis animalia terris,
Mutuum ac turpe pecus, glandem atque cubilia propter,
Unguibus et pugnis, dein fustibus, atque ita porro
Pugnabant armis, quæ post fabricaverat usus.
Hor. Sat. L. i. S. 3

world—and finally the dreadful art of fighting by proclamation seems to endow the demon of war with ubiquity and omnipotence!

This, indeed, is grand!—this, indeed, marks the powers of mind, and bespeaks that divine endowment of reason, which distinguishes us from the animals, our inferiors. The unenlightened brutes content themselves with the native force which Providence has assigned them—The angry bull butts with his horns, as did his progenitors before him—the lion, the leopard, and the tiger seek only with their talons and their fangs to gratify their sanguinary fury; and even the subtle serpent darts the same venom, and uses the same wiles, as did his sire before the flood. Man alone, blessed with the inventive mind, goes on from discovery to discovery—enlarges and multiplies his powers of destruction; arrogates the tremendous weapons of Deity itself, and tasks creation to assist him in murdering his brother worm!

In proportion as the art of war has increased in improvement has the art of preserving peace advanced in equal ratio; and as we have discovered, in this age of wonders and inventions, that proclamation is the most formidable engine in war, so have we discovered the no less ingenious mode of maintaining peace by perpetual negotiations.

A treaty, or, to speak more correctly, a negotiation, therefore, according to the acceptation of experienced statesmen, learned in these matters, is no longer an attempt to accommodate differences, to ascertain rights, and to establish an equitable exchange of kind offices; but a contest of skill between two powers, which shall overreach and take in the other. It is a cunning endeavor to obtain by peaceful manœuvre, and the chicanery of cabinets, those advantages which a nation would otherwise have wrested by force of arms; in the same manner as a conscientious highwayman reforms and becomes a quiet and praiseworthy citizen, contenting himself with cheating his neighbor out of that property he would formerly have seized with open violence.

In fact, the only time when two nations can be said to be in a state of perfect amity is when a negotiation is open, and a treaty pending. Then, when there are no stipulations entered into, no bonds to restrain the will, no specific limits to awaken the captious jealousy of right implanted in our nature; when each party has some advantage to hope and expect from the other, then it is that the two nations are wonderfully gracious and friendly; their ministers professing the highest mutual regard, exchanging billets-doux, making fine speeches, and indulging in all those little diplomatic flirtations, coquetries, and fondlings, that do so marvellously tickle the good humor of the respective nations. Thus it may paradoxically be said, that there is never so good an understanding between two nations as when there is a little misunderstanding—and that so long as they are on no terms at all, they are on the best terms in the world!

I do not by any means pretend to claim the merit of having made the above discovery. It has, in fact, long been secretly acted upon by certain enlightened cabinets, and is, together with divers other notable theories, privately copied out of the common-place book of an illustrious gentleman, who has been member of congress, and enjoyed the unlimited confidence of heads of departments. To this principle may be ascribed the wonderful ingenuity shown of late years in protracting and interrupting negotiations.—Hence the cunning measure of appointing as ambassador some political pettifogger skilled in delays, sophisms, and misapprehensions, and dexterous in the art of baffling argument—or some blundering statesman, whose errors and misconstructions may be a plea for refusing to ratify his engagements. And hence, too, that most notable expedient, so popular with our government, of sending out a brace of ambassadors; between whom, having each an individual will to consult, character to establish, and interest to promote, you may as well look for unanimity and concord as between two lovers with one mistress, two dogs with one bone, or two naked rogues with one pair of breeches. This disagreement, therefore, is continually breeding delays and impediments, in consequence of which the negotiation goes on swimmingly—inasmuch as there is no prospect of its ever coming to a close. Nothing is lost by these delays and obstacles but time; and in a negotiation, according to the theory I have exposed, all time lost is in reality so much time gained:—with what delightful paradoxes does modern political economy abound!

Now all that I have here advanced is so notoriously true, that I almost blush to take up the time of my readers with treating of matters which must many a time have stared them in the face. But the proposition to which I would most earnestly call their attention is this, that though a negotiation be the most harmonizing of all national transactions, yet a treaty of peace is a great political evil, and one of the most fruitful sources of war.

I have rarely seen an instance of any special contract between individuals that did not produce jealousies, bickerings, and often downright ruptures between them; nor did I ever know of a treaty between two nations that did not occasion continual misunderstandings. How many worthy country neighbors have I known, who, after living in peace and good fellowship for years, have been thrown into a state of distrust, cavilling, and animosity, by some ill-starred agreement about fences, runs of water, and stray cattle! And how many well-meaning nations, who would otherwise have remained in the most amicable disposition towards each other, have been brought to swords' points about the infringement or misconstruction of some treaty, which in an evil hour they had concluded, by way of making their amity more sure!

Treaties at best are but complied with so long as interest requires their fulfilment; consequently they are virtually binding on the weaker party only, or, in plain truth, they are not binding at all. No nation will wantonly go to war with another if it has nothing to gain thereby, and therefore needs no treaty to restrain it from violence; and if it have any thing to gain, I much question, from what I have witnessed of the righteous conduct of nations, whether any treaty could be made so strong that it could not thrust the sword through—nay, I would hold ten to one, the treaty itself would be the very source to which resort would be had to find a pretext for hostilities.

Thus, therefore, I conclude—that though it is the best of all policies for a nation to keep up a constant negotiation with its neighbors, yet it is the summit of folly for it ever to be beguiled into a treaty; for then comes on non-fulfilment and infraction, then remonstrance, then altercation, then retaliation, then recrimination, and finally open war. In a word, negotiation is like courtship, a time of sweet words, gallant speeches, soft looks, and endearing caresses—but the marriage ceremony is the signal for hostilities.

If my painstaking reader be not somewhat perplexed by the ratiocination of the foregoing passage, he will perceive, at a glance, that the Great Peter, in concluding a treaty with his Eastern neighbors, was guilty of lamentable error in policy. In fact, to this unlucky agreement may be traced a world of bickerings and heart-burnings between the parties, about fancied or pretended infringements of treaty stipulations; in all which the Yankees were prone to indemnify themselves by a "dig into the sides" of the New Netherlands. But, in sooth, these border feuds, albeit they gave great annoyance to the good burghers of Manna-hata, were so painful in their nature, that a grave historian like myself, who grudges the time spent in any thing less than the revolutions of states and fall of empires, would deem them unworthy of being inscribed on his page. The reader is, therefore, to take it for granted, though I scorn to waste, in the detail, that time which my furrowed brow and trembling hand inform me is invaluable, that all the while the Great Peter was occupied in those tremendous and bloody contests which I shall shortly rehearse, there was a continued series of little, dirty, snivelling scourings, broils, and maraudings, kept up on the eastern frontiers by the moss-troopers of Connecticut. But, like that mirror of chivalry, the sage and valorous Don Quixote, I leave these petty contests for some future Sancho Panza of a historian, while I reserve my prowess and my pen for achievements of higher dignity; for at this moment I hear a direful and portentous note issuing from the bosom of the great council of the league, and resounding throughout the regions of the East, menacing the fame and fortunes of Peter Stuyvesant. I call, therefore, upon the reader to leave behind him all the paltry brawls of the Connecticut borders, and to press forward with me to the relief of our favorite hero, who, I foresee, will be wofully beset by the implacable Yankees in the next chapter.

CHAPTER V.

How Peter Stuyvesant Was Grievously Belied by the Great Council of the League; and How He Sent Antony the Trumpeter to Take to the Council a Piece of His Mind.

That the reader may be aware of the peril at this moment menacing Peter Stuyvesant and his capital, I must remind him of the old charge advanced in the council of the league in the time of William the Testy, that the Nederlanders were carrying on a trade "damnable and injurious to the colonists," in furnishing the savages with "guns, powther, and shott." This, as I then suggested, was a crafty device of the Yankee confederacy to have a snug cause of war *in petto*, in case any favorable opportunity should present of attempting the conquest of the New Nederlands: the great object of Yankee ambition.

Accordingly we now find, when every other ground of complaint had apparently been removed by treaty, this nefarious charge revived with tenfold virulence, and hurled like a thunderbolt at the very head of Peter Stuyvesant; happily his head, like that of the great bull of the Wabash, was proof against such missiles.

To be explicit, we are told that, in the year 1651, the great confederacy of the East accused the immaculate Peter, the soul of honor and heart of steel, of secretly endeavoring, by gifts and promises, to instigate the Narroheganset, Mohaque, and Pequot Indians, to surprise and massacre the Yankee settlements. "For," as the grand council observed, "the Indians round about for divers hundred miles cercute seeme to have drunk deepe of an intoxicating cupp, att or from the Manhattoes against the English, whoe have sought their good, both in bodily and spirituall respects."

This charge they pretended to support by the evidence of divers Indians, who were probably moved by that spirit of truth which is said to reside in the bottle, and who swore to the fact as sturdily as though they had been so many Christian troopers.

Though descended from a family which suffered much injury from the losel Yankees of those times, my great-grandfather having had a yoke of oxen and his best pacer stolen, and having received a pair of black eyes and a bloody nose in one of these border wars; and my grandfather, when a very little boy tending pigs, having been kidnapped and severely flogged by a long-sided Connecticut schoolmaster—yet I should have passed over all these wrongs with forgiveness and oblivion—I could even have suffered them to have broken Everet Ducking's head; to have kicked the doughty Jacobus Van Curlet and his ragged regiment out of doors; to have carried every hog into captivity, and depopulated every hen-roost on the face of the earth with perfect impunity— but this wanton attack upon one of the most gallant and irreproachable heroes of modern times, is too much even for me to digest; and has overset, with a single puff, the patience of the historian, and the forbearance of the Dutchman.

Oh reader, it was false! I swear to thee, it was false!—If thou hast any respect to my word—if the undeviating character for veracity, which I have endeavored to maintain throughout this work, has its due weight with thee, thou wilt not give thy faith to this tale of slander; for I pledge my honor and my immortal fame to thee, that the gallant Peter Stuyvesant was not only innocent of this foul conspiracy, but would have suffered his right arm or even his wooden leg to consume with slow and everlasting flames, rather than attempt to destroy his enemies in any other way than open, generous warfare—beshrew those caitiff scouts, that conspired to sully his honest name by such an imputation!

Peter Stuyvesant, though haply he may never have heard of a knight-errant, had as true a heart of chivalry as ever beat at the round table of King Arthur. In the honest bosom of this heroic Dutchman dwelt the seven noble virtues of knighthood, flourishing among his hardy qualities like wild flowers among rocks. He was, in truth, a hero of chivalry struck off by nature at a single heat, and though little care may have been taken to refine her workmanship, he stood forth a miracle of her skill. In all his dealings he was headstrong perhaps, but open and above board; if there was anything in the whole world he most loathed and despised it was cunning and secret wile; "straight forward" was his motto, and he would at any time rather run his hard head against a stone wall than attempt to get round it.

Such was Peter Stuyvesant, and if my admiration of him has on this occasion transported my style beyond the sober gravity which becomes the philosophic recorder of historic events, I must plead as an apology, that though a little gray-headed Dutchman, arrived almost at the down-hill of life, I still retain a lingering spark of that fire which kindles in the eye of youth when contemplating the virtues of ancient worthies. Blessed, thrice and nine times blessed be the good St. Nicholas, if I have indeed escaped that apathy which chills the sympathies of age and paralyzes every glow of enthusiasm.

The first measure of Peter Stuyvesant, on hearing of this slanderous charge, would have been worthy of a man who had studied for years in the chivalrous library of Don Quixote. Drawing his sword and laying it across the table, to put him in proper tune, he took pen in hand and indited a proud and lofty letter to the council of the league, reproaching them with giving ear to the slanders of heathen savages against a Christian, a soldier, and a cavalier; declaring that whoever charged him with the plot in question, lied in his throat; to prove which he offered to meet the president of the council or any of his compeers; or their champion, Captain Alicxsander Partridg, that mighty man of Rhodes, in single combat; wherein he trusted to vindicate his honor by the prowess of his arm.

This missive was intrusted to his trumpeter and squire, Antony Van Corlear, that man of emergencies, with orders to travel night and day, sparing neither whip nor spur, seeing that he carried the vindication of his patron's fame in his saddle-bags.

The loyal Antony accomplished his mission with great speed and considerable loss of leather. He delivered his missive with becoming ceremony, accompanying it with a flourish of defiance on his trumpet to the whole council, ending with a significant and nasal twang full in the face of Captain Partridg, who nearly jumped out of his skin in an ecstasy of astonishment.

The grand council was composed of men too cool and practical to be put readily in a heat, or to indulge in knight-errantry; and above all to run a tilt with such a fiery hero as Peter the Headstrong. They knew the advantage, however, to have always a snug, justifiable cause of war in reserve with a neighbor, who had territories worth invading; so they devised a reply to Peter Stuyvesant, calculated to keep up the "raw" which they had established.

On receiving this answer, Antony Van Corlear remounted the Flanders mare which he always rode, and trotted merrily back to the Manhattoes, solacing himself by the way according to his wont—twanging his trumpet like a very devil, so that the sweet valleys and banks of the Connecticut resounded with the warlike melody—bringing all the folks to the windows as he passed through Hartford and Pyquag, and Middletown, and all the other border towns, ogling and winking at the women, and making aerial windmills from the end of his nose at their husbands—and stopping occasionally in the villages to eat pumpkin-pies, dance at country frolics, and bundle with the Yankee lasses—whom he rejoiced exceedingly with his soul-stirring instrument.

CHAPTER VI.

How Peter Stuyvesant Demanded a Court of Honor—and of the Court of Honor Awarded to Him.

The reply of the grand council to Peter Stuyvesant was couched in the coolest and most diplomatic language. They assured him that "his confident denials of the barbarous plot alleged against him would weigh little against the testimony of divers sober and respectable Indians;" that "his guilt was proved to their perfect satisfaction," so that they must still require and seek due *satisfaction and security;* ending with—"so we rest, sir—Yours in ways of righteousness."

I forbear to say how the lion-hearted Peter roared and ramped at finding himself more and more entangled in the meshes thus artfully drawn round him by the knowing Yankees. Impatient, however, of suffering so gross an aspersion to rest upon his honest name, he sent a second messenger to the council, reiterating his denial of the treachery imputed to him, and offering to submit his conduct to the scrutiny of a court of honor. His offer was readily accepted; and now he looked forward with confidence to an august tribunal to be assembled at the Manhattoes, formed of high-minded cavaliers, peradventure governors and commanders of the confederate plantations, where the matter might be investigated by his peers, in a manner befitting his rank and dignity.

While he was awaiting the arrival of such high functionaries, behold, one sunshiny afternoon there rode into the great gate of the Manhattoes two lean, hungry-looking Yankees, mounted on Narraganset pacers, with saddle-bags under their bottoms, and green satchels under their arms, who looked marvellously like two pettifogging attorneys beating the hoof from one county court to another in quest of lawsuits: and, in sooth, though they may have passed under different names at the time, I have reason to suspect they were the identical varlets who had negotiated the worthy Dutch commissioners out of the Connecticut river.

It was a rule with these indefatigable missionaries never to let the grass grow under their feet. Scarce had they, therefore, alighted at the inn and deposited their saddle-bags, than they made their way to the residence of the governor. They found him, according to custom, smoking his afternoon pipe on the "stoop," or bench at the porch of his house, and announced themselves, at once, as commissioners sent by the grand council of the East to investigate the truth of certain charges advanced against him.

The good Peter took his pipe from his mouth, and gazed at them for a moment in mute astonishment. By way of expediting business, they were proceeding on the spot to put some preliminary questions; asking him, peradventure, whether he pleaded guilty or not guilty, considering him something in the light of a culprit at the bar; when they were brought to a pause by seeing him lay down his pipe and begin to fumble with his walking-staff. For a moment, those present would not have given half a crown for both the crowns of the commissioners; but Peter Stuyvesant repressed his mighty wrath and stayed his hand; he scanned the varlets from head to foot, satchels and all, with a look of ineffable scorn; then strode into the house, slammed the door after him, and commanded that they should never again be admitted to his presence.

The knowing commissioners winked to each other, and made a certificate on the spot that the governor had refused to answer their interrogatories or to submit to their examination. They then proceeded to rummage about the city for two or three days, in quest of what they called evidence, perplexing Indians and old women with their cross-questioning until they had stuffed their satchels and saddle-bags with all kinds of apocryphal tales, rumors and calumnies: with these they mounted their Narraganset pacers and travelled back to the grand council; neither did the proud-hearted Peter trouble himself to hinder their researches nor impede their departure; he was too mindful of their sacred character as envoys; but I warrant me had they played the same tricks with William the Testy, he would have had them tucked up by the waist-band and treated to an aerial gambol on his patent gallows.

CHAPTER VII.

How "Drum Ecclesiastic" Was Beaten throughout Connecticut for a Crusade against the New Netherlands, and How Peter Stuyvesant Took Measures to Fortify His Capital.

THE GRAND COUNCIL of the East held a solemn meeting on the return of their envoys. As no advocate appeared in behalf of Peter Stuyvesant everything went against him. His haughty refusal to submit to the questioning of the commissioners was construed into a consciousness of guilt. The contents of the satchels and saddle-bags were poured forth before the council and appeared a mountain of evidence. A pale bilious orator took the floor, and declaimed for hours and in belligerent terms. He was one of those furious zealots who blow the bellows of faction until the whole furnace of politics is red-hot with sparks and cinders. What was it to him if he should set the house on fire, so that he might boil his pot by the blaze? He was from the borders of Connecticut; his constituents lived by marauding their Dutch neighbors, and were the greatest poachers in Christendom, excepting the Scotch border nobles. His eloquence had its effect, and it was determined to set on foot an expedition against the Nieuw Nederlands.

It was necessary, however, to prepare the public mind for this measure. Accordingly the arguments of the orator were echoed from the pulpit for several succeeding Sundays, and a crusade was preached up against Peter Stuyvesant and his devoted city.

This is the first we hear of the "drum ecclesiastic" beating up for recruits in worldly warfare in our country. It has since been called into frequent use. A cunning politician often lurks under the clerical robe; things spiritual and things temporal are strangely jumbled together, like drugs on an apothecary's shelf; and instead of a peaceful sermon, the simple seeker after righteousness has often a political pamphlet thrust down his throat, labelled with a pious text from Scripture.

And now nothing was talked of but an expedition against the Manhattoes. It pleased the populace, who had a vehement prejudice against the Dutch, considering them a vastly inferior race, who had sought the new world for the lucre of gain, not the liberty of conscience; who were mere heretics and infidels, inasmuch as they refused to believe in witches and sea-serpents, and had faith in the virtues of horse-shoes nailed to the door; ate pork without molasses; held pumpkins in contempt, and were in perpetual breach of the eleventh commandment of all true Yankees, "Thou shalt have codfish dinners on Saturdays."

No sooner did Peter Stuyvesant get wind of the storm that was brewing in the East than he set to work to prepare for it. He was not one of those economical rulers, who postpone the expense of fortifying until the enemy is at the door. There is nothing, he would say, that keeps off enemies and crows more than the smell of gunpowder. He proceeded, therefore, with all diligence, to put the province and its metropolis in a posture of defence.

Among the remnants which remained from the days of William the Testy, were the militia laws; by which the inhabitants were obliged to turn out twice a year, with such military equipments as it pleased God; and were put under the command of tailors and man-milliners, who, though on ordinary occasions they might have been the meekest, most pippin-hearted little men in the world, were very devils at parades, when they had cocked hats on their heads and swords by their sides. Under the instructions of these periodical warriors, the peaceful burghers of the Manhattoes were schooled in iron war, and became so hardy in the process of time, that they could march through sun and rain, from one end of the town to the other, without flinching; and so intrepid and adroit, that they could face to the right, wheel to the left, and fire without winking or blinking.

Peter Stuyvesant, like all old soldiers who have seen service and smelt gunpowder, had no great respect for militia troops; however, he determined to give them a trial, and accordingly called for a general muster, inspection, and review. But, oh Mars and Bellona! what a turning out was here! Here came old Roelant Cuckaburt, with a short blunderbuss on his shoulder, and a long horseman's sword trailing by his side; and Barent Dirkson, with something that looked like a copper kettle turned upside down on his head, and a couple of old horse-pistols in his belt; and Dirk Volkertson, with a long duck fowling-piece without any ramrod; and a host more, armed higgledy-piggledy—with swords, hatchets, snickersnees, crowbars, broomsticks, and what not; the officers distinguished from the rest by having their slouched hats cocked up with pins, and surmounted with cock-tail feathers.

The sturdy Peter eyed this nondescript host with some such rueful aspect as a man would eye the devil, and determined to give his feathered soldiers a seasoning. He accordingly put them through their manual exercise over and over again; trudged them backwards and forwards about the streets of New

Amsterdam until their short legs ached and their fat sides sweated again, and finally encamped them in the evening on the summit of a hill without the city, to give them a taste of camp life, intending the next day to renew the toils and perils of the field. But so it came to pass that in the night there fell a great and heavy rain, and melted away the army, so that in the morning when Gaffer Phoebus shed his first beams upon the camp scarce a warrior remained excepting Peter Stuyvesant and his trumpeter Van Corlear.

This awful desolation of a whole army would have appalled a commander of less nerve; but it served to confirm Peter's want of confidence in the militia system, which he thenceforward used to call, in joke—for he sometimes indulged in a joke—William the Testy's broken reed. He now took into his service a goodly number of burly, broad-shouldered, broad-bottomed Dutchmen; whom he paid in good silver and gold, and of whom he boasted that whether they could stand fire or not, they were at least water-proof.

He fortified the city, too, with pickets and pallisadoes, extending across the island from river to river; and above all, cast up mud batteries or redoubts on the point of the island, where it divided the beautiful bosom of the bay.

These latter redoubts, in process of time, came to be pleasantly overrun by a carpet of grass and clover, and overshadowed by wide-spreading elms and sycamores; among the branches of which the birds would build their nests and rejoice the ear with their melodious notes. Under these trees, too, the old burghers would smoke their afternoon pipe; contemplating the golden sun as he sank in the west, an emblem of the tranquil end toward which they were declining. Here, too, would the young men and maidens of the town take their evening stroll, watching the silver moonbeams as they trembled along the calm bosom of the bay, or lit up the sail of some gliding bark; and peradventure interchanging the soft vows of honest affection; for to evening strolls in this favored spot were traced most of the marriages in New Amsterdam.

Such was the origin of that renowned promenade, THE BATTERY, which though ostensibly devoted to the stern purposes of war, has ever been consecrated to the sweet delights of peace. The scene of many a gambol in happy childhood—of many a tender assignation in riper years—of many a soothing walk in declining age—the healthful resort of the feeble invalid—the Sunday refreshment of the dusty tradesman—in fine, the ornament and delight of New York, and the pride of the lovely island of Manna-hata.

CHAPTER VIII.

How the Yankee Crusade against the New Netherlands Was Baffled by the Sudden Outbreak of Witchcraft among the People of the East.

HAVING thus provided for the temporary security of New Amsterdam, and guarded it against any sudden surprise, the gallant Peter took a hearty pinch of snuff, and snapping his fingers, set the great council of Amphictyons and their champion, the redoubtable Alicxsander Partridg, at defiance. In the meantime the moss-troopers of Connecticut; the warriors of New Haven and Hartford, and Pyquag, otherwise called Weathersfield, famous for its onions and its witches—and of all the other border towns were in a prodigious turmoil; furbishing up their rusty weapons; shouting aloud for war, and anticipating easy conquests, and glorious rummaging of the fat little Dutch villages.

In the midst of these warlike preparations, however, they received the chilling news that the colony of Massachusetts refused to back them in this righteous war. It seems that the gallant conduct of Peter Stuyvesant, the generous warmth of his vindication and the chivalrous spirit of his defiance, though lost upon the grand council of the league, had carried conviction to the general court of Massachusetts, which nobly refused to believe him guilty of the villanous plot laid at his door.[1]

The defection of so important a colony paralyzed the councils of the league, some such dissension arose among its members as prevailed of yore in the camp of the brawling warriors of Greece, and in the end the crusade against the Manhattoes was abandoned.

It is said that the moss-troopers of Connecticut were sorely disappointed; but well for them that their belligerent cravings were not gratified: for by my faith, whatever might have been the ultimate result of a conflict with all the powers of the East, in the interim the stomachful heroes of Pyquag would have been choked with their own onions, and all the border towns of Connecticut would have had such a scouring from the lion-hearted Peter and his robustious myrmidons, that I warrant me they would not have had the stomach to squat on the land or invade the hen-roost of a Nederlander for a century to come.

But it was not merely the refusal of Massachusetts to join in their unholy crusade that confounded the councils of the league; for about this time broke out in the New England provinces the awful plague of witchcraft, which spread like pestilence through the land. Such a howling abomination could not be suffered to remain long unnoticed; it soon excited the fiery indignation of those guardians of the commonwealth, who whilom had evinced such active benevolence in the conversion of Quakers and Anabaptists. The grand council of the league publicly set their faces against the crime, and bloody laws were enacted against all "solem conversing or compacting with the divil by the way of conjuration or the like."[2] Strict search too was made after witches, who were easily detected by devil's pinches; by being able to weep but three tears, and those out of the left eye; and by having a most suspicious predilection for black cats and broomsticks! What is particularly worthy of admiration is, that this terrible art, which has baffled the studies and researches of philosophers, astrologers, theurgists, and other sages, was chiefly confined to the most ignorant, decrepit, and ugly old women in the community, with scarce more brains than the broomsticks they rode upon.

[1] Hazard's State Papers.
[2] New Plymouth Record.

When once an alarm is sounded, the public, who dearly love to be in a panic, are always ready to keep it up. Raise but the cry of yellow fever, and immediately every headache, indigestion, and overflowing of the bile is pronounced the terrible epidemic; cry out mad dog, and every unlucky cur in the street is in jeopardy: so in the present instance, whoever was troubled with colic or lumbago was sure to be bewitched—and woe to any unlucky old woman living in the neighborhood.

It is incredible the number of offences that were detected, "for every one of which," says the reverend Cotton Mather, in that excellent work, the History of New England, "we have such a sufficient evidence, that no reasonable man in this whole country ever did question them; *and it will be unreasonable to do it in any other*."[3]

Indeed, that authentic and judicious historian, John Josselyn, Gent., furnishes us with unquestionable facts on this subject. "There are none," observes he, "that beg in this country, but there be witches too many—bottle-bellied witches and others, that produce many strange apparitions, if you will believe report of a shallop at sea manned with women—and of a ship and great red horse standing by the main-mast; the ship being in a small cove to the eastward vanished of a sudden," etc.

The number of delinquents, however, and their magical devices, were not more remarkable than their diabolical obstinacy. Though exhorted in the most solemn, persuasive, and affectionate manner, to confess themselves guilty, and be burnt for the good of religion, and the entertainment of the public; yet did they most pertinaciously persist in asserting their innocence. Such incredible obstinacy was in itself deserving of immediate punishment, and was sufficient proof, if proof were necessary, that they were in league with the devil, who is perverseness itself. But their judges were just and merciful, and were determined to punish none that were not convicted on the best of testimony; not that they needed any evidence to satisfy their own minds, for, like true and experienced judges, their minds were perfectly made up, and they were thoroughly satisfied of the guilt of the prisoners before they proceeded to try them: but still something was necessary to convince the community at large—to quiet those prying quidnuncs who should come after them—in short, the world must be satisfied. Oh the world—the world!—all the world knows the world of trouble the world is eternally occasioning!—The worthy judges, therefore, were driven to the necessity of sifting, detecting, and making evident as noon-day, matters which were at the commencement all clearly understood and firmly decided upon in their own pericraniums—so that it may truly be said, that the witches were burnt to gratify the populace of the day—but were tried for the satisfaction of the whole world that should come after them!

Finding therefore, that neither exhortation, sound reason, nor friendly entreaty had any avail on these hardened offenders, they resorted to the more urgent arguments of torture; and having thus absolutely wrung the truth

[3]Mather's Hist. New Eng. B. 6 ch. 7.

from their stubborn lips, they condemned them to undergo the roasting due unto the heinous crimes they had confessed. Some even carried their perverseness so far as to expire under the torture, protesting their innocence to the last; but these were looked upon as thoroughly and absolutely possessed by the devil, and the pious bystanders only lamented that they had not lived a little longer, to have perished in the flames.

In the city of Ephesus, we are told that the plague was expelled by stoning a ragged old beggar to death, whom Apollonius pointed out as being the evil spirit that caused it, and who actually showed himself to be a demon, by changing into a shagged dog. In like manner, and by measures equally sagacious, a salutary check was given to this growing evil. The witches were all burnt, banished, or panic-struck, and in a little while there was not an ugly old woman to be found throughout New England—which is doubtless one reason why all the young women there are so handsome. Those honest folk who had suffered from their incantations gradually recovered, excepting such as had been afflicted with twitches and aches, which, however, assumed the less alarming aspects of rheumatisms, sciatics, and lumbagos—and the good people of New England, abandoning the study of the occult sciences, turned their attention to the more profitable hocus pocus of trade, and soon became expert in the legerdemain art of turning a penny. Still, however, a tinge of the old leaven is discernible, even unto this day, in their characters—witches occasionally start up among them in different disguises, as physicians, civilians, and divines. The people at large show a keenness, a cleverness, and a profundity of wisdom, that savors strongly of witchcraft—and it has been remarked, that whenever any stones fall from the moon, the greater part of them is sure to tumble into New England!

BOOK VI.

CONTAINING THE SECOND PART OF THE REIGN OF PETER THE HEAD-STRONG, AND HIS GALLANT ACHIEVEMENTS ON THE DELAWARE.

CHAPTER I.

IN WHICH IS EXHIBITED A WARLIKE PORTRAIT OF THE GREAT PETER—OF THE WINDY CONTEST OF GENERAL VAN POFFENBURGH AND GENERAL PRINTZ, AND OF THE MOSQUITO WAR ON THE DELAWARE.

HITHERTO, most venerable and courteous reader, have I shown thee the administration of the valorous Stuyvesant, under the mild moonshine of peace, or rather the grim tranquillity of awful expectation; but now the war drum rumbles from afar, the brazen trumpet brays its thrilling note, and the rude clash of hostile arms speaks fearful prophecies of coming troubles. The gallant warrior starts from soft repose; from golden visions, and voluptuous ease; where in the dulcet, "piping time of peace," he sought sweet solace after all his toils. No more in beauty's siren lap reclined, he weaves fair garlands for his lady's brows; no more entwines with flowers his shining sword, nor through the livelong lazy summer's day chants forth his love-sick soul in madrigals. To manhood roused, he spurns the amorous flute; doffs from his brawny back the robe of peace, and clothes his pampered limbs in panoply of steel. O'er his dark brow, where late the myrtle waved, where wanton roses breathed enervate love, he rears the beaming casque and nodding plume; grasps the bright shield, and shakes the ponderous lance; or mounts with eager pride his fiery steed, and burns for deeds of glorious chivalry!

But soft, worthy reader! I would not have you imagine that any *preux chevalier*, thus hideously begirt with iron, existed in the city of New Amsterdam. This is but a lofty and gigantic mode, in which we heroic writers always talk of war, thereby to give it a noble and imposing aspect; equipping our warriors with bucklers, helms, and lances, and such like outlandish and obsolete weapons, the like of which perchance they had never seen or heard of; in the same manner that a cunning statuary arrays a modern general or an admiral in the accoutrements of a Cæsar or an Alexander. The simple truth then of all this oratorical flourish is this—that the valiant Peter Stuyvesant all of a sudden found it necessary to scour his rusty blade, which too long had rusted in its scabbard, and prepare himself to undergo those hardy toils of war, in which his mighty soul so much delighted.

Methinks I at this moment behold him in my imagination—or rather, I behold his goodly portrait, which still hangs up in the family mansion of the Stuyvesants—arrayed in all the terrors of a true Dutch general. His regimental coat of German blue, gorgeously decorated with a goodly show of large brass buttons, reaching from his waistband to his chin: the voluminous skirts turned up at the corners and separating gallantly behind, so as to display the seat of a sumptuous pair of brimstone-colored trunk-breeches—a graceful style still prevalent among the warriors of our day, and which is in conformity to the custom of ancient heroes, who scorned to defend themselves in rear. His face rendered exceeding terrible and warlike by a pair of black mustachios; his hair strutting out on each side in stiffly pomatumed ear-locks, and descending in a rat-tail queue below his waist; a shining stock of black leather supporting his chin, and a little but fierce cocked hat, stuck with a gallant and fiery air over his left eye. Such was the chivalric port of Peter the Headstrong; and when he made a sudden halt, planted himself firmly on his solid supporter, with his wooden leg inlaid with silver a little in advance, in order to strengthen his position, his right hand grasping a gold-headed cane, his left resting upon the pommel of his sword, his head dressing spiritedly to the right, with a most appalling and hard-favored frown upon his brow—he presented altogether one of the most commanding, bitter-looking and soldier-like figures that ever strutted upon canvas.—Proceed we now to inquire the cause of this warlike preparation.

We have spoken of the founding of Fort Casimir, and of the merciless warfare waged by its commander upon cabbages, sunflowers and pumpkins, for want of better occasion to flesh his sword. Now it came to pass that higher up the Delaware, at his stronghold of Tinnekonk, resided one Jan Printz, who styled himself Governor of New Sweden. If history belie not this redoubtable Swede, he was a rival worthy of the windy and inflated commander of Fort Casimir, for master David Pieterzen de Vrie, in his excellent book of voyages, describes him as "weighing upwards of four hundred pounds," a huge feeder and bowser in proportion, taking three potations pottle-deep at every meal. He had a garrison after his own heart at Tinnekonk, guzzling, deep-drinking swashbucklers, who made the wild woods ring with their carousals.

No sooner did this robustious commander hear of the erection of Fort Casimir, than he sent a message to Van Poffenburgh, warning him off the land, as being within the bounds of his jurisdiction.

To this General Van Poffenburgh replied that the land belonged to their High Mightinesses, having been regularly purchased of the natives, as discoverers from the Manhattoes, as witness the breeches of their land measurer, Ten Broeck.

To this the governor rejoined that the land had previously been sold by the Indians to the Swedes, and consequently was under the petticoat government of her Swedish majesty, Christina; and woe be to any mortal that wore a breeches who should dare to meddle even with the hem of her sacred garment.

I forbear to dilate upon the war of words which was kept up for some time by these windy commanders; Van Poffenburgh, however, had served under William the Testy, and was a veteran in this kind of warfare. Governor Printz, finding he was not to be dislodged by these long shots, now determined upon coming to closer quarters. Accordingly he descended the river in great force and fume, and erected a rival fortress just one Swedish mile below Fort Casimir, to which he gave the name of Helsenburg.

And now commenced a tremendous rivalry between these two doughty commanders; striving to outstrut and outswell each other like a couple of belligerent turkeycocks. There was a contest who should run up the tallest flag-staff and display the broadest flag; all day long there was a furious rolling of drums and twanging of trumpets in either fortress, and, whichever had the wind in its favor, would keep up a continual firing of cannon, to taunt its antagonist with the smell of gunpowder.

On all these points of windy warfare the antagonists were well matched; but so it happened that the Swedish fortress being lower down the river, all the Dutch vessels bound to Fort Casimir with supplies, had to pass it. Governor Printz at once took advantage of this circumstance, and compelled them to lower their flags as they passed under the guns of his battery.

This was a deadly wound to the Dutch pride of General Van Poffenburgh, and sorely would he swell when from the ramparts of Fort Casimir he beheld the flag of their High Mightinesses struck to the rival fortress. To heighten his vexation, Governor Printz, who, as has been shown, was a huge trencherman, took the liberty of having the first rummage of every Dutch merchant-ship, and securing to himself and his guzzling garrison all the little round Dutch cheeses, all the Dutch herrings, the gingerbread, the sweetmeats, the curious stone jugs of gin, and all the other Dutch luxuries, on their way for the solace of Fort Casimir. It is possible he may have paid to the Dutch skippers the full value of their commodities, but what consolation was this to Jacobus Van Poffenburgh and his garrison, who thus found their favorite supplies cut off, and diverted into the larders of the hostile camp? For some time this war of the cupboard was carried on to the great festivity and jollification of the Swedes, while the warriors of Fort Casimir found their hearts, or rather their stomachs, daily failing them. At length the summer heats and summer showers set in, and now, lo and behold, a great miracle was wrought for the relief of the Nederlands, not a little resembling one of the plagues of Egypt; for it came to pass that a great cloud of mosquitoes arose out of the marshy borders of the river and settled upon the fortress of Helsenburg, being, doubtless, attracted by the scent of the fresh blood of these Swedish gormandizers. Nay, it is said that the body of Jan Printz alone, which was as big and as full of blood as that of a prize ox, was sufficient to attract the mosquitoes from every part of the country. For some time the garrison endeavored to hold out, but it was all in vain; the mosquitoes penetrated into every chink and crevice, and gave them no rest day nor night; and as to Governor Jan Printz, he moved about as in a cloud, with mosquito music in his ears, and mosquito stings to the very end of his nose. Finally the garrison was fairly driven out of the fortress, and obliged to retreat to Tinnekonk; nay, it is said that the mosquitoes followed Jan Printz even thither, and absolutely drove him out of the country; certain it is, he embarked for Sweden shortly afterwards, and Jan Claudius Risingh was sent to govern New Sweden in his stead.

Such was the famous mosquito war on the Delaware, of which General Van Poffenburgh would fain have been the hero; but the devout people of the Nieuw Nederlands always ascribed the discomfiture of the Swedes to the miraculous intervention of Saint Nicholas. As to the fortress of Helsenburg, it fell to ruin, but the story of its strange destruction was perpetuated by the Swedish name of Myggen-borg, that is to say, Mosquito Castle.[1]

CHAPTER II.

OF JAN RISINGH, HIS GIANTLY PERSON AND CRAFTY DEEDS; AND OF THE CATASTROPHE AT FORT CASIMIR.

JAN CLAUDIUS RISINGH, who succeeded to the command of New Sweden, looms largely in ancient records as a gigantic Swede, who, had he not been rather knock-kneed and splay-footed, might have served for the model of a Samson or a Hercules. He was no less rapacious than mighty, and, withal, as crafty as he was rapacious, so that there is very little doubt that, had he lived some four or five centuries since, he would have figured as one of those wicked giants, who took a cruel pleasure in pocketing beautiful princesses and distressed

[1]Acrelius' History N. Sweden. For some notice of this miraculous discomfiture of the Swedes, see N. Y. Hist. Col., new series, vol. 1, p. 412.

damsels, when gadding about the world, and locking them up in enchanted castles, without a toilet, a change of linen, or any other convenience.—In consequence of which enormities they fell under the high displeasure of chivalry, and all true, loyal, and gallant knights were instructed to attack and slay outright any miscreant they might happen to find above six feet high; which is doubtless one reason why the race of large men is nearly extinct, and the generations of latter ages are so exceedingly small.

Governor Risingh, notwithstanding his giantly condition, was, as I have hinted, a man of craft. He was not a man to ruffle the vanity of General Van Poffenburgh, or to rub his self-conceit against the grain. On the contrary, as he sailed up the Delaware, he paused before Fort Casimir, displayed his flag, and fired a royal salute before dropping anchor. The salute would doubtless have been returned, had not the guns been dismounted; as it was, a veteran sentinel, who had been napping at his post, and had suffered his match to go out, returned the compliment by discharging his musket with the spark of a pipe borrowed from a comrade. Governor Risingh accepted this as a courteous reply, and treated the fortress to a second salute; well knowing its commander was apt to be marvellously delighted with these little ceremonials, considering them so many acts of homage paid to his greatness. He then prepared to land with a military retinue of thirty men, a prodigious pageant in the wilderness.

And now took place a terrible rummage and racket in Fort Casimir, to receive such a visitor in proper style, and to make an imposing appearance. The main guard was turned out as soon as possible, equipped to the best advantage in the few suits of regimentals, which had to do duty by turns with the whole garrison. One tall, lank fellow appeared in a little man's coat, with the buttons between his shoulders; the skirts scarce covering his bottom; his hands hanging like spades out of the sleeves; and the coat linked in front by worsted loops made out of a pair of red garters. Another had a cocked hat stuck on the back of his head, and decorated with a bunch of cock's tails; a third had a pair of rusty gaiters hanging about his heels—while a fourth, a little duck-legged fellow, was equipped in a pair of the general's cast-off breeches, which he held up with one hand while he grasped his firelock with the other. The rest were accoutred in similar style, excepting three ragamuffins without shirts, and with but a pair and a half of breeches between them, wherefore they were sent to the black hole, to keep them out of sight, that they might not disgrace the fortress.

His men being thus gallantly arrayed—those who lacked muskets shouldering spades and pickaxes, and every man being ordered to tuck in his shirt-tail and pull up his brogues—General Van Poffenburgh first took a sturdy draught of foaming ale, which, like the magnanimous More of More-hall,[1] was his invariable practice on all great occasions; this done, he put himself at their

---

[1]"————— as soon as he rose,
   To make him strong and mighty,
 He drank by the tale, six pots of ale,
   And a quart of aqua vitæ."

Dragon of Wantley.

head, and issued forth from his castle, like a mighty giant, just refreshed with
wine. But when the two heroes met, then began a scene of warlike parade that
beggars all description. The shrewd Risingh, who had grown gray much before
his time, in consequence of his craftiness, saw at one glance the ruling passion
of the great Van Poffenburgh, and humored him in all his valorous fantasies.

Their detachments were accordingly drawn up in front of each other; they
carried arms and they presented arms; they gave the standing salute and the
passing salute; they rolled their drums, they flourished their fifes, and they
waved their colors; they faced to the left, and they faced to the right, and
they faced to the right about; they wheeled forward, and they wheeled back-
ward, and they wheeled into *échellon;* they marched and they countermarched,
by grand divisions, by single divisions, and by subdivisions; by platoons, by
sections, and by files; in quick time, in slow time, and in no time at all; for,
having gone through all the evolutions of two great armies, including the
eighteen manœuvres of Dundas; having exhausted all that they could recollect
or imagine of military tactics, including sundry strange and irregular evolutions, the like of which were never seen before nor since, excepting among
certain of our newly-raised militia, the two commanders and their respective
troops came at length to a dead halt, completely exhausted by the toils of war.
Never did two valiant train-band captains, or two buskined theatric heroes, in
the renowned tragedies of Pizarro, Tom Thumb, or any other heroical and
fighting tragedy, marshal their gallows-looking, duck-legged, heavy-heeled
myrmidons with more glory and self-admiration.

These military compliments being finished, General Van Poffenburgh escorted his illustrious visitor, with great ceremony, into the fort; attended him
throughout the fortifications; showed him the horn-works, crown-works, half-
moons, and various other outworks, or rather the places where they ought to
be erected, and where they might be erected if he pleased; plainly demonstrat-
ing that it was a place of "great capability," and though at present but a little
redoubt, yet that it was evidently a formidable fortress, in embryo. This survey
over, he next had the whole garrison put under arms, exercised, and reviewed;
and concluded by ordering the three bridewell birds to be hauled out of the
black hole, brought up to the halberds, and soundly flogged, for the amusement
of his visitor, and to convince him that he was a great disciplinarian.

The cunning Risingh, while he pretended to be struck dumb outright with
the puissance of the great Van Poffenburgh, took silent note of the incompe-
tency of his garrison, of which he gave a wink to his trusty followers, who
tipped each other the wink, and laughed most obstreperously—in their sleeves.

The inspection, review, and flogging being concluded, the party adjourned
to the table; for among his other great qualities, the general was remarkably
addicted to huge carousals, and in one afternoon's campaign would leave more
dead men on the field than he ever did in the whole course of his military
career. Many bulletins of these bloodless victories do still remain on record;
and the whole province was once thrown in amaze by the return of one of his
campaigns; wherein it was stated, that though, like Captain Bobadil, he had
only twenty men to back him, yet in the short space of six months he had

conquered and utterly annihilated sixty oxen, ninety hogs, one hundred sheep, ten thousand cabbages, one thousand bushels of potatoes, one hundred and fifty kilderkins of small beer, two thousand seven hundred and thirty-five pipes, seventy-eight pounds of sugarplums, and forty bars of iron, besides sundry small meats, game, poultry, and garden-stuff:—an achievement unparalleled since the days of Pantagruel and his all devouring army, and which showed that it was only necessary to let Van Poffenburgh and his garrison loose in an enemy's country, and in a little while they would breed a famine, and starve all the inhabitants.

No sooner, therefore, had the general received intimation of the visit of Governor Risingh, than he ordered a great dinner to be prepared; and privately sent out a detachment of his most experienced veterans, to rob all the hen-roosts in the neighborhood, and lay the pigsties under contribution;—a service which they discharged with such zeal and promptitude, that the garrison table groaned under the weight of their spoils.

I wish, with all my heart, my readers could see the valiant Van Poffenburgh, as he presided at the head of the banquet; it was a sight worth beholding:—there he sat, in his greatest glory surrounded by his soldiers, like that famous wine-bibber, Alexander, whose thirsty virtues he did most ably imitate—telling astounding stories of his hair-breadth adventures and heroic exploits; at which, though all his auditors knew them to be incontinent lies and outrageous gasconadoes, yet did they cast up their eyes in admiration, and utter many interjections of astonishment. Nor could the general pronounce any thing that bore the remotest resemblance to a joke, but the stout Risingh would strike his brawny fist upon the table till every glass rattled again, throw himself back in the chair, utter gigantic peals of laughter, and swear most horribly it was the best joke he ever heard in his life.—Thus all was rout and revelry and hideous carousal within Fort Casimir, and so lustily did Van Poffenburgh ply the bottle, that in less than four short hours he made himself and his whole garrison, who all sedulously emulated the deeds of their chieftain, dead drunk, with singing songs, quaffing bumpers, and drinking patriotic toasts, none of which but was as long as a Welsh pedigree or a plea in chancery.

No sooner did things come to this pass, than Risingh and his Swedes, who had cunningly kept themselves sober, rose on their entertainers, tied them neck and heels, and took formal possession of the fort, and all its dependencies, in the name of Queen Christina of Sweden; administering at the same time an oath of allegiance to all the Dutch soldiers who could be made sober enough to swallow it. Risingh then put the fortifications in order, appointed his discreet and vigilant friend Suen Schüte, otherwise called Skytte, a tall, wind-dried, water-drinking Swede, to the command, and departed, bearing with him this truly amiable garrison and its puissant commander; who, when brought to himself by a sound drubbing, bore no little resemblance to a "deboshed fish," or bloated sea-monster, caught upon dry land.

The transportation of the garrison was done to prevent the transmission of intelligence to New Amsterdam; for much as the cunning Risingh exulted in his stratagem, yet did he dread the vengeance of the sturdy Peter Stuyvesant;

whose name spread as much terror in the neighborhood as did whilom that of the unconquerable Scanderbeg among his scurvy enemies the Turks.

CHAPTER III.

Showing How Profound Secrets Are Often Brought to Light; with the Proceedings of Peter the Headstrong When He Heard of the Misfortunes of General Van Poffenburgh.

Whoever first described common fame, or rumor, as belonging to the sager sex, was a very owl for shrewdness. She has in truth certain feminine qualities to an astonishing degree; particularly that benevolent anxiety to take care of the affairs of others, which keeps her continually hunting after secrets, and gadding about proclaiming them. Whatever is done openly and in the face of the world, she takes but transient notice of; but whenever a transaction is done in a corner, and attempted to be shrouded in mystery, then her goddess-ship is at her wits' end to find it out, and takes a most mischievous and lady-like pleasure in publishing it to the world.

It is this truly feminine propensity which induces her continually to be prying into the cabinets of princes, listening at the key-holes of senate-chambers, and peering through chinks and crannies, when our worthy congress are sitting with closed doors, deliberating between a dozen excellent modes of ruining the nation. It is this which makes her so baneful to all wary statesmen and intriguing commanders—such a stumbling-block to private negotiations and secret expeditions; betraying them by means and instruments which never would have been thought of by any but a female head.

Thus it was in the case of the affair of Fort Casimir. No doubt the cunning Risingh imagined, that, by securing the garrison, he should for a long time prevent the history of its fate from reaching the ears of the gallant Stuyvesant; but his exploit was blown to the world when he least expected; and by one of the last beings he would ever have suspected of enlisting as trumpeter to the wide-mouthed deity.

This was one Dirk Schuiler (or Skulker), a kind of hanger-on to the garrison, who seemed to belong to nobody and in a manner to be self-outlawed. He was one of those vagabond cosmopolites who shark about the world, as if they had no right or business in it, and who infest the skirts of society like poachers and interlopers. Every garrison and country village has one or more scape-goats of this kind, whose life is a kind of enigma, whose existence is without motive, who comes from the Lord knows where, who lives the Lord knows how, and who seems created for no other earthly purpose but to keep up the ancient and honorable order of idleness. This vagrant philosopher was supposed to have some Indian blood in his veins, which was manifested by a certain Indian complexion and cast of countenance; but more especially by his propensities and habits. He was a tall, lank fellow, swift of foot, and long-winded. He was generally equipped in a half Indian dress, with belt, leggings, and moccasins. His hair hung in straight gallows locks about his ears, and added not a little to his sharking demeanor. It is an old remark, that persons of Indian mixture are half civilized, half savage and half devil—a third half being provided for their particular convenience. It is for similar reasons, and probably with equal truth, that the backwoodsmen of Kentucky are styled half man, half horse, and half alligator, by the settlers on the Mississippi, and held accordingly in great respect and abhorrence.

The above character may have presented itself to the garrison as applicable to Dirk Schuiler, whom they familiarly dubbed Gallows Dirk. Certain it is, he acknowledged allegiance to no one—was an utter enemy to work, holding it in no manner of estimation—but lounging about the fort, depending upon chance for a subsistence, getting drunk whenever he could get liquor and stealing whatever he could lay his hands on. Every day or two he was sure to get a sound rib-roasting for some of his misdemeanors; which, however, as it broke no bones, he made very light of, and scrupled not to repeat the offence whenever another opportunity presented. Sometimes, in consequence of some flagrant villany, he would abscond from the garrison, and be absent for a month at a time; skulking about the woods and swamps, with a long fowling-piece on his shoulder, lying in ambush for game—or squatting himself down on the edge of a pond catching fish for hours together, and bearing no little resemblance to that notable bird of the crane family, ycleped the Mudpoke. When he thought his crimes had been forgotten or forgiven, he would sneak back to the fort with a bundle of skins, or a load of poultry, which, perchance, he had stolen, and would exchange them for liquor, with which having well soaked his carcass, he would lie in the sun and enjoy all the luxurious indolence of that swinish philosopher Diogenes. He was the terror of all the farm-yards in the country, into which he made fearful inroads; and sometimes he would make his sudden appearance in the garrison at daybreak, with the whole neighborhood at his heels; like the scoundrel thief of a fox, detected in his maraudings and hunted to his hole. Such was this Dirk Schuiler; and from the total indifference he showed to the world and its concerns, and from his truly Indian stoicism and taciturnity, no one would ever have dreamt that he would have been the publisher of the treachery of Risingh.

When the carousal was going on, which proved so fatal to the brave Poffenburgh and his watchful garrison, Dirk skulked about from room to room, being a kind of privileged vagrant, or useless hound, whom nobody noticed. But though a fellow of few words, yet, like your taciturn people, his eyes and ears were always open, and in the course of his prowlings he overheard the whole plot of the Swedes. Dirk immediately settled in his own mind how he should turn the matter to his own advantage. He played the perfect jack-of-both-sides—that is to say, he made a prize of everything that came in his reach, robbed both parties, stuck the copper-bound cocked hat of the puissant Van Poffenburgh on his head, whipped a huge pair of Risingh's jack-boots under his arms, and took to his heels, just before the catastrophe and confusion at the garrison.

Finding himself completely dislodged from his haunt in this quarter, he directed his flight towards his native place, New Amsterdam, whence he had formerly been obliged to abscond precipitately, in consequence of misfortune in business—that is to say, having been detected in the act of sheep-stealing. After wandering many days in the woods, toiling through swamps, fording brooks, swimming various rivers, and encountering a world of hardships that would have killed any other being but an Indian, a backwoodsman, or the devil, he at length arrived, half-famished, and lank as a starved weasel, at Communipaw, where he stole a canoe, and paddled over to New Amsterdam. Immediately on landing, he repaired to Governor Stuyvesant, and in more words than he had ever spoken before in the whole course of his life, gave an account of the disastrous affair.

On receiving these direful tidings, the valiant Peter started from his seat—dashed the pipe he was smoking against the back of the chimney—thrust a prodigious quid of tobacco into his left cheek—pulled up his galligaskins, and strode up and down the room, humming, as was customary with him when in a passion, a hideous northwest ditty. But, as I have before shown, he was not a man to vent his spleen in idle vaporing. His first measure, after the paroxysm of wrath had subsided, was to stump up-stairs to a huge wooden chest, which served as his armory, from whence he drew forth that identical suit of regimentals described in the preceding chapter. In these portentous habiliments he arrayed himself, like Achilles in the armor of Vulcan, maintaining all the while an appalling silence, knitting his brows, and drawing his breath through his clinched teeth. Being hastily equipped, he strode down into the parlor and jerked down his trusty sword from over the fireplace, where it was usually suspended; but before he girded it on his thigh, he drew it from its scabbard, and as his eye coursed along the rusty blade, a grim smile stole over his iron visage—it was the first smile that had visited his countenance for five long weeks; but every one who beheld it prophesied that there would soon be warm work in the province!

Thus armed at all points, with grisly war depicted in each feature, his very cocked hat assuming an air of uncommon defiance, he instantly put himself upon the alert, and despatched Antony Van Corlear hither and thither, this way and that way, through all the muddy streets and crooked lanes of the city, summoning by sound of trumpet his trusty peers to assemble in instant council.—This done, by way of expediting matters, according to the custom of people in a hurry, he kept in continual bustle, shifting from chair to chair, popping his head out of every window, and stumping up and down stairs with his wooden leg in such a brisk and incessant motion, that, as we are informed by an authentic historian of the times, the continual clatter bore no small resemblance to the music of a cooper hooping a flour-barrel.

A summons so peremptory, and from a man of the governor's mettle, was not to be trifled with: the sages forthwith repaired to the council-chamber, seated themselves with the utmost tranquillity, and lighting their long pipes, gazed with unruffled composure on his excellency and his regimentals; being, as all counsellors should be, not easily flustered, nor taken by surprise. The governor, looking around for a moment with a lofty and soldier-like air, and resting one hand on the pommel of his sword, and flinging the other forth in a free and spirited manner, addressed them in a short but soul-stirring harangue.

I am extremely sorry that I have not the advantages of Livy, Thucydides, Plutarch, and others of my predecessors, who were furnished, as I am told, with the speeches of all their heroes, taken down in shorthand by the most accurate stenographers of the time; whereby they were enabled wonderfully to enrich their histories, and delight their readers with sublime strains of eloquence. Not having such important auxiliaries, I cannot possibly pronounce what was the tenor of Governor Stuyvesant's speech. I am bold, however, to say, from the tenor of his character, that he did not wrap his rugged subject in silks and ermines, and other sickly trickeries of phrase; but spoke forth like a man of nerve and vigor, who scorned to shrink in words from those dangers which he stood ready to encounter in very deed. This much is certain, that he concluded by announcing his determination to lead on his troops in person, and rout these costard-monger Swedes from their usurped quarters at Fort Casimir. To this hardy resolution, such of his council as were awake gave their usual signal of concurrence; and as to the rest, who had fallen asleep about the middle of the harangue (their "usual custom in the afternoon"), they made not the least objection.

And now was seen in the fair city of New Amsterdam a prodigious bustle and preparation for iron war. Recruiting parties marched hither and thither, calling lustily upon all the scrubs, the runagates, and tatterdemalions of the Manhattoes and its vicinity, who had any ambition of sixpence a day, and immortal fame into the bargain, to enlist in the cause of glory:—for I would have you note that your warlike heroes who trudge in the rear of conquerors are generally of that illustrious class of gentlemen, who are equal candidates for the army or the bridewell—the halberds or the whipping-post—for whom Dame Fortune has cast an even die, whether they shall make their exit by the sword or the halter—and whose deaths shall, at all events, be a lofty example to their countrymen.

But, notwithstanding all this martial rout and invitation, the ranks of honor were but scantily supplied; so averse were the peaceful burghers of New Amsterdam from enlisting in foreign broils, or stirring beyond that home, which rounded all their earthly ideas. Upon beholding this, the great Peter, whose noble heart was all on fire with war and sweet revenge, determined to wait no longer for the tardy assistance of these oily citizens, but to muster up his merry men of the Hudson, who, brought up among woods, and wilds, and savage beasts, like our yeomen of Kentucky, delighted in nothing so much as desperate adventures and perilous expeditions through the wilderness. Thus resolving, he ordered his trusty squire Antony Van Corlear to have his state galley prepared and duly victualled; which being performed, he attended public service at the great church of St. Nicholas, like a true and pious governor; and then leaving peremptory orders with his council to have the chivalry of the Manhattoes marshalled out and appointed against his return, departed upon his recruiting voyage, up the waters of the Hudson.

CHAPTER IV.

Now did the soft breezes of the south steal sweetly over the face of nature, tempering the panting heats of summer into genial and prolific warmth; when that miracle of hardihood and chivalric virtue, the dauntless Peter Stuyvesant, spread his canvas to the wind, and departed from the fair island of Manna-hata. The galley in which he embarked was sumptuously adorned with pendants and streamers of gorgeous dyes, which fluttered gayly in the wind, or drooped their ends into the bosom of the stream. The bow and poop of this majestic vessel were gallantly bedight, after the rarest Dutch fashion, with figures of little pursy Cupids with periwigs on their heads, and bearing in their hands garlands of flowers, the like of which are not to be found in any book of botany; being the matchless flowers which flourished in the golden age, and exist no longer, unless it be in the imaginations of ingenious carvers of wood and discolorers of canvas.

Thus rarely decorated, in style befitting the puissant potentate of the Manhattoes, did the galley of Peter Stuyvesant launch forth upon the bosom of the lordly Hudson, which, as it rolled its broad waves to the ocean, seemed to pause for a while and swell with pride, as if conscious of the illustrious burden it sustained.

But trust me, gentlefolk, far other was the scene presented to the contemplation of the crew from that which may be witnessed at this degenerate day. Wildness and savage majesty reigned on the borders of this mighty river—the hand of cultivation had not as yet laid low the dark forest, and tamed the features of the landscape—nor had the frequent sail of commerce broken in upon the profound and awful solitude of ages. Here and there might be seen a rude wigwam perched among the cliffs of the mountains with its curling column of smoke mounting in the transparent atmosphere—but so loftily situated that the whoopings of the savage children, gambolling on the margin of the dizzy heights, fell almost as faintly on the ear as do the notes of the lark, when lost in the azure vault of heaven. Now and then, from the beetling brow of some precipice, the wild deer would look timidly down upon the splendid pageant as it passed below; and then, tossing his antlers in the air, would bound away into the thickets of the forest.

Through such scenes did the stately vessel of Peter Stuyvesant pass. Now did they skirt the bases of the rocky heights of Jersey, which spring up like everlasting walls, reaching from the waves unto the heavens, and were fashioned, if tradition may be believed, in times long past, by the mighty spirit Manetho, to protect his favorite abodes from the unhallowed eyes of mortals. Now did they career it gayly across the vast expanse of Tappan Bay, whose wide-extended shores present a variety of delectable scenery—here the bold promontory, crowned with embowering trees, advancing into the bay—there the long woodland slope, sweeping up from the shore in rich luxuriance, and terminating in the upland precipice—while at a distance a long waving line of rocky heights threw their gigantic shades across the water. Now would they pass where some modest little interval, opening among these stupendous scenes, yet retreating as it were for protection into the embraces of the neighboring mountains, displayed a rural paradise, fraught with sweet and pastoral beauties; the velvet-tufted lawn—the bushy copse—the tinkling rivulet, stealing through the fresh and vivid verdure—on whose banks was situated some little Indian village, or, peradventure, the rude cabin of some solitary hunter.

The different periods of the revolving day seemed each, with cunning magic, to diffuse a different charm over the scene. Now would the jovial sun break gloriously from the East, blazing from the summits of the hills, and sparkling the landscape with a thousand dewy gems; while along the borders of the river were seen heavy masses of mist, which, like midnight caitiffs, disturbed at his approach, made a sluggish retreat, rolling in sullen reluctance up the mountains. At such times all was brightness, and life, and gayety—the atmosphere was of an indescribable pureness and transparency—the birds broke forth in wanton madrigals, and the freshening breezes wafted the vessel merrily on her course. But when the sun sunk amid a flood of glory in the West, mantling the heavens and the earth with a thousand gorgeous dyes—then all was calm, and silent, and magnificent. The late swelling sail hung lifelessly against the mast—the seaman, with folded arms, leaned against the shrouds, lost in that involuntary musing which the sober grandeur of nature commands in the rudest of her children. The vast bosom of the Hudson was like an unruffled mirror, reflecting the golden splendor of the heavens; excepting that now and then a bark canoe would steal across its surface, filled with painted savages, whose gay feathers glared brightly, as perchance a lingering ray of the setting sun gleamed upon them from the western mountains.

But when the hour of twilight spread its majestic mists around, then did the face of nature assume a thousand fugitive charms, which to the worthy heart that seeks enjoyment in the glorious works of its Maker are inexpressibly captivating. The mellow dubious light that prevailed just served to tinge with illusive colors the softened features of the scenery. The deceived but delighted eye sought vainly to discern in the broad masses of shade, the separating line between the land and water; or to distinguish the fading objects that seemed sinking into chaos. Now did the busy fancy supply the feebleness of vision, producing with industrious craft a fairy creation of her own. Under her plastic wand the barren rocks frowned upon the watery waste, in the semblance of lofty towers, and high embattled castles—trees assumed the direful forms of mighty giants, and the inaccessible summits of the mountains seemed peopled with a thousand shadowy beings.

Now broke forth from the shores the notes of an innumerable variety of insects, which filled the air with a strange but not inharmonious concert—while ever and anon was heard the melancholy plaint of the Whip-poor-will, who, perched on some lone tree, wearied the ear of night with his incessant moan-

A HISTORY OF NEW YORK

145

ings. The mind, soothed into a hallowed melancholy, listened with pensive stillness to catch and distinguish each·sound that vaguely echoed from the shore —now and then startled perchance by the whoop of some straggling savage, or by the dreary howl of a wolf, stealing forth upon his nightly prowlings.

Thus happily did they pursue their course, until they entered upon those awful defiles denominated THE HIGHLANDS, where it would seem that the gigantic Titans had erst waged their impious war with heaven, piling up cliffs on cliffs, and hurling vast masses of rock in wild confusion. But in sooth very different is the history of these cloud-capt mountains.—These in ancient days, before the Hudson poured its waters from the lakes, formed one vast prison, within whose rocky bosom the omnipotent Manetho confined the rebellious spirits who repined at his control. Here, bound in adamantine chains, or jammed in rifted pines, or crushed by ponderous rocks, they groaned for many an age.—At length the conquering Hudson, in its career towards the ocean, burst open their prison-house, rolling its tide triumphantly through the stupendous ruins.

Still, however, do many of them lurk about their old abodes; and these it is, according to venerable legends, that cause the echoes which resound throughout these awful solitudes; which are nothing but their angry clamors when any noise disturbs the profoundness of their repose.—For when the elements are agitated by tempest, when the winds are up and the thunder rolls, then horrible is the yelling and howling of these troubled spirits, making the mountains to rebellow with their hideous uproar; for at such times it is said that they think the great Manetho is returning once more to plunge them in gloomy caverns, and renew their intolerable captivity.

But all these fair and glorious scenes were lost upon the gallant Stuyvesant; naught occupied his mind but thoughts of iron war, and proud anticipations of hardy deeds of arms. Neither did his honest crew trouble their heads with any romantic speculations of the kind. The pilot at the helm quietly smoked his pipe, thinking of nothing either past, present, or to come—those of his comrades who were not industriously smoking under the hatches were listening with open mouths to Antony Van Corlear; who, seated on the windlass, was relating to them the marvellous history of those myriads of fireflies, that sparkled like gems and spangles upon the dusky robe of night. These, according to tradition, were originally a race of pestilent sempiternous beldames, who peopled these parts long before the memory of man; being of that abominated race emphatically called *brimstones;* and who, for their innumerable sins against the children of men, and to furnish an awful warning to the beauteous sex, were doomed to infest the earth in the shape of these threatening and terrible little bugs; enduring the internal torments of that fire, which they formerly carried in their hearts and breathed forth in their words; but now are sentenced to bear about forever—in their tails!

And now I am going to tell a fact, which I doubt much my readers will hesitate to believe; but if they do, they are welcome not to believe a word in this whole history—for nothing which it contains is more true. It must be known then that the nose of Antony the Trumpeter was of a very lusty size, strutting boldly from his countenance like a mountain of Golconda; being sumptuously bedecked with rubies and other precious stones—the true regalia of a king of good fellows, which jolly Bacchus grants to all who bouse it heartily at the flagon. Now thus it happened, that bright and early in the morning, the good Antony, having washed his burly visage, was leaning over the quarter railing of the galley, contemplating it in the glassy wave below.—Just at this moment the illustrious sun, breaking in all his splendor from behind a high bluff of the highlands, did dart one of his most potent beams full upon the refulgent nose of the sounder of brass—the reflection of which shot straightway down, hissing hot, into the water, and killed a mighty sturgeon that was sporting beside the vessel! This huge monster being with infinite labor hoisted on board, furnished a luxurious repast to all the crew, being accounted of excellent flavor, excepting about the wound, where it smacked a little of brimstone—and this, on my veracity, was the first time that ever sturgeon was eaten in these parts by Christian people.[1]

When this astonishing miracle came to be made known to Peter Stuyvesant, and that he tasted of the unknown fish, he, as may well be supposed, marvelled exceedingly; and as a monument thereof, he gave the name of *Antony's Nose* to a stout promontory in the neighborhood—and it has continued to be called Antony's Nose ever since that time.

But hold: whither am I wandering? By the mass, if I attempt to accompany the good Peter Stuyvesant on this voyage, I shall never make an end; for never was there a voyage so fraught with marvellous incidents, nor a river so abounding with transcendent beauties, worthy of being severally recorded. Even now I have it on the point of my pen to relate how his crew were most horribly frightened, on going on shore above the highlands, by a gang of merry roistering devils, frisking and curveting on a flat rock, which projected into the river—and which is called the *Duyvel's Dans-Kamer* to this very day.—But no! Diedrich Knickerbocker—it becomes thee not to idle thus in thy historic wayfaring.

Recollect that while dwelling with the fond garrulity of age over these fairy scenes, endeared to thee by the recollections of thy youth, and the charms of a thousand legendary tales, which beguiled the simple ear of thy childhood; recollect that thou art trifling with those fleeting moments which should be devoted to loftier themes.—Is not Time—relentless Time! shaking, with palsied hand, his almost exhausted hour-glass before thee?—hasten then to pursue thy weary task, lest the last sands be run ere thou hast finished thy history of the Manhattoes.

Let us, then, commit the dauntless Peter, his brave galley, and his loyal crew, to the protection of the blessed St. Nicholas; who, I have no doubt, will prosper him in his voyage, while we await his return at the great city of New Amsterdam.

[1]The learned Hans Megapolonsis, treating of the country about Albany, in a letter which was written sometime after the settlement thereof, says, "There is in the river great plenty of sturgeon, which we Christians do not make use of, but the Indians eat them greedily."

CHAPTER V.

DESCRIBING THE POWERFUL ARMY THAT ASSEMBLED AT THE CITY OF
NEW AMSTERDAM—TOGETHER WITH THE INTERVIEW BETWEEN PETER
THE HEADSTRONG AND GENERAL VAN POFFENBURGH, AND PETER'S
SENTIMENTS TOUCHING UNFORTUNATE GREAT MEN.

WHILE thus the enterprising Peter was coasting, with flowing sail, up the
shores of the lordly Hudson, and arousing all the phlegmatic little Dutch
settlements upon its borders, a great and puissant concourse of warriors was
assembling at the city of New Amsterdam. And here that invaluable fragment
of antiquity, the Stuyvesant manuscript, is more than commonly particular;
by which means I am enabled to record the illustrious host that encamped itself
in the public square in front of the fort, at present denominated the Bowling
Green.

In the centre, then, was pitched the tent of the men of battle of the Manhattoes, who being the inmates of the metropolis, composed the lifeguards of
the governor. These were commanded by the valiant Stoffel Brinkerhoof, who
whilom had acquired such immortal fame at Oyster Bay—they displayed as a
standard a beaver *rampant* on a field of orange; being the arms of the province,
and denoting the persevering industry and the amphibious origin of the
Nederlanders.[1]

On their right hand might be seen the vassals of that renowned Mynheer,
Michael Paw[2] who lorded it over the fair regions of ancient Pavonia, and the
lands away south, even unto the Navesink mountains,[3] and was moreover
patroon of Gibbet Island. His standard was borne by his trusty squire, Cornelius
Van Vorst; consisting of a huge oyster *recumbent* upon a sea-green field; being
the armorial bearings of his favorite metropolis, Communipaw. He brought to
the camp a stout force of warriors, heavily armed, being each clad in ten pair
of linsey-woolsey breeches, and overshadowed by broad-brimmed beavers,
with short pipes twisted in their hatbands. These were the men who vegetated
in the mud along the shores of Pavonia; being of the race of genuine copperheads, and were fabled to have sprung from oysters.

[1]This was likewise the great seal of the New Netherlands, as may still be seen
in ancient records.

[2]Besides what is related in the Stuyvesant MS. I have found mention made of this
illustrious patroon in another manuscript, which says: "De Heer (or the squire)
Michael Paw, a Dutch subject, about 10th Aug. 1630, by deed purchased Staten-Island.
N. B. The same Michael Paw had what the Dutch call a colonie at Pavonia, on the
Jersey shore, opposite New York, and his overseer in 1636 was named Corns. Van
Vorst—a person of the same name in 1769, owned Pawles Hook, and a large farm
at Pavonia, and is a lineal descendant from Van Vorst."

[3]So called from the Navesink tribe of Indians that inhabited these parts—at present
they are erroneously denominated the Neversink, or Neversunk mountains.

At a little distance was encamped the tribe of warriors who came from the neighborhood of Hell-gate. These were commanded by the Suy Dams, and the Van Dams, incontinent hard swearers, as their names betoken—they were terrible looking fellows, clad in broad-skirted gabardines, of that curious colored cloth called thunder and lightning—and bore as a standard three Devil's darning-needles, *volent*, in a flame-colored field.

Hard by was the tent of the men of battle from the marshy borders of the Waale-Boght[4] and the country thereabouts—these were of a sour aspect, by reason that they lived on crabs, which abound in these parts. They were the first institutors of that honorable order of knighthood, called *Fly-market shirks*, and if tradition speak true, did likewise introduce the far-famed step in dancing, called "double trouble." They were commanded by the fearless Jacobus Varra Vanger, and had, moreover, a jolly band of Breuckelen[5] ferry-men, who performed a brave concerto on conch shells.

But I refrain from pursuing this minute description, which goes on to describe the warriors of Bloemen-dael, and Weehawk, and Hoboken, and sundry other places, well known in history and song—for now do the notes of martial music alarm the people of New Amsterdam, sounding afar from beyond the walls of the city. But this alarm was in a little while relieved, for lo, from the midst of a vast cloud of dust, they recognized the brimstone-colored breeches and splendid silver leg of Peter Stuyvesant, glaring in the sunbeams; and beheld him approaching at the head of a formidable army, which he had mustered along the banks of the Hudson. And here the excellent but anonymous writer of the Stuyvesant manuscript breaks out into a brave and glorious description of the forces, as they defiled through the principal gate of the city, that stood by the head of Wall-street.

First of all came the Van Bummels, who inhabit the pleasant borders of the Bronx: these were short fat men, wearing exceeding large trunk-breeches, and were renowned for feats of the trencher—they were the first inventors of suppawn or mush and milk.—Close in their rear marched the Van Voltens, of Kaatskill, horrible quaffers of new cider, and arrant braggarts in their liquor.—After them came the Van Pelts of Groodt Esopus, dextrous horsemen, mounted upon goodly switch-tailed steeds of the Esopus breed—these were mighty hunters of minks and muskrats, whence came the word *Peltry*.—Then the Van Nests of Kinderhoeck, valiant robbers of birds' nests, as their name denotes; to these, if report may be believed, are we indebted for the invention of slap-jacks, or buckwheat cakes.—Then the Van Higginbottoms, of Wapping's creek; these came armed with ferules and birchen rods, being a race of school-masters, who first discovered the marvellous sympathy between the seat of honor and the seat of intellect—and that the shortest way to get knowledge into the head was to hammer it into the bottom.—Then the Van Grolls, of Anthony's Nose, who carried their liquor in fair round little pottles, by reason they could not bouse it out of their canteens, having such rare long noses.—

[4]Since corrupted into the *Wallabout;* the bay where the Navy Yard is situated.
[5]Now spelt Brooklyn.

Then the Gardeniers, of Hudson and thereabouts, distinguished by many triumphant feats, such as robbing watermelon patches, smoking rabbits out of their holes, and the like, and by being great lovers of roasted pigs' tails; these were the ancestors of the renowned congressman of that name.—Then the Van Hoesens, of Sing Sing, great choristers and players upon the jewsharp; these marched two and two, singing the great song of St. Nicholas.—Then the Couenhovens, of Sleepy Hollow; these gave birth to a jolly race of publicans, who first discovered the magic artifice of conjuring a quart of wine into a pint bottle.—Then the Van Kortlandts, who lived on the wild banks of the Croton, and were great killers of wild ducks, being much spoken of for their skill in shooting with the long bow.—Then the Van Bunschotens, of Nayack and Kakiat, who were the first that did ever kick with the left foot; they were gallant bush-whackers and hunters of raccoons by moonlight.—Then the Van Winkles, of Haerlem, potent suckers of eggs, and noted for running of horses, and running up of scores at taverns; they were the first that ever winked with both eyes at once.—Lastly came the KNICKERBOCKERS, of the great town of Scaghtikoke, where the folk lay stones upon the houses in windy weather, lest they should be blown away. These derive their name, as some say, from *Knicker*, to shake, and *Beker*, a goblet, indicating thereby that they were sturdy toss-pots of yore; but, in truth, it was derived from *Knicker*, to nod, and *Boeken*, books; plainly meaning that they were great nodders or dozers over books—from them did descend the writer of this history.

Such was the legion of sturdy bush-beaters that poured in at the grand gate of New Amsterdam; the Stuyvesant manuscript indeed speaks of many more, whose names I omit to mention, seeing that it behooves me to hasten to matters of greater moment. Nothing could surpass the joy and martial pride of the lion-hearted Peter as he reviewed this mighty host of warriors, and he determined no longer to defer the gratification of his much-wished-for revenge, upon the scoundrel Swedes at Fort Casimir.

But before I hasten to record those unmatchable events, which will be found in the sequel of this faithful history, let me pause to notice the fate of Jacobus Van Poffenburgh, the discomfited commander-in-chief of the armies of the New Netherlands. Such is the inherent uncharitableness of human nature, that scarcely did the news become public of his deplorable discomfiture at Fort Casimir, than a thousand scurvy rumors were set afloat in New Amsterdam, wherein it was insinuated, that he had in reality a treacherous understanding with the Swedish commander; that he had long been in the practice of privately communicating with the Swedes; together with divers hints about "secret service money."—To all which deadly charges I do not give a jot more credit than I think they deserve.

Certain it is, that the general vindicated his character by the most vehement oaths and protestations, and put every man out of the ranks of honor who dared to doubt his integrity. Moreover, on returning to New Amsterdam, he paraded up and down the streets with a crew of hard swearers at his heels—sturdy bottle companions, whom he gorged and fattened, and who were ready to bolster him through all the courts of justice—heroes of his own kidney, fierce-whiskered, broad-shouldered, colbrand-looking swaggerers—not one of whom but looked as though he could eat up an ox, and pick his teeth with the horns. These lifeguard men quarrelled all his quarrels, were ready to fight all his battles, and scowled at every man that turned up his nose at the general, as though they would devour him alive. Their conversation was interspersed with oaths like minute-guns, and every bombastic rodomontade was rounded off by a thundering execration, like a patriotic toast honored with a discharge of artillery.

All these valorous vaporings had a considerable effect in convincing certain profound sages, who began to think the general a hero, of unmatchable loftiness and magnanimity of soul; particularly as he was continually protesting *on the honor of a soldier*—a marvellously high-sounding asseveration. Nay, one of the members of the council went so far as to propose they should immortalize him by an imperishable statue of plaster of Paris.

But the vigilant Peter the Headstrong was not thus to be deceived. Sending privately for the commander-in-chief of all the armies, and having heard all his story, garnished with the customary pious oaths, protestations, and ejaculations—"Harkee, comrade," cried he, "though by your own account you are the most brave, upright, and honorable man in the whole province, yet do you lie under the misfortune of being damnably traduced, and immeasurably despised. Now, though it is certainly hard to punish a man for his misfortunes, and though it is very possible you are totally innocent of the crimes laid to your charge; yet as heaven, doubtless for some wise purpose, sees fit at present to withhold all proofs of your innocence, far be it from me to counteract its sovereign will. Beside, I cannot consent to venture my armies with a commander whom they despise, nor to trust the welfare of my people to a champion whom they distrust. Retire therefore, my friend, from the irksome toils and cares of public life, with this comforting reflection—that if guilty, you are but enjoying your just reward—and if innocent, you are not the first great and good man who has most wrongfully been slandered and maltreated in this wicked world—doubtless to be better treated in a better world, where there shall be neither error, calumny, nor persecution. In the meantime let me never see your face again, for I have a horrible antipathy to the countenances of unfortunate great men like yourself."

CHAPTER VI.

IN WHICH THE AUTHOR DISCOURSES VERY INGENUOUSLY OF HIMSELF —AFTER WHICH IS TO BE FOUND MUCH INTERESTING HISTORY ABOUT PETER THE HEADSTRONG AND HIS FOLLOWERS.

As MY READERS and myself are about entering on as many perils as ever-a confederacy of meddlesome knights-errant wilfully ran their heads into, it is meet that, like those hardy adventurers, we should join hands, bury all differences, and swear to stand by one another, in weal or woe, to the end of the enterprise. My readers must doubtless perceive how completely I have altered my tone and deportment since we first set out together. I warrant they then thought me a crabbed, cynical, impertinent little son of a Dutchman; for I scarcely ever gave them a civil word, nor so much as touched my beaver, when I had occasion to address them. But as we jogged along together on the high road of my history, I gradually began to relax, to grow more courteous, and occasionally to enter into familiar discourse, until at length I came to conceive a most social, companionable kind of regard for them. This is just my way—I am always a little cold and reserved at first, particularly to people whom I neither know nor care for, and am only to be completely won by long intimacy.

Besides, why should I have been sociable to the crowd of how-d'ye-do acquaintances that flocked around me at my first appearance? Many were merely attracted by a new face; and having stared me full in the title-page, walked off without saying a word; while others lingered yawningly through the preface, and, having gratified their short-lived curiosity, soon dropped off one by one. But, more especially to try their mettle, I had recourse to an expedient, similar to one which we are told was used by that peerless flower of chivalry, King Arthur; who, before he admitted any knight to his intimacy, first required that he should show himself superior to danger or hardships, by encountering unheard-of mishaps, slaying some dozen giants, vanquishing wicked enchanters, not to say a word of dwarfs, hippogriffs, and fiery dragons. On a similar principle did I cunningly lead my readers, at the first sally, into two or three knotty chapters, where they were most wofully belabored and buffeted, by a host of pagan philosophers and infidel writers. Though naturally a very grave man, yet could I scarce refrain from smiling outright at seeing the utter confusion and dismay of my valiant cavaliers. Some dropped down dead (asleep) on the field; others threw down my book in the middle of the first chapter, took to their heels, and never ceased scampering until they had fairly run it out of sight; then they stopped to take breath, to tell their friends what troubles they had undergone, and to warn all others from venturing on so thankless an expedition. Every page thinned my ranks more and more; and of the vast multitude that first set out, but a comparatively few made shift to survive, in exceedingly battered condition, through the five introductory chapters.

What, then! would you have had me take such sunshine, faint-hearted recreants to my bosom at our first acquaintance? No—no; I reserved my friendship for those who deserved it, for those who undauntedly bore me company, in despite of difficulties, dangers and fatigues. And now, as to those who adhere to me at present, I take them affectionately by the hand.— Worthy and thrice-beloved readers! brave and well-tried comrades! who have faithfully followed my footsteps through all my wanderings—I salute you from my heart—I pledge myself to stand by you to the last; and to conduct you (so heaven speed this trusty weapon which I now hold between my fingers) triumphantly to the end of this our stupendous undertaking.

But, hark! while we are thus talking, the city of New Amsterdam is in a bustle. The host of warriors encamped in the Bowling Green are striking their tents; the brazen trumpet of Antony Van Corlear makes the welkin

to resound with portentous clangor—the drums beat—the standards of the
Manhattoes, of Hell-gate, and of Michael Paw, wave proudly in the air.
And now behold where the mariners are busily employed, hoisting the sails
of yon topsail schooner, and those clump-built sloops, which are to waft
the army of the Nederlanders to gather immortal honors on the Delaware!

The entire population of the city, man, woman, and child, turned out to
behold the chivalry of New Amsterdam, as it paraded the streets previous
to embarkation. Many a handkerchief was waved out of the windows; many
a fair nose was blown in melodious sorrow on the mournful occasion. The
grief of the fair dames and beauteous damsels of Granada could not have
been more vociferous on the banishment of the gallant tribe of Abencerrages,
than was that of the kind-hearted fair ones of New Amsterdam on the departure
of their intrepid warriors. Every love-sick maiden fondly crammed the pockets
of her hero with gingerbread and doughnuts—many a copper ring was exchanged, and crooked sixpence broken, in pledge of eternal constancy—and
there remain extant to this day some love-verses written on that occasion,
sufficiently crabbed and incomprehensible to confound the whole universe.

But it was a moving sight to see the buxom lasses, how they hung about
the doughty Antony Van Corlear—for he was a jolly, rosy-faced, lusty
bachelor, fond of his joke, and withal a desperate rogue among the women.
Fain would they have kept him to comfort them while the army was away;
for besides what I have said of him, it is no more than justice to add, that
he was a kind-hearted soul, noted for his benevolent attentions in comforting
disconsolate wives during the absence of their husbands—and this made him
to be very much regarded by the honest burghers of the city. But nothing
could keep the valiant Antony from following the heels of the old governor,
whom he loved as he did his very soul—so embracing all the young vrouws,
and giving every one of them that had good teeth and rosy lips a dozen
hearty smacks, he departed loaded with their kind wishes.

Nor was the departure of the gallant Peter among the least causes of public
distress. Though the old governor was by no means indulgent to the follies
and waywardness of his subjects, yet somehow or other he had become
strangely popular among the people. There is something so captivating in
personal bravery, that, with the common mass of mankind, it takes the lead
of most other merits. The simple folk of New Amsterdam looked upon
Peter Stuyvesant as a prodigy of valor. His wooden leg, that trophy of
his martial encounters, was regarded with reverence and admiration. Every
old burgher had a budget of miraculous stories to tell about the exploits of
Hardkoppig Piet, wherewith he regaled his children of a long winter night;
and on which he dwelt with as much delight and exaggeration, as do our
honest country yeomen on the hardy adventures of old General Putnam
(or, as he is familiarly termed, *Old Put*) during our glorious revolution. Not
an individual but verily believed the old governor was a match for Beelzebub
himself; and there was even a story told, with great mystery, and under the
rose, of his having shot the devil with a silver bullet one dark stormy night,
as he was sailing in a canoe through Hell-gate—but this I do not record as

being an absolute fact. Perish the man who would let fall a drop to discolor the pure stream of history!

Certain it is, not an old woman in New Amsterdam but considered Peter Stuyvesant as a tower of strength, and rested satisfied that the public welfare was secure, so long as he was in the city. It is not surprising, then, that they looked upon his departure as a sore affliction. With heavy hearts they draggled at the heels of his troop, as they marched down to the river side to embark. The governor from the stern of his schooner gave a short but truly patriarchal address to his citizens, wherein he recommended them to comport like loyal and peaceable subjects—to go to church regularly on Sundays, and to mind their business all the week besides. That the women should be dutiful and affectionate to their husbands—looking after nobody's concerns but their own; eschewing all gossipings, and morning gaddings—and carrying short tongues and long petticoats. That the men should abstain from intermeddling in public concerns, intrusting the cares of government to the officers appointed to support them—staying at home, like good citizens, making money for themselves, and getting children for the benefit of their country. That the burgomasters should look well to the public interest—not oppressing the poor nor indulging the rich—not tasking their ingenuity to devise new laws, but faithfully enforcing those which were already made—rather bending their attention to prevent evil than to punish it; ever recollecting that civil magistrates should consider themselves more as guardians of public morals than rat-catchers employed to entrap public delinquents. Finally, he exhorted them, one and all, high and low, rich and poor, to conduct themselves *as well as they could*, assuring them that if they faithfully and conscientiously complied with this golden rule, there was no danger but that they would all conduct themselves well enough. This done, he gave them a paternal benediction; the sturdy Antony sounded a most loving farewell with his trumpet, the jolly crews put up a shout of triumph, and the invincible armada swept off proudly down the bay.

The good people of New Amsterdam crowded down to the Battery—that blest resort, from whence so many a tender prayer has been wafted, so many a fair hand waved, so many a tearful look been cast by a love-sick damsel, after the lessening bark, bearing her adventurous swain to distant climes!—Here the populace watched with straining eyes the gallant squadron, as it slowly floated down the bay, and when the intervening land at the Narrows shut it from their sight, gradually dispersed with silent tongues and downcast countenances.

A heavy gloom hung over the late bustling city—the honest burghers smoked their pipes in profound thoughtfulness, casting many a wistful look to the weather-cock on the church of St. Nicholas; and all the old women, having no longer the presence of Peter Stuyvesant to hearten them, gathered their children home, and barricaded the doors and windows every evening at sundown.

In the meanwhile the armada of the sturdy Peter proceeded prosperously on its voyage, and after encountering about as many storms, and water-spouts, and whales, and other horrors and phenomena, as generally befall adventurous landsmen in perilous voyages of the kind; and after undergoing a severe scouring from that deplorable and unpitied malady called sea-sickness, the whole squadron arrived safely in the Delaware.

Without so much as dropping anchor and giving his wearied ships time to breathe, after laboring so long on the ocean, the intrepid Peter pursued his course up the Delaware, and made a sudden appearance before Fort Casimir. Having summoned the astonished garrison by a terrific blast from the trumpet of the long-winded Van Corlear, he demanded, in a tone of thunder, an instant surrender of the fort. To this demand, Suen Skytte, the wind-dried commandant, replied in a shrill whiffling voice, which, by reason of his extreme spareness, sounded like the wind whistling through a broken bellows—"that he had no very strong reason for refusing, except that the demand was particularly disagreeable, as he had been ordered to maintain his post to the last extremity." He requested time, therefore, to consult with Governor Risingh, and proposed a truce for that purpose.

The choleric Peter, indignant at having his rightful fort so treacherously taken from him, and thus pertinaciously withheld, refused the proposed armistice, and swore by the pipe of St. Nicholas, which, like the sacred fire, was never extinguished, that unless the fort were surrendered in ten minutes, he would incontinently storm the works, make all the garrison run the gauntlet, and split their scoundrel of a commander like a pickled shad. To give this menace the greater effect, he drew forth his trusty sword, and shook it at them with such a fierce and vigorous motion, that doubtless, if it had not been exceeding rusty, it would have lightened terror into the eyes and hearts of the enemy. He then ordered his men to bring a broadside to bear upon the fort, consisting of two swivels, three muskets, a long duck fowling-piece, and two brace of horse-pistols.

In the meantime the sturdy Van Corlear marshalled all his forces, and commenced his warlike operations. Distending his cheeks like a very Boreas, he kept up a most horrific twanging of his trumpet—the lusty choristers of Sing Sing broke forth into a hideous song of battle—the warriors of Breuckelen and the Wallabout blew a potent and astounding blast on their conch shells, altogether forming as outrageous a concerto as though five thousand French fiddlers were displaying their skill in a modern overture.

Whether the formidable front of war thus suddenly presented smote the garrison with sore dismay—or whether the concluding terms of the summons, which mentioned that he should surrender "at discretion," were mistaken by Suen Skytte, who, though a Swede was a very considerate, easy-tempered man —as a compliment to his discretion, I will not take upon me to say; certain it is he found it impossible to resist so courteous a demand. Accordingly, in the very nick of time, just as the cabin-boy had gone after a coal of fire, to discharge the swivel, a chamade was beat on the rampart by the only drum in the garrison, to the no small satisfaction of both parties; who, not-withstanding their great stomach for fighting, had full as good an inclination to eat a quiet dinner as to exchange black eyes and bloody noses.

Thus did this impregnable fortress once more return to the domination of their High Mightinesses; Skytte and his garrison of twenty men were allowed to march out with the honors of war, and the victorious Peter, who was as generous as brave, permitted them to keep possession of all their arms and ammunition—the same on inspection being found totally unfit for service, having long rusted in the magazine of the fortress, even before it was wrested by the Swedes from the windy Van Poffenburgh. But I must not omit to mention, that the governor was so well pleased with the service of his faithful squire Van Corlear, in the reduction of this great fortress, that he made him on the spot lord of a goodly domain in the vicinity of New Amsterdam—which goes by the name of Corlear's Hook unto this very day.

The unexampled liberality of Peter Stuyvesant towards the Swedes, occasioned great surprise in the city of New Amsterdam—nay, certain factious individuals, who had been enlightened by political meetings in the days of William the Testy, but who had not dared to indulge their meddlesome habits under the eye of their present ruler, now, emboldened by his absence, gave vent to their censures in the street. Murmurs were heard in the very council-chamber of New Amsterdam; and there is no knowing whether they might not have broken out into downright speeches and invectives, had not Peter Stuyvesant privately sent home his walking-staff, to be laid as a mace on the table of the council-chamber, in the midst of his counsellors; who, like wise men, took the hint, and for ever after held their peace.

CHAPTER VII.

SHOWING THE GREAT ADVANTAGE THAT THE AUTHOR HAS OVER HIS READER IN TIME OF BATTLE—TOGETHER WITH DIVERS PORTENTOUS MOVEMENTS; WHICH BETOKEN THAT SOMETHING TERRIBLE IS ABOUT TO HAPPEN.

LIKE as a mighty alderman, when at a corporation feast the first spoonful of turtle-soup salutes his palate, feels his appetite but tenfold quickened, and re-doubles his vigorous attacks upon the tureen; while his projecting eyes roll greedily round, devouring everything at table—so did the mettlesome Peter Stuyvesant feel that hunger for martial glory, which raged within his bowels, inflamed by the capture of Fort Casimir, and nothing could allay it but the conquest of all New-Sweden. No sooner, therefore, had he secured his conquest, than he stumped resolutely on, flushed with success, to gather fresh laurels at Fort Christina.[1]

This was the grand Swedish post, established on a small river (or, as it is improperly termed, creek) of the same name; and here that crafty governor

[1] At present a flourishing town, called Christiana, or Christeen, about thirty-seven miles from Philadelphia, on the post-road to Baltimore.

Jan Risingh lay grimly drawn up, like a gray-bearded spider in the citadel of his web.

But before we hurry into the direful scenes which must attend the meeting of two such potent chieftains, it is advisable to pause for a moment, and hold a kind of warlike council. Battles should not be rushed into precipitately by the historian and his readers, any more than by the general and his soldiers. The great commanders of antiquity never engaged the enemy without previously preparing the minds of their followers by animating harangues; spiriting them up to heroic deeds, assuring them of the protection of the gods, and inspiring them with a confidence in the prowess of their leaders. So the historian should awaken the attention and enlist the passions of his readers; and having set them all on fire with the importance of his subject, he should put himself at their head, flourish his pen, and lead them on to the thickest of the fight.

An illustrious example of this rule may be seen in that mirror of historians the immortal Thucydides. Having arrived at the breaking out of the Peloponnesian war, one of his commentators observes that "he sounds the charge in all the disposition and spirit of Homer. He catalogues the allies on both sides. He awakens our expectations, and fast engages our attention. All mankind are concerned in the important point now going to be decided. Endeavors are made to disclose futurity. Heaven itself is interested in the dispute. The earth totters, and nature seems to labor with the great event. This is his solemn, sublime manner of setting out. Thus he magnifies a war between two, as Rapin styles them, petty states; and thus artfully he supports a little subject by treating it in a great and noble method."

In like manner, having conducted my readers into the very teeth of peril—having followed the adventurous Peter and his band into foreign regions—surrounded by foes, and stunned by the horrid din of arms—at this important moment, while darkness and doubt hang o'er each coming chapter, I hold it meet to harangue them, and prepare them for the events that are to follow.

And here I would premise one great advantage which, as historian, I possess over my reader; and this it is, that though I cannot save the life of my favorite hero, nor absolutely contradict the event of a battle (both which liberties, though often taken by the French writers of the present reign, I hold to be utterly unworthy of a scrupulous historian), yet I can now and then make him bestow on his enemy a sturdy back stroke sufficient to fell a giant; though, in honest truth, he may never have done anything of the kind—or I can drive his antagonist clear round and round the field, as did Homer make that fine fellow Hector scamper like a poltroon round the walls of Troy; for which, if ever they have encountered one another in the Elysian fields, I'll warrant the prince of poets has had to make the most humble apology.

I am aware that many conscientious readers will be ready to cry out "foul play!" whenever I render a little assistance to my hero—but I consider it one of those privileges exercised by historians of all ages—and one which has never been disputed. An historian is, in fact, as it were, bound in honor to stand by his hero—the fame of the latter is intrusted to his hands, and it is his duty to do the best by it he can. Never was there a general, an admiral, or any other commander, who, in giving an account of any battle he had fought, did not sorely belabor the enemy; and I have no doubt that, had my heroes written the history of their own achievements, they would have dealt much harder blows than any that I shall recount. Standing forth, therefore, as the guardian of their fame, it behooves me to do them the same justice they would have done themselves; and if I happen to be a little hard upon the Swedes, I give free leave to any of their descendants, who may write a history of the State of Delaware, to take fair retaliation, and belabor Peter Stuyvesant as hard as they please.

Therefore stand by for broken heads and bloody noses!—My pen hath long itched for a battle—siege after siege have I carried on without blows or bloodshed; but now I have at length got a chance, and I vow to Heaven and St. Nicholas, that, let the chronicles of the times say what they please, neither Sallust, Livy, Tacitus, Polybius, nor any other historian, did ever record a fiercer fight than that in which my valiant chieftains are now about to engage.

And you, oh most excellent readers, whom, for your faithful adherence, I could cherish in the warmest corner of my heart—be not uneasy—trust the fate of our favorite Stuyvesant with me—for by the rood, come what may, I'll stick by Hardkoppig Piet to the last. I'll make him drive about these losels vile, as did the renowned Lancelot of the Lake a herd of recreant Cornish knights—and if he does fall, let me never draw my pen to fight another battle in behalf of a brave man, if I don't make these lubberly Swedes pay for it.

No sooner had Peter Stuyvesant arrived before Fort Christina than he proceeded without delay to intrench himself, and immediately on running his first parallel, despatched Antony Van Corlear to summon the fortress to surrender. Van Corlear was received with all due formality, hoodwinked at the portal, and conducted through a pestiferous smell of salt fish and onions to the citadel, a substantial hut built of pine logs. His eyes were here uncovered, and he found himself in the august presence of Governor Risingh. This chieftain, as I have before noted, was a very giantly man; and was clad in a coarse blue coat, strapped round the waist with a leathern belt, which caused the enormous skirts and pockets to set off with a very warlike sweep. His ponderous legs were cased in a pair of foxy-colored jack-boots, and he was straddling in the attitude of the Colossus of Rhodes, before a bit of broken looking-glass, shaving himself with a villanously dull razor. This afflicting operation caused him to make a series of horrible grimaces, which heightened exceedingly the grisly terrors of his visage. On Antony Van Corlear's being announced, the grim commander paused for a moment, in the midst of one of his most hard-favored contortions, and after eying him askance over the shoulder, with a kind of snarling grin on his countenance, resumed his labors at the glass.

This iron harvest being reaped, he turned once more to the trumpeter, and demanded the purport of his errand. Antony Van Corlear delivered in a few words, being a kind of short-hand speaker, a long message from his excellency, recounting the whole history of the province, with a recapitulation of grievances, and enumeration of claims, and concluding with a peremptory demand of instant surrender; which done, he turned aside, took his nose between his thumb and finger, and blew a tremendous blast, not unlike the flourish of a trumpet of defiance—which it had doubtless learned from a long and intimate neighborhood with that melodious instrument.

Governor Risingh heard him through, trumpet and all, but with infinite impatience; leaning at times, as was his usual custom, on the pommel of his sword, and at times twirling a huge steel watch-chain, or snapping his fingers. Van Corlear having finished, he bluntly replied, that Peter Stuyvesant and his summons might go to the d——l, whither he hoped to send him and his crew of ragamuffins before supper-time. Then unsheathing his brass-hilted sword, and throwing away the scabbard—" 'Fore gad," quod he, "but I will not sheathe thee again until I make a scabbard of the smoke-dried leathern hide of this runagate Dutchman." Then having flung a fierce defiance in the teeth of his adversary, by the lips of his messenger, the latter was reconducted to the portal, with all the ceremonious civility due to the trumpeter, squire, and ambassador of so great a commander; and being again unblinded, was courteously dismissed with a tweak of the nose, to assist him in recollecting his message.

No sooner did the gallant Peter receive this insolent reply than he let fly a tremendous volley of red-hot execrations, which would infallibly have battered down the fortifications, and blown up the powder magazine about the ears of the fiery Swede, had not the ramparts been remarkably strong, and the magazine bomb-proof. Perceiving that the works withstood this terrific blast, and that it was utterly impossible (as it really was in those unphilosophic days) to carry on a war with words, he ordered his merry men all to prepare for an immediate assault. But here a strange murmur broke out among his troops, beginning with the tribe of the Van Bummels, those valiant trenchermen of the Bronx, and spreading from man to man, accompanied with certain mutinous looks and discontented murmurs. For once in his life, and only for once, did the great Peter turn pale, for he verily thought his warriors were going to falter in this hour of perilous trial, and thus to tarnish forever the fame of the province of New Netherlands.

But soon did he discover, to his great joy, that in this suspicion he deeply wronged this most undaunted army; for the cause of this agitation and uneasiness simply was, that the hour of dinner was at hand, and it would have almost broken the hearts of these regular Dutch warriors to have broken in upon the invariable routine of their habits. Besides, it was an established rule among our ancestors always to fight upon a full stomach; and to this may be doubtless attributed the circumstance that they came to be so renowned in arms.

And now are the hearty men of the Manhattoes, and their no less hearty comrades, all lustily engaged under the trees, buffeting stoutly with the contents of their wallets, and taking such affectionate embraces of their canteens and pottles, as though they verily believed they were to be the last. And as I foresee we shall have hot work in a page or two, I advise my readers to do the same, for which purpose I will bring this chapter to a close; giving them my word of honor, that no advantage shall be taken of this armistice to surprise, or in any wise molest, the honest Nederlanders, while at their vigorous repast.

CHAPTER VIII.

Containing the Most Horrible Battle Ever Recorded in Poetry or Prose; with the Admirable Exploits of Peter the Headstrong.

"Now had the Dutchmen snatched a huge repast," and finding themselves wonderfully encouraged and animated thereby, prepared to take the field. Expectation, says the writer of the Stuyvesant manuscript—Expectation now stood on stilts. The world forgot to turn round, or rather stood still, that it might witness the affray; like a round-bellied alderman, watching the combat of two chivalrous flies upon his jerkin. The eyes of all mankind, as usual in such cases, were turned upon Fort Christina. The sun, like a little man in a crowd at a puppet-show, scampered about the heavens, popping his head here and there, and endeavoring to get a peep between the unmannerly clouds that obtruded themselves in his way. The historians filled their inkhorns— the poets went without their dinners, either that they might buy paper and goose-quills, or because they could not get any thing to eat—Antiquity scowled sulkily out of its grave, to see itself outdone—while even Posterity stood mute, gazing in gaping ecstasy of retrospection on the eventful field.

The immortal deities, who whilom had seen service at the "affair" of Troy, now mounted their feather-bed clouds, and sailed over the plain, or mingled among the combatants in different disguises, all itching to have a finger in the pie. Jupiter sent off his thunderbolt to a noted coppersmith, to have it furbished up for the direful occasion. Venus vowed by her chastity to patronize the Swedes, and in semblance of a blear-eyed trull paraded the battlements of Fort Christina, accompanied by Diana, as a sergeant's widow, of cracked reputation. The noted bully, Mars, stuck two horse-pistols into his belt, shouldered a rusty firelock, and gallantly swaggered at their elbow, as a drunken corporal—while Apollo trudged in their rear, as a bandy-legged fifer, playing most villanously out of tune.

On the other side, the ox-eyed Juno, who had gained a pair of black eyes over night, in one of her curtain lectures with old Jupiter, displayed her haughty beauties on a baggage-wagon—Minerva, as a brawny gin-sutler, tucked up her skirts, brandished her fists, and swore most heroically, in exceeding bad Dutch, (having but lately studied the language), by way of keeping up the spirits of the soldiers; while Vulcan halted as a club-footed blacksmith, lately promoted to be a captain of militia. All was silent awe, or bustling preparation: war reared his horrid front, gnashed loud his iron fangs, and shook his direful crest of bristling bayonets.

And now the mighty chieftains marshalled out their hosts. Here stood stout Risingh, firm as a thousand rocks—incrusted with stockades, and intrenched to the chin in mud batteries. His valiant soldiery lined the breast-work in grim array, each having his mustachios fiercely greased, and his hair pomatumed back, and queued so stiffly, that he grinned above the ramparts like a grisly death's head.

There came on the intrepid Peter—his brows knit, his teeth set, his fists clenched, almost breathing forth volumes of smoke, so fierce was the fire that raged within his bosom. His faithful squire Van Corlear trudged valiantly at his heels, with his trumpet gorgeously bedecked with red and yellow ribands, the remembrances of his fair mistresses at the Manhattoes. Then came waddling on the sturdy chivalry of the Hudson. There were the Van Wycks, and the Van Dycks, and the Ten Eycks—the Van Nesses, the Van Tassels, the Van Grolls; the Van Hœsens, the Van Giesons, and the Van Blarcoms—the Van Warts, the Van Winkles, the Van Dams; the Van Pelts, the Van Rippers, and the Van Brunts. There were the Van Horns, the Van Hooks, the Van Bunschotens; the Van Gelders, the Van Arsdales, and the Van Bummels; the Vander Belts, the Vander Hoofs, the Vander Voorts, the Vander Lyns, the Vander Pools, and the Vander Spiegles— there came the Hoffmans, the Hooghlands, the Hoppers, the Cloppers, the Ryckmans, the Dyckmans, the Hogebooms, the Rosebooms, the Oothouts, the Quackenbosses, the Roerbacks, the Garrebrantzes, the Bensons, the Brouwers, the Waldrons, the Onderdonks, the Varra Vangers, the Schermerhorns, the Stoutenburghs, the Brinkerhoffs, the Bontecous, the Knickerbockers, the Hockstrassers, the Ten Breecheses and the Tough Breecheses, with a host more of worthies, whose names are too crabbed to be written, or if they could be written, it would be impossible for man to utter—all fortified with a mighty dinner, and to use the words of a great Dutch poet,

"Brimful of wrath and cabbage."

For an instant the mighty Peter paused in the midst of his career, and mounting on a stump, addressed his troops in eloquent Low Dutch, exhorting them to fight like *duyvels*, and assuring them that if they conquered, they should get plenty of booty—if they fell, they should be allowed the satisfaction, while dying, of reflecting that it was in the service of their country—and after they were dead, of seeing their names inscribed in the temple of renown, and handed down, in company with all the other great men of the year, for the admiration of posterity.—Finally, he swore to them, on the word of a governor (and they knew him too well to doubt it for a moment), that if he caught any mother's son of them looking pale, or playing craven, he would curry his hide till he made him run out of it like a snake in springtime.—Then lugging out his trusty sabre, he brandished it three times over his head, ordered Van Corlear to sound a charge, and shouting the words "St. Nicholas and the Manhattoes!" courageously dashed forwards. His warlike followers, who had employed the interval in lighting their pipes, instantly stuck them into their mouths, gave a furious puff, and charged gallantly, under cover of the smoke.

The Swedish garrison, ordered by the cunning Risingh not to fire until they could distinguish the whites of their assailants' eyes, stood in horrid silence on the covert-way, until the eager Dutchmen had ascended the glacis. Then did they pour into them such a tremendous volley, that the very hills quaked around, and were terrified even unto an incontinence of water, insomuch that certain springs burst forth from their sides, which continue to run unto the present day. Not a Dutchman but would have bitten the dust beneath that dreadful fire, had not the protecting Minerva kindly taken care that the Swedes should, one and all, observe their usual custom of shutting their eyes and turning away their heads at the moment of discharge.

The Swedes followed up their fire by leaping the counterscarp, and falling tooth and nail upon the foe with furious outcries. And now might be seen prodigies of valor, unmatched in history or song. Here was the sturdy Stoffel Brinkerhoff brandishing his quarter-staff, like the giant Blanderon his oak-tree (for he scorned to carry any other weapon), and drumming a horrific tune upon the hard heads of the Swedish soldiery. There were the Van Kortlandts, posted at a distance, like the Locrian archers of yore, and plying it most potently with the long bow, for which they were so justly renowned. On a rising knoll were gathered the valiant men of Sing Sing, assisting marvellously in the fight, by chanting the great song of St. Nicholas; but as to the Gardeniers of Hudson, they were absent on a marauding party, laying waste the neighboring water-melon patches.

In a different part of the field were the Van Grolls of Anthony's Nose, struggling to get to the thickest of the fight, but horribly perplexed in a defile between two hills, by reason of the length of their noses. So also the Van Bunschotens of Nyack and Kakiat, so renowned for kicking with the left foot, were brought to a stand for want of wind, in consequence of the hearty dinner they had eaten, and would have been put to utter rout but for the arrival of a gallant corps of voltigeurs, composed of the Hoppers, who advanced nimbly to their assistance on one foot. Nor must I omit to mention the valiant achievements of Antony Van Corlear, who, for a good quarter of an hour, waged stubborn fight with a little pursy Swedish drummer; whose hide he drummed most magnificently, and whom he would infallibly have annihilated on the spot, but that he had come into the battle with no other weapon but his trumpet.

But now the combat thickened.—On came the mighty Jacobus Varra Vanger and the fighting men of the Wallabout; after them thundered the Van Pelts of Esopus, together with the Van Rippers and the Van Brunts, bearing down all before them—then the Suy Dams, and the Van Dams, pressing forward with many a blustering oath, at the head of the warriors of Hell-gate, clad in their thunder and lightning gabardines; and lastly, the standard-bearers and body-guards of Peter Stuyvesant, bearing the great beaver of the Manhattoes.

And now commenced the horrid din, the desperate struggle, the maddening ferocity, the frantic desperation, the confusion and self-abandonment of war. Dutchman and Swede commingled, tugged, panted, and blowed. The heavens were darkened with a tempest of missives. Bang! went the guns—whack!

went the broadswords—thump! went the cudgels—crash! went the musket-stocks—blows—kicks—cuffs—scratches—black eyes and bloody noses swelling the horrors of the scene! Thick thwack, cut and hack, helter-skelter, higgledy-piggledy, hurly-burly, head over heels, rough and tumble!—Dunder and blixum! swore the Dutchmen—Splitter and splutter! cried the Swedes—Storm the works! shouted Hardkoppig Peter—Fire the mine! roared stout Risingh—Tanta-ra-ra-ra! twanged the trumpet of Antony Van Corlear—until all voice and sound became unintelligible—grunts of pain, yells of fury, and shouts of triumph mingling in one hideous clamor. The earth shook as if struck with a paralytic stroke—trees shrunk aghast, and withered at the sight—rocks burrowed in the ground like rabbits—and even Christina creek turned from its course, and ran up a hill in breathless terror!

Long hung the contest doubtful, for though a heavy shower of rain, sent by the "cloud-compelling Jove," in some measure cooled their ardor, as doth a bucket of water thrown on a group of fighting mastiffs, yet did they but pause for a moment, to return with tenfold fury to the charge. Just at this juncture a vast and dense column of smoke was seen slowly rolling toward the scene of battle. The combatants paused for a moment, gazing in mute astonishment until the wind, dispelling the murky cloud, revealed the flaunting banner of Michael Paw the Patroon of Communipaw. That valiant chieftain came fearlessly on at the head of a phalanx of oyster-fed Pavonians and a *corps de reserve* of the Van Arsdales and Van Bummels, who had remained behind to digest the enormous dinner they had eaten. These now trudged manfully forward, smoking their pipes with outrageous vigor, so as to raise the awful cloud that has been mentioned; but marching exceedingly slow, being short of leg, and of great rotundity in the belt.

And now the deities who watched over the fortunes of the Nederlanders having unthinkingly left the field and stepped into a neighboring tavern to refresh themselves with a pot of beer, a direful catastrophe had well nigh ensued. Scarce had the myrmidons of Michael Paw attained the front of battle, when the Swedes, instructed by the cunning Risingh, levelled a shower of blows full at their tobacco-pipes. Astounded at this assault, and dismayed at the havoc of their pipes, these ponderous warriors gave way, and like a drove of frightened elephants broke through the ranks of their own army. The little Hoppers were borne down in the surge: the sacred banner emblazoned with the gigantic oyster of Communipaw was trampled in the dirt: on blundered and thundered the heavy-sterned fugitives, the Swedes pressing on their rear and applying their feet *a parte poste* of the Van Arsdales and the Van Bummels with a vigor that prodigiously accelerated their movements —nor did the renowned Michael Paw himself fail to receive divers grievous and dishonorable visitations of shoe leather.

But what, oh Muse! was the rage of Peter Stuyvesant, when from afar he saw his army giving way! In the transports of his wrath he sent forth a roar, enough to shake the very hills. The men of the Manhattoes plucked up new courage at the sound; or rather, they rallied at the voice of their leader, of whom they stood more in awe than of all the Swedes in Christendom.

Without waiting for their aid, the daring Peter dashed sword in hand into the thickest of the foe. Then might be seen achievements worthy of the days of the giants. Wherever he went, the enemy shrank before him; the Swedes fled to right and left, or were driven, like dogs, into their own ditch; but, as he pushed forward singly with headlong courage, the foe closed behind and hung upon his rear. One aimed a blow full at his heart; but the protecting power which watches over the great and good turned aside the hostile blade and directed it to a side-pocket, where reposed an enormous iron tobacco-box, endowed, like the shield of Achilles, with supernatural powers, doubtless from bearing the portrait of the blessed St. Nicholas. Peter Stuyvesant turned like an angry bear upon the foe, and seizing him as he fled, by an immeasurable queue, "Ah whoreson caterpillar," roared he, "here's what shall make worms' meat of thee!" So saying, he whirled his sword and dealt a blow that would have decapitated the varlet, but that the pitying steel struck short and shaved the queue forever from his crown. At this moment an arquebusier levelled his piece from a neighboring mound, with deadly aim; but the watchful Minerva, who had just stopped to tie up her garter, seeing the peril of her favorite hero, sent old Boreas with his bellows, who, as the match descended to the pan, gave a blast that blew the priming from the touch-hole.

Thus waged the fight, when the stout Risingh, surveying the field from the top of a little ravelin, perceived his troops banged, beaten, and kicked by the invincible Peter. Drawing his falchion and uttering a thousand anathemas, he strode down to the scene of combat with some such thundering strides as Jupiter is said by Hesiod to have taken, when he strode down the spheres to hurl his thunderbolts at the Titans.

When the rival heroes came face to face, each made a prodigious start in the style of a veteran stage champion. Then did they regard each other for a moment with the bitter aspect of two furious ram-cats on the point of a clapper-clawing. Then did they throw themselves into one attitude, then into another, striking their swords on the ground first on the right side, then on the left—at last at it they went, with incredible ferocity. Words cannot tell the prodigies of strength and valor displayed in this direful encounter— an encounter compared to which the far-famed battles of Ajax with Hector, of Æneas with Turnus, Orlando with Rodomont, Guy of Warwick with Colbrand the Dane, or of that renowned Welsh knight, Sir Owen of the Mountains, with the giant Guylon, were all gentle sports and holiday recreations. At length the valiant Peter, watching his opportunity, aimed a blow, enough to cleave his adversary to the very chine; but Risingh, nimbly raising his sword, warded it off so narrowly, that glancing on one side, it shaved away a huge canteen in which he carried his liquor; thence pursuing its trenchant course, it severed off a deep coat pocket, stored with bread and cheese—which provant rolling among the armies, occasioned a fearful scrambling between the Swedes and Dutchmen, and made the general battle to wax ten times more furious than ever.

Enraged to see his military stores laid waste, the stout Risingh, collecting all his forces, aimed a mighty blow full at the hero's crest. In vain did his fierce little cocked hat oppose its course. The biting steel clove through the stubborn ram beaver, and would have cracked the crown of any one not endowed with supernatural hardness of head; but the brittle weapon shivered in pieces on the skull of Hardkoppig Piet, shedding a thousand sparks, like beams of glory round his grizzly visage.

The good Peter reeled with the blow, and turning up his eyes beheld a thousand suns, beside moons and stars, dancing about the firmament—at length, missing his footing, by reason of his wooden leg, down he came on his seat of honor with a crash which shook the surrounding hills, and might have wrecked his frame, had he not been received into a cushion softer than velvet, which Providence or Minerva, or St. Nicholas, or some kindly cow had benevolently prepared for his reception.

The furious Risingh, in despite of the maxim, cherished by all true knights, that "fair play is a jewel," hastened to take advantage of the hero's fall; but, as he stooped to give a fatal blow, Peter Stuyvesant dealt him a thwack over the sconce with his wooden leg, which set a chime of bells ringing triple bob majors in his cerebellum. The bewildered Swede staggered with the blow, and the wary Peter seizing a pocket-pistol, which lay hard by, discharged it full at the head of the reeling Risingh. Let not my reader mistake; it was not a murderous weapon loaded with powder and ball; but a little sturdy stone pottle charged to the muzzle with a double dram of true Dutch courage, which the knowing Antony Van Corlear carried about him by way of replenishing his valor; and which had dropped from his wallet during his furious encounter with the drummer. The hideous weapon sang through the air, and true to its course as was the fragment of a rock discharged at Hector by bully Ajax, encountered the head of the gigantic Swede with matchless violence.

This heaven-directed blow decided the battle. The ponderous pericranium of General Jan Risingh sank upon his breast; his knees tottered under him; a death-like torpor seized upon his frame, and he tumbled to the earth with such violence, that old Pluto started with affright, lest he should have broken through the roof of his infernal palace.

His fall was the signal of defeat and victory—the Swedes gave way—the Dutch pressed forward; the former took to their heels, the latter hotly pursued. —Some entered with them, pell-mell, through the sally-port—others stormed the bastion, and others scrambled over the curtain. Thus in a little while the fortress of Fort Christina, which, like another Troy, had stood a seige of full ten hours, was carried by assault, without the loss of a single man on either side. Victory, in the likeness of a gigantic ox-fly, sat perched upon the cocked hat of the gallant Stuyvesant, and it was declared, by all the writers whom he hired to write the history of his expedition, that on this memorable day he gained a sufficient quantity of glory to immortalize a dozen of the greatest heroes in Christendom.

CHAPTER IX.

IN WHICH THE AUTHOR AND THE READER, WHILE REPOSING AFTER
THE BATTLE, FALL INTO A VERY GRAVE DISCOURSE—AFTER WHICH
IS RECORDED THE CONDUCT OF PETER STUYVESANT AFTER HIS VICTORY.

THANKS to St. Nicholas, we have safely finished this tremendous battle: let
us sit down, my worthy reader, and cool ourselves, for I am in a prodigious
sweat and agitation—truly this fighting of battles is hot work! and if your great
commanders did but know what trouble they give their historians, they would
not have the conscience to achieve so many horrible victories. But methinks
I hear my reader complain, that throughout this boasted battle there is not
the least slaughter, nor a single individual maimed, if we except the unhappy
Swede, who was shorn of his queue by the trenchant blade of Peter Stuyvesant;
all which, he observes, is a great outrage on probability, and highly injurious to
the interest of the narration.

This is certainly an objection of no little moment, but it arises entirely
from the obscurity enveloping the remote periods of time about which I have
undertaken to write. Thus, though doubtless, from the importance of the
object, and the prowess of the parties concerned, there must have been terrible
carnage, and prodigies of valor displayed before the walls of Christina, yet,
notwithstanding that I have consulted every history, manuscript, and tradition,
touching this memorable though long-forgotten battle, I cannot find mention
made of a single man killed or wounded in the whole affair. . . .

BOOK VII.

CONTAINING THE THIRD PART OF THE REIGN OF PETER THE HEADSTRONG—HIS
TROUBLES WITH THE BRITISH NATION, AND THE DECLINE AND FALL OF THE
DUTCH DYNASTY.

CHAPTER I.

HOW PETER STUYVESANT RELIEVED THE SOVEREIGN PEOPLE FROM THE
BURDEN OF TAKING CARE OF THE NATION; WITH SUNDRY PARTICULARS
OF HIS CONDUCT IN TIME OF PEACE, AND OF THE RISE OF A GREAT
DUTCH ARISTOCRACY.

THE HISTORY of the reign of Peter Stuyvesant furnishes an edifying picture of
the cares and vexations inseparable from sovereignty, and a solemn warning to
all who are ambitious of attaining the seat of honor. Though returning in
triumph and crowned with victory, his exultation was checked on observing

the abuses which had sprung up in New Amsterdam during his short absence. His walking-staff, which he had sent home to act as his vicegerent, had, it is true, kept his council-chamber in order; the counsellors eying it with awe, as it lay in grim repose upon the table, and smoking their pipes in silence; but its control extended not out of doors.

The populace unfortunately had had too much their own way under the slack though fitful reign of William the Testy; and though upon the accession of Peter Stuyvesant they had felt, with the instinctive perception which mobs as well as cattle possess, that the reins of government had passed into stronger hands, yet could they not help fretting and chafing and champing upon the bit, in restive silence.

Scarcely, therefore, had he departed on his expedition against the Swedes, than the old factions of William Kieft's reign had again thrust their heads above water. Pot-house meetings were again held to "discuss the state of the nation," where cobblers, tinkers, and tailors, the self-dubbed "friends of the people," once more felt themselves inspired with the gift of legislation, and undertook to lecture on every movement of government.

Now, as Peter Stuyvesant had a singular inclination to govern the province by his individual will, his first move, on his return, was to put a stop to this gratuitous legislation. Accordingly, one evening, when an inspired cobbler was holding forth to an assemblage of the kind, the intrepid Peter suddenly made his appearance, with his ominous walking-staff in his hand, and a countenance sufficient to petrify a mill-stone. The whole meeting was thrown into confusion—the orator stood aghast, with open mouth and trembling knees, while "horror! tyranny! liberty! rights! taxes! death! destruction!" and a host of other patriotic phrases were bolted forth before he had time to close his lips. Peter took no notice of the skulking throng, but strode up to the brawling bully-ruffian, and pulling out a huge silver watch, which might have served in times of yore as a town-clock, and which is still retained by his descendants as a family curiosity, requested the orator to mend it, and set it going. The orator humbly confessed it was utterly out of his power, as he was unacquainted with the nature of its construction. "Nay, but," said Peter, "try your ingenuity, man: you see all the springs and wheels, and how easily the clumsiest hand may stop it, and pull it to pieces; and why should it not be equally easy to regulate as to stop it?" The orator declared that his trade was wholly different—that he was a poor cobbler, and had never meddled with a watch in his life—that there were men skilled in the art, whose business it was to attend to those matters; but for his part, he should only mar the workmanship and put the whole in confusion—"Why, harkee, master of mine," cried Peter, turning suddenly upon him, with a countenance that almost petrified the patcher of shoes into a perfect lapstone—"dost thou pretend to meddle with the movements of government—to regulate, and correct, and patch, and cobble a complicated machine, the principles of which are above thy comprehension, and its simplest operations too subtle for thy understanding, when thou canst not correct a trifling error in a common piece of mechanism, the whole mystery of which is open to thy inspection?—Hence with thee to the leather and stone, which are emblems of thy head; cobble thy shoes, and confine thyself to the vocation for which Heaven has fitted thee—but," elevating his voice until it made the welkin ring, "if ever I catch thee, or any of thy tribe, meddling again with affairs of government, by St. Nicholas, but I'll have every mother's bastard of ye flay'd alive, and your hides stretched for drum-heads, that ye may thenceforth make a noise to some purpose!"

This threat, and the tremendous voice in which it was uttered, caused the whole multitude to quake with fear. The hair of the orator rose on his head like his own swine's bristles, and not a knight of the thimble present but his heart died within him, and he felt as though he could have verily escaped through the eye of a needle. The assembly dispersed in silent consternation; the pseudo statesmen who had hitherto undertaken to regulate public affairs were now fain to stay at home, hold their tongues, and take care of their families; and party feuds died away to such a degree, that many thriving keepers of taverns and dram-shops were utterly ruined for want of business. But though this measure produced the desired effect in putting an extinguisher on the new lights just brightening up: yet did it tend to injure the popularity of the Great Peter with the thinking part of the community: that is to say, that part which think for others instead of for themselves; or, in other words, who attend to every body's business but their own. These accused the old governor of being highly aristocratical, and in truth there seems to have been some ground for such an accusation; for he carried himself with a lofty soldier-like air, and was somewhat particular in his dress, appearing, when not in uniform, in rich apparel of the antique flaundrish cut, and was especially noted for having his sound leg (which was a very comely one) always arrayed in a red stocking and high-heeled shoe.

Justice he often dispensed in the primitive patriarchal way, seated on the "stoep" before his door, under the shade of a great button-wood tree; but all visits of form and state were received with something of court ceremony in the best parlor; where Antony the Trumpeter officiated as high chamberlain. On public occasions he appeared with great pomp of equipage, and always rode to church in a yellow wagon with flaming red wheels.

These symptoms of state and ceremony, as we have hinted, were much cavilled at by the thinking (and talking) part of the community. They had been accustomed to find easy access to their former governors, and in particular had lived on terms of extreme intimacy with William the Testy, and they accused Peter Stuyvesant of assuming too much dignity and reserve, and of wrapping himself in mystery. Others, however, have pretended to discover in all this a shrewd policy on the part of the old governor. It is certainly of the first importance, say they, that a country should be governed by wise men: but then it is almost equally important that the people should think them wise; for this belief alone can produce willing subordination. To keep up, however, this desirable confidence in rulers, the people should be allowed to see as little of them as possible. It is the mystery which envelopes great men, that gives them half their greatness. There is a kind of superstitious reverence for office which leads us to exaggerate the merits of the occupant; and to suppose that he must be wiser than common men. He, however, who gains access to cabinets, soon finds out by what foolishness the world is governed. He finds that there is quackery in legislation as in everything else; that rulers have their whims and errors as well as other men, and are not so wonderfully superior as he had imagined, since even he may occasionally confute them in argument. Thus awe subsides into confidence, confidence inspires familiarity, and familiarity produces contempt. Such was the case, say they, with William the Testy. By making himself too easy of access he enabled every scrub-politician to measure wits with him, and to find out the true dimensions not only of his person but of his mind: and thus it was that, by being familiarly scanned, he was discovered to be a very little man. Peter Stuyvesant, on the contrary, say they, by conducting himself with dignity and loftiness, was looked up to with great reverence. As he never gave his reasons for anything he did, the public gave him credit for very profound ones; every movement, however intrinsically unimportant, was a matter of speculation; and his very red stockings excited some respect as being different from the stockings of other men.

Another charge against Peter Stuyvesant was that he had a great leaning in favor of the patricians: and indeed in his time rose many of those mighty Dutch families which have taken such vigorous root, and branched out so luxuriantly in our State. Some, to be sure, were of earlier date, such as the Van Kortlandts, the Van Zandts, the Ten Broecks, the Harden Broecks, and others of Pavonian renown, who gloried in the title' of "Discoverers," from having been engaged in the nautical expedition from Communipaw, in which they so heroically braved the terrors of Hell-gate and Buttermilk-channel, and discovered a site for New Amsterdam.

Others claimed to themselves the appellation of Conquerors, from their gallant achievements in New Sweden and their victory over the Yankees at Oyster Bay. Such was that list of warlike worthies heretofore enumerated, beginning with the Van Wycks, the Van Dycks, and the Ten Eycks, and extending to the Rutgers, the Bensons, the Brinkerhoffs, and the Schermerhorns; a roll equal to the Doomsday Book of William the Conqueror, and establishing the heroic origin of many an ancient aristocratical Dutch family. These, after all, are the only legitimate nobility and lords of the soil; these are the real "beavers of the Manhattoes;" and much does it grieve me in modern days to see them elbowed aside by foreign invaders, and more especially by those ingenious people, "the Sons of the Pilgrims;" who out-bargain them in the market, out-speculate them on the exchange, out-top them in fortune, and run up mushroom palaces so high, that the tallest Dutch family mansion has not wind enough left for its weather-cock.

In the proud days of Peter Stuyvesant, however, the good old Dutch aristocracy loomed out in all its grandeur. The burly burgher, in round-crowned flaundrish hat with brim of vast circumference; in portly gabardine and bulbous multiplicity of breeches, sat on his "stoep" and smoked his pipe in lordly silence, nor did it ever enter his brain that the active, restless

Yankee, whom he saw through his half-shut eyes worrying about in dog-day heat, ever intent on the main chance, was one day to usurp control over these goodly Dutch domains. Already, however, the races regarded each other with disparaging eye. The Yankees sneeringly spoke of the round-crowned burghers of the Manhattoes as the "Copperheads;" while the latter, glorying in their own nether rotundity, and observing the slack galligaskins of their rivals, flapping like an empty sail against the mast, retorted upon them with the opprobrious appellation of "Platter-breeches."

CHAPTER II.

How Peter Stuyvesant Labored to Civilize the Community—How He Was a Great Promoter of Holidays—How He Instituted Kissing on New Year's Day—How He Distributed Fiddles Throughout the New Netherlands—How He Ventured to Reform the Ladies' Petticoats, and How He Caught a Tartar.

From what I have recounted in the foregoing chapter I would not have it imagined that the great Peter was a tyrannical potentate, ruling with a rod of iron. On the contrary, where the dignity of office permitted he abounded in generosity and condescension. If he refused the brawling multitude the right of misrule, he at least endeavored to rule them in righteousness. To spread abundance in the land, he obliged the bakers to give thirteen loaves to the dozen—a golden rule which remains a monument of his beneficence. So far from indulging in unreasonable austerity, he delighted to see the poor and the laboring man rejoice; and for this purpose he was a great promoter of holidays. Under his reign there was a great cracking of eggs at Paas or Easter; Whitsuntide or Pinxter also flourished in all its bloom; and never were stockings better filled on the eve of the blessed St. Nicholas.

New Year's day, however, was his favorite festival, and was ushered in by the ringing of bells and firing of guns. On that genial day the fountains of hospitality were broken up, and the whole community was deluged with cherry-brandy, true Hollands, and mulled cider; every house was a temple to the jolly god; and many a provident vagabond got drunk out of pure economy, taking in liquor enough gratis to serve him half a year afterwards.

The great assemblage, however, was at the governor's house, whither repaired all the burghers of New Amsterdam with their wives and daughters, pranked out in their best attire. On this occasion the good Peter was devoutly observant of the pious Dutch rite of kissing the women-kind for a happy New Year; and it is traditional that Antony the Trumpeter, who acted as gentleman usher, took toll of all who were young and handsome, as they passed through the ante-chamber. This venerable custom, thus happily introduced, was followed with such zeal by high and low, that on New Year's day, during the reign of Peter Stuyvesant, New Amsterdam was the most thoroughly be-kissed community in all Christendom.

Another great measure of Peter Stuyvesant for public improvement was the distribution of fiddles throughout the land. These were placed in the hands of veteran negroes, who were despatched as missionaries to every part of the province. This measure, it is said, was first suggested by Antony the Trumpeter; and the effect was marvellous. Instead of those "indignation meetings" set on foot in the time of William the Testy, where men met together to rail at public abuses, groan over the evils of the times, and make each other miserable, there were joyous gatherings of the two sexes to dance and make merry. Now were instituted "quilting bees," and "husking bees," and other rural assemblages, where, under the inspiring influence of the fiddle, toil was enlivened by gayety and followed up by the dance. "Raising bees" also were frequent, where houses sprang up at the wagging of the fiddle-stick, as the walls of Thebes sprang up of yore to the sound of the lyre of Amphion.

Jolly autumn, which pours its treasures over hill and dale, was in those days a season for the lifting of the heel as well as the heart; labor came dancing in the train of abundance, and frolic prevailed throughout the land. Happy days! when the yeomanry of the Nieuw Nederlands were merry rather than wise; and when the notes of the fiddle, those harbingers of good humor and good will, resounded at the close of the day from every hamlet along the Hudson!

Nor was it in rural communities alone that Peter Stuyvesant introduced his favorite engine of civilization. Under his rule the fiddle acquired that potent sway in New Amsterdam which it has ever since retained. Weekly assemblages were held, not in heated ball-rooms at midnight hours, but on Saturday afternoons, by the golden light of the sun, on the green lawn of the battery; with Antony the Trumpeter for master of ceremonies. Here would the good Peter take his seat under the spreading trees, among the old burghers and their wives, and watch the mazes of the dance. Here would he smoke his pipe, crack his joke, and forget the rugged toils of war, in the sweet oblivious festivities of peace, giving a nod of approbation to those of the young men who shuffled and kicked most vigorously; and, now and then a hearty smack, in all honesty of soul, to the buxom lass who held out longest, and tired down every competitor, infallible proof of her being the best dancer.

Once it is true the harmony of these meetings was in danger of interruption. A young belle just returned from a visit to Holland, who of course led the fashions, made her appearance in not more than half a dozen petticoats, and these of alarming shortness. A whisper and a flutter ran through the assembly. The young men of course were lost in admiration, but the old ladies were shocked in the extreme, especially those who had marriageable daughters; the young ladies blushed and felt excessively for the "poor thing," and even the governor himself appeared to be in some kind of perturbation.

To complete the confusion of the good folks she undertook, in the course of a jig, to describe some figures in algebra taught her by a dancing-master at Rotterdam. Unfortunately, at the highest flourish of her feet some vagabond zephyr obtruded his services, and a display of the graces took place, at which all the ladies present were thrown into great consternation; several grave country members were not a little moved, and the good Peter Stuyvesant himself was grievously scandalized.

The shortness of the female dresses, which had continued in fashion ever since the days of William Kieft, had long offended his eye; and though extremely averse to meddling with the petticoats of the ladies, yet he immediately recommended that every one should be furnished with a flounce to the bottom. He likewise ordered that the ladies, and indeed the gentlemen, should use no other step in dancing than "shuffle and turn," and "double trouble;" and forbade, under pain of his high displeasure, any young lady thenceforth to attempt what was termed "exhibiting the graces."

These were the only restrictions he ever imposed upon the sex, and these were considered by them as tyrannical oppressions, and resisted with that becoming spirit manifested by the gentle sex whenever their privileges are invaded. In fact, Antony Van Corlear, who, as has been shown, was a sagacious man, experienced in the ways of women, took a private occasion to intimate to the governor that a conspiracy was forming among the young vrouws of New Amsterdam; and that, if the matter were pushed any further, there was danger of their leaving off petticoats altogether; whereupon the good Peter shrugged his shoulders, dropped the subject, and ever after suffered the women to wear their petticoats and cut their capers as high as they pleased; a privilege which they have jealously maintained in the Manhattoes unto the present day.

CHAPTER III.

How the Yankees Secretly Sought the Aid of the British Cabinet in Their Hostile Schemes Against the Manhattoes.

Now so it happened that while the great and good Peter Stuyvesant, followed by his trusty squire, was making his chivalric progress through the East Country, a dark and direful scheme of war against his beloved province was forming in that nursery of monstrous projects, the British Cabinet.

This, we are confidently informed, was the result of the secret instigations of the great council of the league; who, finding themselves totally incompetent to vie in arms with the heavy-sterned warriors of the Manhattoes and their iron-headed commander, sent emissaries to the British government, setting forth in eloquent language the wonders and delights of this delicious little Dutch Canaan, and imploring that a force might be sent out to invade it by sea, while they should co-operate by land.

These emissaries arrived at a critical juncture, just as the British Lion was beginning to bristle up his mane and wag his tail; for we are assured by the anonymous writer of the Stuyvesant manuscript, that the astounding victory of Peter Stuyvesant at Fort Christina had resounded throughout Europe; and his annexation of the territory of New Sweden had awakened the jealousy of the British cabinet for their wild lands at the South. This jealousy was brought to a head by the representations of Lord Baltimore, who declared that the territory thus annexed lay within the lands granted to him by the British crown, and he claimed to be protected in his rights. Lord Sterling, another British subject, claimed the hole of Nassau or Long Island, once the Ophir of William the Testy, but now the kitchen-garden of the Manhattoes, which he declared to be British territory by the right of discovery, but unjustly usurped by the Nederlanders.

The result of all these rumors and representations was a sudden zeal on the part of his majesty Charles the Second, for the safety and well-being of his transatlantic possessions, and especially for the recovery of the New Netherlands, which Yankee logic had, somehow or other, proved to be a continuity of the territory taken possession of for the British crown by the Pilgrims, when they landed on Plymouth rock, fugitives from British oppression. All this goodly land, thus wrongfully held by the Dutchmen, he presented, in a fit of affection, to his brother the Duke of York: a donation truly royal, since none but great sovereigns have a right to give away what does not belong to them. That this munificent gift might not be merely nominal, his majesty ordered that an armament should be straightway despatched to invade the city of New Amsterdam by land and water, and put his brother in complete possession of the premises.

Thus critically situated are the affairs of the New Netherlanders. While the honest burghers are smoking their pipes in sober security, and the privy councillors are snoring in the council chamber; while Peter the Headstrong is undauntedly making his way through the East Country in the confident hope by honest words and manly deeds to bring the grand council to terms, a hostile fleet is sweeping like a thunder cloud across the Atlantic, soon to rattle a storm of war about the ears of the dozing Nederlanders, and to put the mettle of their governor to the trial.

But come what may, I here pledge my veracity, that in all warlike conflicts and doubtful perplexities, he will ever acquit himself like a gallant, noble-minded, obstinate old cavalier.—Forward then to the charge! Shine out, propitious stars, on the renowned city of the Manhattoes; and the blessing of St. Nicholas go with thee—honest Peter Stuyvesant.

CHAPTER IV.

How the People of New Amsterdam Were Thrown Into a Great Panic, by the News of the Threatened Invasion, and the Manner in Which They Fortified Themselves.

There is no sight more truly interesting to a philosopher than a community, where every individual has a voice in public affairs; where every individual considers himself the Atlas of the nation; and where every individual thinks it his duty to bestir himself for the good of his country—I say, there is nothing more interesting to a philosopher than such a community in a sudden bustle of war. Such clamor of tongues—such patriotic bawling—such running hither and thither—everybody in a hurry—everybody in trouble—everybody in the way, and everybody interrupting his neighbor—who is busily employed in doing nothing! It is like witnessing a great fire, where the whole community are agog—some dragging about empty engines—others scampering with full buckets, and spilling the contents into their neighbors' boots—and others ringing the church bells all night, by way of putting out the fire. Little firemen—like sturdy little knights storming a breach, clambering up and down scaling-ladders, and bawling through tin trumpets, by way of directing the attack.—Here a fellow, in his great zeal to save the property of the unfortunate, catches up an anonymous chamber utensil, and gallants it off with an air of as much self-importance as if he had rescued a pot of money—there another throws looking-glasses and china out of the window, to save them from the flames—whilst those who can do nothing else run up and down the streets, keeping up an incessant cry of *Fire! Fire! Fire!*

"When the news arrived at Sinope," says Lucian—though I own the story is rather trite—"that Philip was about to attack them, the inhabitants were thrown into a violent alarm. Some ran to furbish up their arms; others rolled stones to build up the walls—everybody, in short, was employed, and everybody in the way of his neighbor. Diogenes alone could find nothing to do—whereupon, not to be idle when the welfare of his country was at stake, he tucked up his robe, and fell to rolling his tub with might and main up and down the Gymnasium." In like manner did every mother's son in the patriotic community of New Amsterdam, on receiving the missives of Peter Stuyvesant, busy himself most mightily in putting things in confusion, and assisting the general uproar. "Every man"—saith the Stuyvesant manuscript—"flew to arms!"—by which is meant, that not one of our honest Dutch citizens would venture to church or to market without an old-fashioned spit of a sword dangling at his side, and a long Dutch fowling-piece on his shoulder—nor would he go out of a night without a lantern; nor turn a corner without first peeping cautiously round, lest he should come unawares upon a British army;—and we are informed that Stoffel Brinkerhoff, who was considered by the old women almost as brave a man as the governor himself, actually had two one-pound swivels mounted in his entry, one pointing out at the front door, and the other at the back.

But the most strenuous measure resorted to on this awful occasion, and one which has since been found of wonderful efficacy, was to assemble popular meetings. These brawling convocations, I have already shown, were extremely offensive to Peter Stuyvesant; but as this was a moment of unusual agitation, and as the old governor was not present to repress them, they broke out with intolerable violence. Hither, therefore, the orators and politicians repaired; striving who should bawl loudest, and exceed the others in hyperbolical bursts of patriotism, and in resolutions to uphold and defend the government. In these sage meetings it was resolved that they were the most enlightened, the most dignified, the most formidable, and the most ancient community upon the face of the earth. This resolution being carried unanimously, another was immediately proposed—whether it were not possible and politic to exterminate Great Britain? upon which sixty-nine members spoke in the affirmative, and only one rose to suggest some doubts—who, as a punishment for his treasonable presumption, was immediately seized by the mob, and tarred and feathered—which punishment being equivalent to the Tarpeian Rock, he was afterwards considered as an outcast from society, and his opinion went for nothing. The question, therefore, being unanimously carried in the affirmative, it was recommended to the grand council to pass it into a law; which was accordingly done. By this measure the hearts of the people at large were wonderfully encouraged, and they waxed exceeding choleric and valorous. Indeed, the first paroxysm of alarm having in some measure subsided—the old women having buried all the money they could lay their hands on, and their husbands daily getting fuddled with what was left—the community began even to stand on the offensive. Songs were manufactured in Low Dutch and sung about the streets, wherein the English were most wofully beaten, and shown no quarter; and popular addresses were made, wherein it was proved to a certainty that the fate of Old England depended upon the will of the New Amsterdammers.

Finally, to strike a violent blow at the very vitals of Great Britain, a multitude of the wiser inhabitants assembled, and having purchased all the British manufactures they could find, they made thereof a huge bonfire; and, in the patriotic glow of the moment, every man present, who had a hat or breeches of English workmanship, pulled it off, and threw it into the flames—to the irreparable detriment, loss, and ruin, of the English manufacturers. In commemoration of this great exploit, they erected a pole on the spot, with a device on the top intended to represent the province of Nieuw Nederlands destroying Great Britain, under the similitude of an Eagle picking the little Island of Old England out of the globe; but either through the unskilfulness of the sculptor, or his ill-timed waggery, it bore a striking resemblance to a goose, vainly striving to get hold of a dumpling.

CHAPTER V.

How the Grand Council of the New Netherlands Were Miraculously Gifted with Long Tongues in the Moment of Emergency—Showing the Value of Words in Warfare.

It will need but little penetration in any one conversant with the ways of that wise but windy potentate, the sovereign people, to discover that notwithstanding all the warlike bluster and bustle of the last chapter, the city of New Amsterdam was not a whit more prepared for war than before. The privy councillors of Peter Stuyvesant were aware of this; and, having received his private orders to put the city in an immediate posture of defence, they called a meeting of the oldest and richest burghers to assist them with their wisdom.

These were that order of citizens commonly termed "men of the greatest weight in the community;" their weight being estimated by the heaviness of their heads and of their purses. Their wisdom in fact is apt to be of a ponderous kind, and to hang like a millstone round the neck of the community.

Two things were unanimously determined in this assembly of venerables: First, that the city required to be put in a state of defence; and Second, that, as the danger was imminent, there should be no time lost: which points being settled, they fell to making long speeches and belaboring one another in endless and intemperate disputes. For about this time was this unhappy city first visited by that talking endemic, so prevalent in this country, and which so invariably evinces itself, wherever a number of wise men assemble together; breaking out in long, windy speeches; caused, as physicians suppose, by the foul air which is ever generated in a crowd. Now it was, moreover, that they first introduced the ingenious method of measuring the merits of an harangue by the hour-glass; he being considered the ablest orator who spoke longest on a question. For which excellent invention, it is recorded, we are indebted to the same profound Dutch critic who judged of books by their size.

This sudden passion for endless harangues, so little consonant with the customary gravity and taciturnity of our sage forefathers, was supposed by certain philosophers to have been imbibed, together with divers others barbarous propensities, from their savage neighbors; who were peculiarly noted for *long talks* and *council fires,* and never undertook any affair of the least importance, without previous debates and harangues among their chiefs and *old men.* But the real cause was, that the people, in electing their representatives to the grand council, were particular in choosing them for their talents at talking, without inquiring whether they possessed the more rare, difficult, and ofttimes important talent of holding their tongues. The consequence was, that this deliberative body was composed of the most loquacious men in the community. As they considered themselves placed there to talk, every man concluded that his duty to his constituents, and, what is more, his popularity with them, required that he should harangue on every subject, whether he understood it or not. There was an ancient mode of burying a chieftain, by every soldier throwing his shield full of earth on the corpse, until a mighty mound was formed; so whenever a question was brought forward in this assembly, every member pressing forward to throw on his quantum of wisdom, the subject was quickly buried under a mountain of words.

We are told, that disciples on entering the school of Pythagoras, were for two years enjoined silence, and forbidden either to ask questions, or make remarks. After they had thus acquired the inestimable art of holding their tongues, they were gradually permitted to make inquiries, and finally to communicate their own opinions.

With what a beneficial effect could this wise regulation of Pythagoras be introduced in modern legislative bodies—and how wonderfully would it have tended to expedite business in the grand council of the Manhattoes!

At this perilous juncture the fatal word economy, the stumbling-block of William the Testy, had been once more set afloat, according to which the cheapest plan of defence was insisted upon as the best; it being deemed a great stroke of policy in furnishing powder to economize in ball.

Thus did dame Wisdom (whom the wags of antiquity have humorously personified as a woman), seem to take a mischievous pleasure in jilting the venerable councillors of New Amsterdam. To add to the confusion, the old factions of Short Pipes and Long Pipes, which had been almost strangled by the herculean grasp of Peter Stuyvesant, now sprang up with tenfold vigor. Whatever was proposed by a Short Pipe was opposed by the whole tribe of Long Pipes, who, like true partisans, deemed it their first duty to effect the downfall of their rivals; their second to elevate themselves, and their third, to consult the public good; though many left the third consideration out of question altogether.

In this great collision of hard heads it is astonishing the number of projects that were struck out; projects which threw the windmill system of William the Testy completely in the background. These were almost uniformly opposed by the "men of the greatest weight in the community!" your weighty men, though slow to devise, being always great at "negativing." Among these were a set of fat, self-important old burghers, who smoked their pipes, and said nothing except to negative every plan of defence proposed. These were that class of "conservatives," who, having amassed a fortune, button up their pockets, shut their mouths, sink, as it were, into themselves, and pass the rest of their lives in the indwelling beatitude of conscious wealth; as some phlegmatic oyster, having swallowed a pearl, closes its shell, sinks in the mud, and devotes the rest of its life to the conservation of its treasure. Every plan of defence seemed to these worthy old gentlemen pregnant with ruin. An armed force was a legion of locusts, preying upon the public property—to fit out a naval armament was to throw their money into the sea—to build fortifications was to bury it in the dirt. In short, they settled it as a sovereign maxim, so long as their pockets were full, no matter how much they were drubbed:— A kick left no scar—a broken head cured itself—but an empty purse was of all maladies the slowest to heal, and one in which nature did nothing for the patient.

Thus did this venerable assembly of sages lavish away that time which the urgency of affairs rendered invaluable, in empty brawls and long-winded speeches, without ever agreeing, except on the point with which they started, namely, that there was no time to be lost, and delay was ruinous. At length, St. Nicholas taking compassion on their distracted situation, and anxious to preserve them from anarchy, so ordered, that in the midst of one of their most noisy debates on the subject of fortification and defence, when they had nearly fallen to loggerheads in consequence of not being able to convince each other, the question was happily settled by the sudden entrance of a messenger, who informed them that a hostile fleet had arrived, and was actually advancing up the bay!

CHAPTER VI.

In Which the Troubles of New Amsterdam Appear to Thicken —Showing the Bravery, in Time of Peril, of a People Who Defend Themselves by Resolutions.

Like as an assemblage of belligerent cats, gibbering and caterwauling; eying one another with hideous grimaces and contortions; spitting in each other's faces, and on the point of a general clapper-clawing, are suddenly put to scampering rout and confusion by the appearance of a house-dog; so was the no less vociferous council of New Amsterdam amazed, astounded, and totally dispersed, by the sudden arrival of the enemy. Every member waddled home as fast as his short legs could carry him, wheezing as he went with corpulency and terror. Arrived at his castle, he barricaded the street-door, and buried himself in the cider-cellar, without venturing to peep out, lest he should have his head carried off by a cannon ball.

The sovereign people crowded into the market-place, herding together with the instinct of sheep, who seek safety in each other's company, when the shepherd and his dog are absent, and the wolf is prowling round the fold. Far from finding relief, however, they only increased each other's terrors. Each man looked ruefully in his neighbor's face, in search of encouragement, but only found in its wobegone lineaments a confirmation of his own dismay. Not a word now was to be heard of conquering Great Britain, not a whisper about the sovereign virtues of economy—while the old women heightened the general gloom by clamorously bewailing their fate, and calling for protection on St. Nicholas and Peter Stuyvesant.

Oh, how did they bewail the absence of the lion-hearted Peter!—and how did they long for the comforting presence of Antony Van Corlear! Indeed a gloomy uncertainty hung over the fate of these adventurous heroes. Day after day had elapsed since the alarming message from the governor, without bringing any further tidings of his safety. Many a fearful conjecture was hazarded as to what had befallen him and his loyal squire. Had they not been devoured alive by the cannibals of Marblehead and Cape Cod?—Had they not been put to the question by the great council of Amphictyons?—Had they not been smothered in onions by the terrible men of Pyquag?—In the midst of this consternation, and perplexity, when horror, like a mighty nightmare, sat brooding upon the little, fat, plethoric city of New Amsterdam, the ears of the multitude were suddenly startled by the distant sound of a trumpet —it approached—it grew louder and louder—and now it resounded at the city gate. The public could not be mistaken in the well-known sound—a shout of joy burst from their lips, as the gallant Peter, covered with dust, and followed by his faithful trumpeter, came galloping into the market-place.

The first transports of the populace having subsided, they gathered round the honest Antony, as he dismounted, overwhelming him with greetings and congratulations. In breathless accents he related to them the marvellous adventures through which the old governor and himself had gone, in making their escape from the clutches of the terrible Amphictyons. But though the Stuyvesant manuscript, with its customary minuteness where anything touching the great Peter is concerned, is very particular as to the incidents of this masterly retreat, the state of the public affairs will not allow me to indulge in a full recital thereof. Let it suffice to say, that, while Peter Stuyvesant was anxiously revolving in his mind how he could make good his escape with honor and dignity, certain of the ships sent out for the conquest of the Manhattoes touched at the Eastern ports to obtain supplies, and to call on the grand council of the league for its promised co-operation. Upon hearing of this, the vigilant Peter, perceiving that a moment's delay were fatal, made a secret and precipitate decampment; though much did it grieve his lofty soul to be obliged to turn his back even upon a nation of foes. Many hair-breadth 'scapes and divers perilous mishaps did they sustain, as they scoured, without sound of trumpet, through the fair regions of the East. Already was the country in an uproar with hostile preparation, and they were obliged to take a large circuit in their flight, lurking along through the woody mountains of the Devil's backbone; whence the valiant Peter sallied forth one day like a lion, and put to rout a whole legion of squatters, consisting of three generations of a prolific family, who were already on their way to take possession of some corner of the New Netherlands. Nay, the faithful Antony had great difficulty, at sundry times, to prevent him, in the excess of his wrath, from descending down from the mountains, and falling, sword in hand, upon certain of the border-towns, who were marshalling forth their draggle-tailed militia.

The first movement of the governor, on reaching his dwelling, was to mount the roof, whence he contemplated with rueful aspect the hostile squadron. This had already come to anchor in the bay, and consisted of two stout frigates, having on board, as John Josselyn, gent., informs us, "three hundred valiant redcoats." Having taken this survey, he sat himself down and wrote an epistle to the commander, demanding the reason of his anchoring in the harbor without obtaining previous permission so to do. This letter was couched in the most dignified and courteous terms, though I have it from undoubted authority that his teeth were clinched, and he had a bitter sardonic grin upon his visage all the while he wrote. Having despatched his letter, the grim Peter stumped to and fro about the town with a most war-betokening countenance, his hands thrust into his breeches pockets, and whistling a Low Dutch psalm-tune, which bore no small resemblance to the music of a northeast wind when a storm is brewing. The very dogs as they eyed him skulked away in dismay; while all the old and ugly women of New Amsterdam ran howling at his heels, imploring him to save them from murder, robbery, and pitiless ravishment!

The reply of Colonel Nicholas, who commanded the invaders, was couched in terms of equal courtesy with the letter of the governor; declaring the right and title of his British Majesty to the province; where he affirmed the Dutch to be mere interlopers; and demanding that the town, forts, etc., should be forthwith rendered into his majesty's obedience and protection; promising, at the same time, life, liberty, estate, and free trade, to every Dutch denizen who should readily submit to his majesty's government.

Peter Stuyvesant read over this friendly epistle with some such harmony of aspect as we may suppose a crusty farmer reads the loving letter of John Stiles, warning him of an action of ejectment. He was not, however, to be taken by surprise; but, thrusting the summons into his breeches pocket, stalked three times across the room, took a pinch of snuff with great vehemence, and then, loftily waving his hand, promised to send an answer the next morning. He now summoned a general meeting of his privy councillors and burgomasters, not to ask their advice, for, confident in his own strong head, he needed no man's counsel, but apparently to give them a piece of his mind on their late craven conduct.

His orders being duly promulgated, it was a piteous sight to behold the late valiant burgomasters, who had demolished the whole British empire in their harangues, peeping ruefully out of their hiding places; crawling cautiously forth; dodging through narrow lanes and alleys; starting at every little dog that barked; mistaking lamp-posts for British grenadiers; and, in the excess of their panic, metamorphosing pumps into formidable soldiers, levelling blunderbusses at their bosoms! Having, however, in despite of numerous perils and difficulties of the kind, arrived safe, without the loss of a single man, at the hall of assembly, they took their seats, and awaited in fearful silence the arrival of the governor. In a few moments the wooden leg of the intrepid Peter was heard in regular and stout-hearted thumps upon the staircase. He entered the chamber, arrayed in full suit of regimentals, and carrying his trusty toledo, not girded on his thigh, but tucked under his arm. As the governor never equipped himself in this portentous manner unless something of martial nature were working within his pericranium, his council regarded him ruefully, as if they saw fire and sword in his iron countenance, and forgot to light their pipes in breathless suspense.

His first words were to rate his council soundly for having wasted in idle debate and party feud the time which should have been devoted to putting the city in a state of defence. He was particularly indignant at those brawlers who had disgraced the councils of the province by empty bickerings and scurrilous invectives against an absent enemy. He now called upon them to make good their words by deeds, as the enemy they had defied and derided was at the gate. Finally, he informed them of the summons he had received to surrender, but concluded by swearing to defend the province as long as Heaven was on his side and he had a wooden leg to stand upon; which warlike sentence he emphasized by a thwack with the flat of his sword upon the table, that quite electrified his auditors.

The privy councillors, who had long since been brought into as perfect discipline as were ever the soldiers of the great Frederick, knew there was no use in saying a word—so lighted their pipes, and smoked away in silence, like fat and discreet councillors. But the burgomasters, being inflated with considerable importance and self-sufficiency, acquired at popular meetings, were not so easily satisfied. Mustering up fresh spirit, when they found there was some chance of escaping from their present jeopardy without the disagreeable alternative of fighting, they requested a copy of the summons to surrender, that they might show it to a general meeting of the people.

So insolent and mutinous a request would have been enough to have roused the gorge of the tranquil Van Twiller himself—what then must have been its effect upon the great Stuyvesant, who was not only a Dutchman, a governor, and a valiant wooden-legged soldier to boot, but withal a man of the most stomachful and gunpowder disposition? He burst forth into a blaze of indignation,—swore not a mother's son of them should see a syllable of it—that as to their advice or concurrence, he did not care a whiff of tobacco for either—that they might go home, and go to bed like old women; for he was determined to defend the colony himself, without the assistance of them or their adherents! So saying, he tucked his sword under his arm, cocked his hat upon his head, and girding up his loins, stumped indignantly out of the council-chamber—everybody making room for him as he passed.

No sooner was he gone than the busy burgomasters called a public meeting in front of the Stadt-house, where they appointed as chairman one Dofue Roerback, formerly a meddlesome member of the cabinet during the reign of William the Testy, but kicked out of office by Peter Stuyvesant on taking the reins of government. He was, withal, a mighty gingerbread baker in the land, and reverenced by the populace as a man of dark knowledge, seeing that he was the first to imprint New Year cakes with the mysterious hieroglyphics of the Cock and Breeches, and such like magical devices.

This burgomaster, who still chewed the cud of ill-will against Peter Stuyvesant, addressed the multitude in what is called a patriotic speech, informing them of the courteous summons which the governor had received, to surrender; of his refusal to comply therewith, and of his denying the public even a sight of the summons, which doubtless contained conditions highly to the honor and advantage of the province.

He then proceeded to speak of his Excellency in high-sounding terms of vituperation, suited to the dignity of his station; comparing him to Nero, Caligula, and other flagrant great men of yore; assuring the people that the history of the world did not contain a despotic outrage equal to the present. That it would be recorded in letters of fire, on the blood-stained tablet of history! That ages would roll back with sudden horror when they came to view it! That the womb of time (by the way, your orators and writers take strange liberties with the womb of time, though some would fain have us believe that time is an old gentleman)—that the womb of time, pregnant as it was with direful horrors, would never produce a parallel enormity!—with a variety of other heart-rending, soul-stirring tropes and figures, which I cannot enumerate; neither, indeed, need I, for they were of the kind which even to the present day form the style of popular harangues and patriotic orations, and may be classed in rhetoric under the general title of RIGMAROLE.

The result of this speech of the inspired burgomaster was a memorial addressed to the governor, remonstrating in good round terms on his conduct. It was proposed that Dofue Roerback himself should be the bearer of this memorial, but this he warily declined, having no inclination of coming again within kicking distance of his Excellency. Who did deliver it has never been named in history, in which neglect he has suffered grievous wrong; seeing that he was equally worthy of blazon with him perpetuated in Scottish song and story by the surname of Bell-the-cat. All we know of the fate of this memorial is that it was used by the grim Peter to light his pipe; which, from the vehemence with which he smoked it, was evidently anything but a pipe of peace.

CHAPTER VII.

Containing a Doleful Disaster of Antony the Trumpeter—and How Peter Stuyvesant, Like a Second Cromwell, Suddenly Dissolved a Rump Parliament.

Now did the high-minded Pieter de Groodt shower down a pannier load of maledictions upon his burgomasters for a set of self-willed, obstinate, factious varlets, who would neither be convinced nor persuaded. Nor did he omit to bestow some left-handed compliments upon the sovereign people, as a herd of poltroons, who had no relish for the glorious hardships and illustrious misadventures of battle—but would rather stay at home, and eat and sleep in ignoble ease, than fight in a ditch for immortality and a broken head.

Resolutely bent, however, upon defending his beloved city, in despite even of itself, he called unto him his trusty Van Corlear, who was his right-hand man in all times of emergency. Him did he adjure to take his war-denouncing trumpet, and mounting his horse, to beat up the country night and day—sounding the alarm along the pastoral borders of the Bronx—startling the wild solitudes of Croton—arousing the rugged yeomanry of Weehawk and Hoboken—the mighty men of battle of Tappan Bay—and the brave boys of Tarry-Town, Petticoat-Lane, and Sleepy-Hollow—charging them one and all to sling their powder-horns, shoulder their fowling-pieces, and march merrily down to the Manhattoes.

Now there was nothing in all the world, the divine sex excepted, that Antony Van Corlear loved better than errands of this kind. So just stopping to take a lusty dinner, and bracing to his side his junk bottle, well charged with heart-inspiring Hollands, he issued jollily from the city gate, which looked out upon what is at present called Broadway; sounding a farewell strain, that rung in sprightly echoes through the winding streets of New Amsterdam—Alas! never more were they to be gladdened by the melody of their favorite trumpeter!

It was a dark and stormy night when the good Antony arrived at the creek (sagely denominated Haerlem *river*) which separates the island of Mannahata from the mainland. The wind was high, the elements were in an uproar, and no Charon could be found to ferry the adventurous sounder of brass across the water. For a short time he vapored like an impatient ghost upon the brink, and then bethinking himself of the urgency of his errand took a hearty embrace of his stone bottle, swore most valorously that he would swim across in spite of the devil! (Spyt den Duyvel,) and daringly plunged into the stream. Luckless Antony! scarce had he buffeted half-way over, when he was observed to struggle violently, as if battling with the spirit of the waters—instinctively he put his trumpet to his mouth, and giving a vehement blast—sank forever to the bottom!

The clangor of his trumpet, like that of the ivory horn of the renowned Paladin Orlando, when expiring in the glorious field of Roncesvalles, rang far and wide through the country, alarming the neighbors round, who hurried in amazement to the spot. Here an old Dutch burgher, famed for his veracity, and who had been a witness of the fact, related to them the melancholy affair; with the fearful addition (to which I am slow of giving belief) that he saw the duyvel, in the shape of a huge moss-bonker, seize the sturdy Antony by the leg, and drag him beneath the waves. Certain it is, the place, with the adjoining promontory, which projects into the Hudson, has been called *Spyt den Duyvel* ever since—the ghost of the unfortunate Antony still haunts the surrounding solitudes, and his trumpet has often been heard by the neighbors, of a stormy night, mingling with the howling of the blast. Nobody ever attempts to swim across the creek after dark; on the contrary, a bridge has been built to guard against such melancholy accidents in future—and as to moss-bonkers, they are held in such abhorrence, that no true Dutchman will admit them to his table, who loves good fish and hates the devil.

Such was the end of Antony Van Corlear—a man deserving of a better fate. He lived roundly and soundly, like a true and jolly bachelor, until the day of his death; but though he was never married, yet did he leave behind some two or three dozen children, in different parts of the country—fine, chubby, brawling, flatulent little urchins; from whom, if legends speak true, (and they are not apt to lie,) did descend the innumerable race of editors, who people and defend this country, and who are bountifully paid by the people for keeping up a constant alarm—and making them miserable. It is hinted, too, that in his various expeditions into the East he did much towards promoting the population of the country; in proof of which is adduced the notorious propensity of the people of those parts to sound their own trumpet.

As some way-worn pilgrim, when the tempest whistles through his locks and night is gathering round, beholds his faithful dog, the companion and solace of his journeying, stretched lifeless at his feet, so did the generous-hearted hero of the Manhattoes contemplate the untimely end of Antony Van Corlear. He had been the faithful attendant of his footsteps; he had charmed him in many a weary hour by his honest gayety and the martial melody of his trumpet, and had followed him with unflinching loyalty and affection through many a scene of direful peril and mishap. He was gone forever! and that, too, at a moment when every mongrel cur was skulking from his side. This—Peter Stuyvesant—was the moment to try thy fortitude; and this was the moment when thou didst indeed shine forth—Peter *the Headstrong!*

The glare of day had long dispelled the horrors of the stormy night; still all was dull and gloomy. The late jovial Apollo hid his face behind lugubrious clouds, peeping out now and then for an instant, as if anxious, yet fearful, to see what was going on in his favorite city. This was the eventful morning when the great Peter was to give his reply to the summons of the invaders. Already was he closeted with his privy counsel, sitting in grim state, brooding over the fate of his favorite trumpeter, and anon boiling with indignation as the insolence of his recreant burgomasters flashed upon his mind. While in this state of irritation, a courier arrived in all haste from Winthrop, the subtle governor of Connecticut, counselling him, in the most affectionate and disinterested manner, to surrender the province, and magnifying the dangers and calamities to which a refusal would subject him.—What a moment was this to intrude officious advice upon a man who never took advice in his whole life!—The fiery old governor strode up and down the chamber with a vehemence that made the bosoms of his councillors to quake with awe— railing at his unlucky fate, that thus made him the constant butt of factious subjects, and jesuitical advisers.

Just at this ill-chosen juncture, the officious burgomasters, who had heard of the arrival of mysterious despatches, came marching in a body into the room, with a legion of schepens and toad-eaters at their heels, and abruptly demanded a persual of the letter. This was too much for the spleen of Peter Stuyvesant. He tore the letter in a thousand pieces—threw it in the face of the nearest burgomaster—broke his pipe over the head of the next—hurled his spitting-box at an unlucky schepen, who was just retreating out at the door, and finally prorogued the whole meeting *sine die*, by kicking them down stairs with his wooden leg.

As soon as the burgomasters could recover from their confusion and had time to breathe, they called a public meeting, where they related at full length, and with appropriate coloring and exaggeration, the despotic and vindictive deportment of the governor; declaring that, for their own parts, they did not value a straw the being kicked, cuffed, and mauled by the timber toe of his excellency, but that they felt for the dignity of the sovereign people, thus rudely insulted by the outrage committed on the seat of honor of their representatives. The latter part of the harangue came home at once to that delicacy of feeling, and jealous pride of character, vested in all true mobs; who, though they may bear injuries without a murmur, yet are marvellously jealous of their sovereign dignity—and there is no knowing to what act of resentment they might have been provoked, had they not been somewhat more afraid of their sturdy old governor than they were of St. Nicholas, the English—or the d—l himself.

CHAPTER VIII.

How Peter Stuyvesant Defended the City of New Amsterdam for Several Days, by Dint of the Strength of His Head.

There is something exceedingly sublime and melancholy in the spectacle which the present crisis of our history presents. An illustrious and venerable little city—the metropolis of a vast extent of uninhabited country—garrisoned by a doughty host of orators, chairmen, committeemen, burgomasters, schepens, and old women—governed by a determined and strong-headed warrior, and fortified by mud batteries, palisadoes, and resolutions—blockaded by sea, beleaguered by land, and threatened with direful desolation from without; while its very vitals are torn with internal faction and commotion! Never did historic pen record a page of more complicated distress, unless it be the strife that distracted the Israelites during the siege of Jerusalem—where discordant parties were cutting each other's throats, at the moment when the victorious legions of Titus had toppled down their bulwarks, and were carrying fire and sword into the very sanctum sanctorum of the temple.

Governor Stuyvesant having triumphantly put his grand council to the rout, and delivered himself from a multitude of impertinent advisers, despatched a categorical reply to the commanders of the invading squadron; wherein he asserted the right and title of their High Mightinesses the Lords States General to the province of New Netherlands, and trusting in the righteousness of his cause, set the whole British nation at defiance!

My anxiety to extricate my readers and myself from these disastrous scenes prevents me from giving the whole of this gallant letter, which concluded in these manly and affectionate terms:

"As touching the threats in your conclusion, we have nothing to answer, only that we fear nothing but what God (who is as just as merciful) shall lay upon us; all things being in his gracious disposal, and we may as well be preserved by him with small forces as by a great army; which makes us to wish you all happiness and prosperity, and recommend you to his protection.— My lords, your thrice humble and affectionate servant and friend,

"P. STUYVESANT."

Thus having thrown his gauntlet, the brave Peter stuck a pair of horse-pistols in his belt, girded an immense powder-horn on his side—thrust his sound leg into a Hessian boot, and clapping his fierce little war-hat on the top of his head—paraded up and down in front of his house, determined to defend his beloved city to the last.

While all these struggles and dissensions were prevailing in the unhappy city of New Amsterdam, and while its worthy but ill-starred governor was framing the above-quoted letter, the English commanders did not remain idle. They had agents secretly employed to foment the fears and clamors of the

populace; and moreover circulated far and wide, through the adjacent
country, a proclamation, repeating the terms they had already held out in
their summons to surrender, at the same time beguiling the simple Nederlanders with the most crafty and conciliating professions. They promised that
every man who voluntarily submitted to the authority of his British Majesty
should retain peaceful possession of his house, his vrouw, and his cabbage-
garden. That he should be suffered to smoke his pipe, speak Dutch, wear as
many breeches as he pleased, and import bricks, tiles, and stone jugs from
Holland, instead of manufacturing them on the spot. That he should on no
account be compelled to learn the English language, nor eat codfish on Saturdays, nor keep accounts in any other way than by casting them upon his
fingers, and chalking them down upon the crown of his hat; as is observed
among the Dutch yeomanry at the present day. That every man should be
allowed quietly to inherit his father's hat, coat, shoe-buckles, pipe, and every
other personal appendage; and that no man should be obliged to conform to
any improvements, inventions, or any other modern innovations; but, on the
contrary, should be permitted to build his house, follow his trade, manage his
farm, rear his hogs, and educate his children, precisely as his ancestors had
done before him from time immemorial. Finally, that he should have all the
benefits of free trade, and should not be required to acknowledge any other
saint in the calendar than St. Nicholas, who should thenceforward, as before,
be considered the tutelar saint of the city.

These terms, as may be supposed, appeared very satisfactory to the people,
who had a great disposition to enjoy their property unmolested, and a most
singular aversion to engage in a contest, where they could gain little more
than honor and broken heads—the first of which they held in philosophic
indifference, the latter in utter detestation. By these insidious means, therefore, did the English succeed in alienating the confidence and affections of
the populace from their gallant old governor, whom they considered as
obstinately bent upon running them into hideous misadventures; and did not
hesitate to speak their minds freely, and abuse him most heartily—behind his
back.

Like as a mighty grampus, when assailed and buffeted by roaring waves
and brawling surges, still keeps on an undeviating course, rising above the
boisterous billows, spouting and blowing as he emerges—so did the inflexible
Peter pursue, unwavering, his determined career, and rise, contemptuous,
above the clamors of the rabble.

But when the British warriors found that he set their power at defiance,
they despatched recruiting officers to Jamaica and Jericho, and Nineveh, and
Quag, and Patchog, and all those towns on Long Island which had been
subdued of yore by Stoffel Brinkerhoff; stirring up the progeny of Preserved
Fish, and Determined Cock, and those other New England squatters, to assail
the city of New Amsterdam by land; while the hostile ships prepared for an
assault by water.

The streets of New Amsterdam now presented a scene of wild dismay and
consternation. In vain did Peter Stuyvesant order the citizens to arm and

assemble on the battery. Blank terror reigned over the community. The whole party of Short Pipes in the course of a single night had changed into arrant old women—a metamorphosis only to be parallel by the prodigies recorded by Livy as having happened at Rome at the approach of Hannibal, when statues sweated in pure affright, goats were converted into sheep, and cocks, turning into hens, ran cackling about the street.

Thus baffled in all attempts to put the city in a state of defence; blockaded from without; tormented from within, and menaced with a Yankee invasion, even the stiff-necked will of Peter Stuyvesant for once gave way, and in spite of his mighty heart, which swelled in his throat until it nearly choked him, he consented to a treaty of surrender.

Words cannot express the transports of the populace, on receiving this intelligence; had they obtained a conquest over their enemies, they could not have indulged greater delight. The streets resounded with their congratulations—they extolled their governor as the father and deliverer of his country—they crowded to his house to testify their gratitude, and were ten times more noisy in their plaudits than when he returned, with victory perched upon his beaver, from the glorious capture of Fort Christina.—But the indignant Peter shut his doors and windows, and took refuge in the innermost recesses of his mansion, that he might not hear the ignoble rejoicings of the rabble.

Commissioners were now appointed on both sides and a capitulation was speedily arranged; all that was wanting to ratify it was that it should be signed by the governor. When the commissioners waited upon him for this purpose they were received with grim and bitter courtesy. His warlike accoutrements were laid aside—an old Indian night-gown was wrapped about his rugged limbs, a red night-cap overshadowed his frowning brow, an iron-gray beard of three days' growth gave additional grimness to his visage. Thrice did he seize a worn-out stump of a pen, and essay to sign the loathsome paper—thrice did he clinch his teeth, and make a horrible countenance, as though a dose of rhubarb, senna, and ipecacuanha, had been offered to his lips; at length, dashing it from him, he seized his brass-hilted sword, and jerking it from the scabbard, swore by St. Nicholas, to sooner die than yield to any power under heaven.

For two whole days did he persist in this magnanimous resolution, during which his house was besieged by the rabble, and menaces and clamorous revilings exhausted to no purpose. And now another course was adopted to soothe, if possible, his mighty ire. A procession was formed by the burgomasters and schepens, followed by the populace, to bear the capitulation in state to the governor's dwelling. They found the castle strongly barricaded, and the old hero in full regimentals, with his cocked hat on his head, posted with a blunderbuss at the garret window.

There was something in this formidable position that struck even the ignoble vulgar with awe and admiration. The brawling multitude could not but reflect with self-abasement upon their own pusillanimous conduct, when they beheld their hardy but deserted old governor, thus faithful to his post, like a forlorn hope, and fully prepared to defend his ungrateful city to the last. These compunctions, however, were soon overwhelmed by the recurring tide of public apprehension. The populace arranged themselves before the house, taking off their hats with most respectful humility—Burgomaster Roerback, who was of that popular class of orators described by Sallust, as being "talkative rather than eloquent," stepped forth and addressed the governor in a speech of three hours' length, detailing, in the most pathetic terms, the calamitous situation of the province, and urging him in a constant repetition of the same arguments and words to sign the capitulation.

The mighty Peter eyed him from his garret window in grim silence—now and then his eye would glance over the surrounding rabble, and an indignant grin, like that of an angry mastiff, would mark his iron visage. But though a man of most undaunted mettle—though he had a heart as big as an ox, and a head that would have set adamant to scorn—yet after all he was a mere mortal. Wearied out by these repeated oppositions, and this eternal haranguing, and perceiving that unless he complied, the inhabitants would follow their own inclination, or rather their fears, without waiting for his consent; or, what was still worse, the Yankees would have time to pour in their forces and claim a share in the conquest, he testily ordered them to hand up the paper. It was accordingly hoisted to him on the end of a pole, and having scrawled his name at the bottom of it, he anathematized them all for a set of cowardly, mutinous, degenerate poltroons—threw the capitulation at their heads, slammed down the window, and was heard stumping down stairs with vehement indignation. The rabble incontinently took to their heels; even the burgomasters were not slow in evacuating the premises, fearing lest the sturdy Peter might issue from his den, and greet them with some unwelcome testimonial of his displeasure.

Within three hours after the surrender, a legion of British beef-fed warriors poured into New Amsterdam, taking possession of the fort and batteries. And now might be heard, from all quarters, the sound of hammers made by the old Dutch burghers, in nailing up their doors and windows, to protect their vrouws from these fierce barbarians, whom they contemplated in silent sulliness from the garret windows as they paraded through the streets.

Thus did Colonel Richard Nichols, the commander of the British forces, enter into quiet possession of the conquered realm as *locum tenens* for the Duke of York. The victory was attended with no other outrage than that of changing the name of the province and its metropolis, which thenceforth were denominated NEW YORK, and so have continued to be called unto the present day. The inhabitants, according to treaty, were allowed to maintain quiet possession of their property; but so inveterately did they retain their abhorrence of the British nation, that in a private meeting of the leading citizens, it was unanimously determined never to ask any of their conquerors to dinners.

NOTE.—Modern historians assert that when the New Netherlands were thus overrun by the British, as Spain in ancient days by the Saracens, a resolute band refused to bend the neck to the invader. Led by one Garret Van Horne, a valorous and gigantic Dutchman, they crossed the bay and buried themselves among the marshes and cabbage-gardens of Communipaw; as did Pelayo and his followers among the mountains of Asturias. Here their descendants have remained ever since, keeping themselves apart, like seed corn, to re-people the city with the genuine breed whenever it shall be effectually recovered from its intruders. It is said the genuine descendants of the Nederlanders who inhabit New York, still look with longing eyes to the green marshes of ancient Pavonia, as did the conquered Spaniards of yore to the stern mountains of Asturias, considering these the regions whence deliverance is to come.

CHAPTER IX

CONTAINING THE DIGNIFIED RETIREMENT, AND MORTAL SURRENDER OF PETER THE HEADSTRONG.

THUS then have I concluded this great historical enterprise; but before I lay aside my weary pen, there yet remains to be performed one pious duty. If among the variety of readers who may peruse this book, there should haply be found any of those souls of true nobility, which glow with celestial fire at the history of the generous and the brave, they will doubtless be anxious to know the fate of the gallant Peter Stuyvesant. To gratify one such sterling heart of gold I would go more lengths than to instruct the cold-blooded curiosity of a whole fraternity of philosophers.

No sooner had that high-mettled cavalier signed the articles of capitulation, than, determined not to witness the humiliation of his favorite city, he turned his back on its walls and made a growling retreat to his *bouwery*, or country-seat, which was situated about two miles off; where he passed the remainder of his days in patriarchal retirement. There he enjoyed that tranquillity of mind, which he had never known amid the distracting cares of government; and tasted the sweets of absolute and uncontrolled authority, which his factious subjects had so often dashed with the bitterness of opposition.

No persuasions could ever induce him to revisit the city—on the contrary, he would always have his great arm-chair placed with its back to the windows which looked in that direction; until a thick grove of trees planted by his own hand grew up and formed a screen that effectually excluded it from the prospect. He railed continually at the degenerate innovations and improvements introduced by the conquerors—forbade a word of their detested language to be spoken in his family, a prohibition readily obeyed, since none of the household could speak anything but Dutch—and even ordered a fine avenue to be cut down in front of his house because it consisted of English cherry-trees.

The same incessant vigilance, which blazed forth when he had a vast province under his care, now showed itself with equal vigor, though in narrower limits. He patrolled with unceasing watchfulness the boundaries of his little territory; repelled every encroachment with intrepid promptness; punished every vagrant depredation upon his orchard or his farm-yard with inflexible severity; and conducted every stray hog or cow in triumph to the pound. But to the indigent neighbor, the friendless stranger, or the weary wanderer, his spacious doors were ever open, and his capacious fireplace, that emblem of his own warm and generous heart, had always a corner to receive and cherish them. There was an exception to this, I must confess, in case the ill-starred applicant were an Englishman or a Yankee; to whom, though he might extend the hand of assistance, he could never be brought to yield the rites of hospitality. Nay, if peradventure some straggling merchant of the East should stop at his door, with his cart-load of tin ware or wooden bowls, the fiery Peter would issue forth like a giant from his castle, and make such a furious clattering among his pots and kettles, that the vender of *"notions"* was fain to betake himself to instant flight.

His suit of regimentals, worn threadbare by the brush, were carefully hung up in the state bedchamber, and regularly aired the first fair day of every month; and his cocked hat and trusty sword were suspended in grim repose over the parlor mantel-piece, forming supporters to a full-length portrait of the renowned admiral Van Tromp. In his domestic empire he maintained strict discipline, and a well-organized despotic government; but though his own will was the supreme law, yet the good of his subjects was his constant object. He watched over, not merely their immediate comforts, but their morals, and their ultimate welfare; for he gave them abundance of excellent admonition, nor could any of them complain, that, when occasion required, he was by any means niggardly in bestowing wholesome correction.

The good old Dutch festivals, those periodical demonstrations of an over-flowing heart and a thankful spirit, which are falling into sad disuse among my fellow-citizens, were faithfully observed in the mansion of Governor Stuyvesant. New Year was truly a day of open-handed liberality, of jocund revelry, and warm-hearted congratulation, when the bosom swelled with genial good-fellowship, and the plenteous table was attended with an unceremonious freedom, and honest broad-mouthed merriment, unknown in these days of degeneracy and refinement. Paas and Pinxter were scrupulously observed throughout his dominions; nor was the day of St. Nicholas suffered to pass by, without making presents, hanging the stocking in the chimney, and complying with all its other ceremonies.

Once a year, on the first day of April, he used to array himself in full regimentals, being the anniversary of his triumphal entry into New Amsterdam, after the conquest of New Sweden. This was always a kind of saturnalia among the domestics, when they considered themselves at liberty, in some measure, to say and do what they pleased; for on this day their master was always observed to unbend, and become exceeding pleasant and jocose, sending the old gray-headed negroes on April-fool's errands for pigeons' milk; not one of whom but allowed himself to be taken in, and humored his old master's jokes, as became a faithful and well-disciplined dependant. Thus did he reign, happily and peacefully on his own land—injuring no man—envying no man—molested by no outward strifes; perplexed by no internal commotions —and the mighty monarchs of the earth, who were vainly seeking to maintain peace, and promote the welfare of mankind, by war and desolation, would have done well to have made a voyage to the little island of Manna-hata, and learned a lesson in government from the domestic economy of Peter Stuyvesant.

In process of time, however, the old governor, like all other children of mortality, began to exhibit evident tokens of decay. Like an aged oak, which, though it long has braved the fury of the elements, and still retains its gigantic proportions, begins to shake and groan with every blast—so was it with the gallant Peter; for though he still bore the port and semblance of what he was in the days of his hardihood and chivalry, yet did age and infirmity begin to sap the vigor of his frame—but his heart, that unconquerable citadel, still triumphed unsubdued. With matchless avidity would he listen to every article of intelligence concerning the battles between the English and Dutch—still would his pulse beat high, whenever he heard of the victories of De Ruyter—and his countenance lower, and his eyebrows knit, when fortune turned in favor of the English. At length, as on a certain day he had just smoked his fifth pipe, and was napping after dinner, in his arm-chair, conquering the whole British nation in his dreams, he was suddenly aroused by a ringing of bells, rattling of drums, and roaring of cannon, that put all his blood in a ferment. But when he learnt that these rejoicings were in honor of a great victory obtained by the combined English and French fleets over the brave De Ruyter, and the younger Van Tromp, it went so much to his heart, that he took to his bed, and, in less than three days, was brought to death's door, by a violent cholera morbus! Even in this extremity he still displayed the unconquerable spirit of Peter *the Headstrong;* holding out to the last gasp, with inflexible obstinacy, against a whole army of old women who were bent upon driving the enemy out of his bowels, in the true Dutch mode of defence, by inundation.

While he thus lay, lingering on the verge of dissolution, news was brought him, that the brave De Ruyter had made good his retreat, with little loss, and meant once more to meet the enemy in battle. The closing eye of the old warrior kindled with martial fire at the words—he partly raised himself in bed —clinched his withered hand, as if he felt within his gripe that sword which waved in triumph before the walls of Fort Christina, and giving a grim smile of exultation, sank back upon his pillow, and expired.

Thus died Peter Stuyvesant, a valiant soldier—a loyal subject—an upright governor, and an honest Dutchman—who wanted only a few empires to desolate, to have been immortalized as a hero!

His funeral obsequies were celebrated with the utmost grandeur and solemnity. The town was perfectly emptied of its inhabitants, who crowded in throngs to pay the last sad honors to their good old governor. All his sterling qualities rushed in full tide upon their recollection, while the memory of his foibles and his faults had expired with him. The ancient burghers contended who should have the privilege of bearing the pall; the populace strove who should walk nearest to the bier, and the melancholy procession was closed by a number of gray-headed negroes, who had wintered and summered in the household of their departed master for the greater part of a century. With sad and gloomy countenances, the multitude gathered round the grave. They dwelt with mournful hearts on the sturdy virtues, the signal services, and the gallant exploits of the brave old worthy. They recalled, with secret upbraidings, their own factious oppositions to his government; and many an ancient burgher, whose phlegmatic features had never been known to relax, nor his eyes to moisten, was now observed to puff a pensive pipe, and the big drop to steal down his cheek; while he muttered, with affectionate accent, and melancholy shake of the head—"Well, den!—Hardkoppig Peter ben gone at last!"

His remains were deposited in the family vault, under a chapel which he had piously erected on his estate, and dedicated to St. Nicholas—and which stood on the identical spot at present occupied by St. Mark's church, where his tombstone is still to be seen. His estate, or *bouwery*, as it was called, has ever continued in the possession of his descendants, who, by the uniform integrity of their conduct, and their strict adherence to the customs and manners that prevailed in the *"good old times,"* have proved themselves worthy of their illustrious ancestor. Many a time and oft has the farm been haunted at night by enterprising money-diggers, in quest of pots of gold, said to have been buried by the old governor—though I cannot learn that any of them have ever been enriched by their researches—and who is there, among my native-born fellow citizens, that does not remember when, in the mischievous days of his boyhood, he conceived it a great exploit to rob "Stuyvesant's orchard" on a holiday afternoon?

At this stronghold of the family may still be seen certain memorials of the immortal Peter. His full-length portrait frowns in martial terrors from the parlor wall—his cocked hat and sword still hang up in the best bedroom—his brimstone-colored breeches were for a long while suspended in the hall, until some years since they occasioned a dispute between a new-married couple— and his silver-mounted wooden leg is still treasured up in the store-room, as an invaluable relique.

SELECTIONS
FROM THE SKETCH BOOK
OF
GEOFFREY CRAYON, GENT`

First Published in 1832

THE AUTHOR'S ACCOUNT OF HIMSELF

I am of this mind with Homer, that as the snaile that crept out of her shel was turned eftsoons into a toad, and thereby was forced to make a stoole to sit on; so the traveller that stragleth from his owne country is in a short time transformed into so monstrous a shape, that he is faine to alter his mansion with his manners, and to live where he can, not where he would.—Lyly's "Euphues."

I was always fond of visiting new scenes, and observing strange characters and manners. Even when a mere child I began my travels, and made many tours of discovery into foreign parts and unknown regions of my native city, to the frequent alarm of my parents, and the emolument of the town-crier. As I grew into boyhood, I extended the range of my observations. My holiday afternoons were spent in rambles about the surrounding country. I made myself familiar with all its places famous in history or fable. I knew every spot where a murder or robbery had been committed, or a ghost seen. I visited the neighbouring villages, and added greatly to my stock of knowledge by noting their habits and customs, and conversing with their sages and great men. I even journeyed one long summer's day to the summit of the most distant hill, whence I stretched my eye over many a mile of *terra incognita*, and was astonished to find how vast a globe I inhabited.

This rambling propensity strengthened with my years. Books of voyages and travels became my passion, and in devouring their contents I neglected the regular exercises of the school. How wistfully would I wander about the pier-heads in fine weather, and watch the parting ships bound to distant climes—with what longing eyes would I gaze after their lessening sails, and waft myself in imagination to the ends of the earth!

Further reading and thinking, though they brought this vague inclination into more reasonable bounds, only served to make it more decided. I visited various parts of my own country; and had I been merely a lover of fine scenery, I should have felt little desire to seek elsewhere its gratification; for on no country have the charms of Nature been more prodigally lavished. Her mighty lakes, like oceans of liquid silver; her mountains, with their bright aërial tints; her valleys, teeming with wild fertility; her tremendous cataracts, thundering in their solitudes; her boundless plains, waving with spontaneous verdure; her broad deep rivers, rolling in solemn silence to the ocean; her trackless forests, where vegetation puts forth all its magnificence; her skies, kindling with the magic of summer clouds and glorious sunshine;—no, never need an American look beyond his own country for the sublime and beautiful of natural scenery.

But Europe held forth the charms of storied and poetical association. There were to be seen the masterpieces of art, the refinements of highly-cultivated society, the quaint peculiarities of ancient and local custom. My native country was full of youthful promise: Europe was rich in the accumulated treasures of age. Her very ruins told the history of times gone by, and every mouldering stone was a chronicle. I longed to wander over the scenes of renowned achievement—to tread, as it were, in the footsteps of antiquity—to loiter about the ruined castle—to meditate on the falling tower—to escape, in short, from the commonplace realities of the present, and lose myself among the shadowy grandeurs of the past.

I had, beside all this, an earnest desire to see the great men of the earth. We have, it is true, our great men in America: not a city but has an ample share of them. I have mingled among them in my time, and been almost withered by the shade into which they cast me; for there is nothing so baleful to a small man as the shade of a great one, particularly the great man of the city. But I was anxious to see the great men of Europe; for I had read in the works of various philosophers, that all animals degenerated in America, and man among the number. A great man of Europe, thought I, must therefore be as superior to a great man of America as a peak of the Alps to a highland of the Hudson; and in this idea I was confirmed by observing the comparative importance and swelling magnitude of many English travellers among us, who, I was assured, were very little people in their own country. I will visit this land of wonders, thought I, and see the gigantic race from which I am degenerated.

It has been either my good or evil lot to have my roving passion gratified. I have wandered through different countries, and witnessed many of the shifting scenes of life. I cannot say that I have studied them with the eye of a philosopher; but rather with the sauntering gaze with which humble lovers of the picturesque stroll from the window of one print-shop to another; caught, sometimes by the delineations of beauty, sometimes by the distortions of caricature, and sometimes by the loveliness of landscape. As it is the fashion for modern tourists to travel pencil in hand, and bring home their portfolios filled with sketches, I am disposed to get up a few for the entertainment of my friends. When, however, I look over the hints and memorandums I have taken down for the purpose, my heart almost fails me at finding how my idle humour has led me aside for the great objects studied by every regular traveller who would make a book. I fear I shall give equal disappointment with an unlucky landscape painter who had travelled on the continent, but, following the bent of his vagrant inclination, had sketched in nooks, and corners, and by-places. His sketch-book was accordingly crowded with cottages, and landscapes, and obscure ruins; but he had neglected to paint St Peter's or the Coliseum, the cascade of Terni or the bay of Naples, and had not a single glacier or volcano in his whole collection.

RIP VAN WINKLE

[The following Tale was found among the papers of the late Diedrich Knickerbocker, an old gentleman of New York, who was very curious in the Dutch history of the province, and the manners of the descendants from its primitive settlers. His historical researches, however, did not lie so much among books as among men; for the former are lamentably scanty on his favourite topics, whereas he found the old burghers, and still more their wives, rich in that legendary lore so invaluable to true history. Whenever, therefore, he happened upon a genuine Dutch family, snugly shut up in its low-roofed farmhouse, under a spreading sycamore, he looked upon it as a little clasped volume of black letter, and studied it with the zeal of a book-worm.

The result of all these researches was a history of the province during the reign of the Dutch governors, which he published some years since. There have been various opinions as to the literary character of his work, and, to tell the truth, it is not a whit better than it should be. Its chief merit is its scrupulous accuracy, which indeed was a little questioned on its first appearance, but has since been completely established; and it is now admitted into all historical collections as a book of unquestionable authority.

The old gentleman died shortly after the publication of his work, and now that he is dead and gone, it cannot do much harm to his memory to say, that his time might have been much better employed in weightier labours. He, however, was apt to ride his hobby his own way; and though it did now and then kick up the dust a little in the eyes of his neighbours, and grieve the spirit of some friends, for whom he felt the truest deference and affection; yet his errors and follies are remembered "more in sorrow than in anger," and it begins to be suspected that he never intended to injure or offend. But however his memory may be appreciated by critics, it is still held dear by many folk whose good opinion is well worth having, particularly by certain biscuit-bakers, who have gone so far as to imprint his likeness on their new-year cakes, and have thus given him a chance for immortality, almost equal to the being stamped on a Waterloo medal or a Queen Anne's farthing.]

RIP VAN WINKLE:

A POSTHUMOUS WRITING OF DIEDRICH KNICKERBOCKER

By Woden, God of Saxons,
From whence comes Wensday, that is Wodensday.
Truth is a thing that ever I will keep
Unto thylke day in which I creep into
My sepulchre——

CARTWRIGHT.

WHOEVER has made a voyage up the Hudson must remember the Kaatskill mountains. They are a dismembered branch of the great Appalachian family, and are seen away to the west of the river, swelling up to a noble height, and lording it over the surrounding country. Every change of season, every change of weather, indeed, every hour of the day, produces some change in the magical hues and shapes of these mountains, and they are regarded by all the good wives, far and near, as perfect barometers. When the weather is fair and settled, they are clothed in blue and purple, and print their bold outlines on the clear evening sky; but sometimes, when the rest of the landscape is cloudless, they will gather a hood of gray vapours about their summits, which, in the last rays of the setting sun, will glow and light up like a crown of glory.

At the foot of these fairy mountains, the voyager may have descried the light smoke curling up from a village, whose shingle-roofs gleam among the trees, just where the blue tints of the upland melt away into the fresh green of the nearer landscape. It is a little village, of great antiquity, having been founded by some of the Dutch colonists, in the early times of the province, just about the beginning of the government of the good Peter Stuyvesant (may he rest in peace!) and there were some of the houses of the original settlers standing within a few years, built of small yellow bricks brought from Holland, having latticed windows and gable fronts, surmounted with weathercocks.

In that same village and in one of these very houses (which, to tell the precise truth, was sadly time-worn and weather-beaten), there lived many years since, while the country was yet a province of Great Britain, a simple good-natured fellow, of the name of Rip Van Winkle. He was a descendant of the Van Winkles who figured so gallantly in the chivalrous days of Peter Stuyvesant, and accompanied him to the siege of Fort Christina. He inherited, however, but little of the martial character of his ancestors. I have observed that he was a simple good-natured man; he was, moreover, a kind neighbour, and an obedient hen-pecked husband. Indeed, to the latter circumstance might be owing that meekness of spirit which gained him such universal popularity; for those men are most apt to be obsequious and conciliating abroad, who are under the discipline of shrews at home. Their tempers, doubtless, are rendered pliant and malleable in the fiery furnace of domestic tribulation, and a curtain lecture is worth all the sermons in the world for teaching the virtues of patience and long-suffering. A termagant wife may, therefore, in some respects, be considered a tolerable blessing; and if so, Rip Van Winkle was thrice blessed.

Certain it is that he was a great favourite among all the good wives of the village, who, as usual with the amiable sex, took his part in all family squabbles; and never failed, whenever they talked those matters over in their evening gossipings, to lay all the blame on Dame Van Winkle. The children of the village, too, would shout with joy whenever he approached. He assisted at their sports, made their playthings, taught them to fly kites and shoot marbles, and told them long stories of ghosts, witches, and Indians. Whenever he went dodging about the village, he was surrounded by a troop of them hanging on his skirts, clambering on his back, and playing a thousand tricks on him with impunity; and not a dog would bark at him throughout the neighbourhood.

The great error in Rip's composition was an insuperable aversion to all kinds of profitable labour. It could not be from the want of assiduity or perseverance;

for he would sit on a wet rock, with a rod as long and heavy as a Tartar's lance, and fish all day without a murmur, even though he should not be encouraged by a single nibble. He would carry a fowling-piece on his shoulder for hours together, trudging through woods and swamps, and up hill and down dale, to shoot a few squirrels or wild pigeons. He would never refuse to assist a neighbour even in the roughest toil, and was a foremost man at all country frolics for husking Indian corn, or building stone fences; the women of the village, too, used to employ him to run their errands, and to do such little odd jobs as their less obliging husbands would not do for them. In a word, Rip was ready to attend to anybody's business but his own; but as to doing family duty, and keeping his farm in order, he found it impossible.

In fact, he declared it was of no use to work on his farm; it was the most pestilent little piece of ground in the whole country; everything about it went wrong, and would go wrong, in spite of him. His fences were continually falling to pieces; his cow would either go astray, or get among the cabbages; weeds were sure to grow quicker in his fields than anywhere else; the rain always made a point of setting in just as he had some out-door work to do; so that though his patrimonial estate had dwindled away under his manage- ment, acre by acre, until there was little more left than a mere patch of Indian corn and potatoes, yet it was the worst conditioned farm in the neighbourhood.

His children, too, were as ragged and wild as if they belonged to nobody. His son Rip, an urchin begotten in his own likeness, promised to inherit the habits, with the old clothes of his father. He was generally seen trooping like a colt at his mother's heels, equipped in a pair of his father's cast-off galligaskins, which he had much ado to hold up with one hand, as a fine lady does her train in bad weather.

Rip Van Winkle, however, was one of those happy mortals, of foolish, well-oiled dispositions, who take the world easy, eat white bread or brown, whichever can be got with least thought or trouble, and would rather starve on a penny than work for a pound. If left to himself, he would have whistled life away in perfect contentment; but his wife kept continually dinning in his ears about his idleness, his carelessness, and the ruin he was bringing on his family. Morning, noon, and night, her tongue was incessantly going, and everything he said or did was sure to produce a torrent of household eloquence. Rip had but one way of replying to all lectures of the kind, and that, by frequent use, had grown into a habit. He shrugged his shoulders, shook his head, cast up his eyes, but said nothing. This, however, always provoked a fresh volley from his wife; so that he was fain to draw off his forces, and take to the outside of the house—the only side which, in truth, belongs to a hen- pecked husband.

Rip's sole domestic adherent was his dog wolf, who was as much hen-pecked as his master; for Dame Van Winkle regarded them as companions in idleness, and even looked upon Wolf with an evil eye, as the cause of his master's going so often astray. True it is, in all points of spirit befitting an honourable dog, he was as courageous an animal as ever scoured the woods—but what courage can withstand the ever-during and all-besetting terrors of a woman's tongue? The moment Wolf entered the house, his crest fell, his tail drooped to the ground, or curled between his legs, he sneaked about with a gallows air, casting many a side-long glance at Dame Van Winkle, and at the least flourish of a broomstick or ladle, he would fly to the door with yelping precipitation.

Times grew worse and worse with Rip Van Winkle as years of matrimony rolled on; a tart temper never mellows with age, and a sharp tongue is the only edged tool that grows keener with constant use. For a long while he used to console himself, when driven from home, by frequenting a kind of perpetual club of the sages, philosophers, and other idle personages of the village; which held its sessions on a bench before a small inn, designated by a rubicund portrait of his Majesty George the Third. Here they used to sit in the shade through a long lazy summer's day, talking listlessly over village gossip, or telling endless sleepy stories about nothing. But it would have been worth any statesman's money to have heard the profound discussions that sometimes took place, when by chance an old newspaper fell into their hands from some passing traveller. How solemnly they would listen to the contents, as drawled out by Derrick Van Bummel, the schoolmaster, a dapper learned little man, who was not to be daunted by the most gigantic word in the dictionary; and how sagely they would deliberate upon public events some months after they had taken place.

The opinions of this junto were completely controlled by Nicholas Vedder, a patriarch of the village, and landlord of the inn, at the door of which he took his seat from morning till night, just moving sufficiently to avoid the sun and keep in the shade of a large tree; so that the neighbours could tell the hour by his movements as accurately as by a sundial. It is true he was rarely heard to speak, but smoked his pipe incessantly. His adherents, however (for every great man has his adherents), perfectly understood him, and knew how to gather his opinions. When anything that was read or related displeased him, he was observed to smoke his pipe vehemently, and to send forth short, frequent, and angry puffs, but when pleased he would inhale the smoke slowly and tranquilly, and emit it in light and placid clouds; and sometimes, taking the pipe from his mouth, and letting the fragrant vapour curl about his nose, would gravely nod his head in token of perfect approbation.

From even this stronghold the unlucky Rip was at length routed by his termagant wife, who would suddenly break in upon the tranquillity of the assemblage and call the members all to naught; nor was that august personage, Nicholas Vedder himself, sacred from the daring tongue of this terrible virago, who charged him outright with encouraging her husband in habits of idleness.

Poor Rip was at last reduced almost to despair; and his only alternative, to escape from the labour of the farm and clamour of his wife, was to take gun in hand and stroll away into the woods. Here he would sometimes seat himself at the foot of a tree, and share the contents of his wallet with Wolf, with whom he sympathised as a fellow-sufferer in persecution. "Poor Wolf," he would say, "thy mistress leads thee a dog's life of it; but never mind, my lad, whilst I live thou shalt never want a friend to stand by thee!" Wolf would wag his tail, look wistfully in his master's face, and if dogs can feel pity, I verily believe he reciprocated the sentiment with all his heart.

In a long ramble of the kind on a fine autumnal day, Rip had unconsciously scrambled to one of the highest parts of the Kaatskill mountains. He was after his favourite sport of squirrel-shooting, and the still solitudes had echoed and re-echoed with the reports of his gun. Panting and fatigued, he threw himself, late in the afternoon, on a green knoll, covered with mountain herbage, that crowned the brow of a precipice. From an opening between the trees he could overlook all the lower country for many a mile of rich woodland. He saw at a distance the lordly Hudson, far, far below him, moving on its silent but majestic course, with the reflection of a purple cloud, or the sail of a lagging bark, here and there sleeping on its glassy bosom, and at last losing itself in the blue highlands.

On the other side he looked down into a deep mountain glen, wild, lonely, and shagged, the bottom filled with fragments from the impending cliffs, and scarcely lighted by the reflected rays of the setting sun. For some time Rip lay musing on this scene; evening was gradually advancing; the mountains began to throw their long blue shadows over the valleys; he saw that it would be dark long before he could reach the village, and he heaved a heavy sigh when he thought of encountering the terrors of Dame Van Winkle.

As he was about to descend, he heard a voice from a distance, hallooing, "Rip Van Winkle! Rip Van Winkle!" He looked round, but could see nothing but a crow winging its solitary flight across the mountain. He thought his fancy must have deceived him, and turned again to descend, when he heard the same cry ring through the still evening air: "Rip Van Winkle! Rip Van Winkle!"—at the same time Wolf bristled up his back, and, giving a loud growl, skulked to his master's side, looking fearfully down into the glen. Rip now felt a vague apprehension stealing over him; he looked anxiously in the same direction, and perceived a strange figure slowly toiling up the rocks, and bending under the weight of something he carried on his back. He was surprised to see any human being in this lonely and unfrequented place; but supposing it to be some one of the neighbourhood in need of his assistance, he hastened down to yield it.

On nearer approach he was still more surprised at the singularity of the stranger's appearance. He was a short, square-built old fellow, with thick bushy hair and a grizzled beard. His dress was of the antique Dutch fashion—a cloth jerkin, strapped round the waist—several pairs of breeches, the outer one of ample volume, decorated with rows of buttons down the sides, and bunches at the knees. He bore on his shoulder a stout keg, that seemed full of liquor, and made signs for Rip to approach and assist him with the load. Though rather shy and distrustful of this new acquaintance, Rip complied with his usual alacrity; and mutually relieving each other, they clambered up a narrow gully, apparently the dry bed of a mountain torrent. As they ascended, Rip every now and then heard long rolling peals, like distant thunder, that seemed to issue out of a deep ravine, or rather cleft, between lofty rocks, toward which their rugged path conducted. He paused for an instant, but supposing it to be the muttering of one of those transient thunder-showers which often take place in mountain heights, he proceeded. Passing through the ravine, they came to a hollow, like a small amphitheatre, surrounded by perpendicular precipices, over the brinks of which impending trees shot their branches, so that you only caught glimpses of the azure sky and the bright evening cloud. During the whole time Rip and his companion had laboured on in silence, for though the former marvelled greatly what could be the object of carrying a keg of liquor up this wild mountain; yet there was something strange and incomprehensible about the unknown, that inspired awe and checked familiarity.

On entering the amphitheatre, new objects of wonder presented themselves. On a level spot in the centre was a company of odd-looking personages playing at nine-pins. They were dressed in a quaint outlandish fashion; some wore short doublets, others jerkins, with long knives in their belts, and most of them had enormous breeches, of similar style with that of the guide's. Their visages, too, were peculiar; one had a large head, broad face, and small piggish eyes; the face of another seemed to consist entirely of nose, and was surmounted by a white sugar-loaf hat, set off with a little red cock's tail. They all had beards, of various shapes and colours. There was one who seemed to be the commander. He was a stout old gentleman, with a weather-beaten countenance; he wore a laced doublet, broad belt and hanger, high-crowned hat and feather, red stockings, and high-heeled shoes, with roses in them. The whole group reminded Rip of the figures in an old Flemish painting, in the parlour of Dominie Van Shaick, the village parson, and which had been brought over from Holland at the time of the settlement.

What seemed particularly odd to Rip was, that though these folks were evidently amusing themselves, yet they maintained the gravest faces, the most mysterious silence, and were, withal, the most melancholy party of pleasure he had ever witnessed. Nothing interrupted the stillness of the scene but the noise of the balls, which, whenever they were rolled, echoed along the mountains like rumbling peals of thunder.

As Rip and his companion approached them, they suddenly desisted from their play, and stared at him with such fixed, statue-like gaze, and such strange, uncouth, lack-lustre countenances, that his heart turned within him, and his knees smote together. His companion now emptied the contents of the keg into large flagons, and made signs to him to wait upon the company. He obeyed with fear and trembling; they quaffed the liquor in profound silence, and then returned to their game.

By degrees Rip's awe and apprehension subsided. He even ventured, when no eye was fixed upon him, to taste the beverage, which he found had much of the flavour of excellent Hollands. He was naturally a thirsty soul, and was soon tempted to repeat the draught. One taste provoked another; and he reiterated his visits to the flagon so often, that at length his senses were overpowered, his eyes swam in his head, his head gradually declined, and he fell into a deep sleep.

On waking, he found himself on the green knoll whence he had first seen the old man of the glen. He rubbed his eyes—it was a bright sunny morning. The birds were hopping and twittering among the bushes, and the eagle was wheeling aloft, and breasting the pure mountain breeze. "Surely," thought Rip, "I have not slept here all night." He recalled the occurrences before he fell asleep. The strange man with a keg of liquor—the mountain ravine—the wild retreat among the rocks—the woe-begone party at nine-pins—the flagon—"Oh! that flagon! that wicked flagon!" thought Rip; "what excuse shall I make to Dame Van Winkle?"

He looked round for his gun, but in place of the clean well-oiled fowling-piece, he found an old firelock lying by him, the barrel incrusted with rust, the lock falling off, and the stock worm-eaten. He now suspected that the grave roysters of the mountain had put a trick upon him, and, having dosed him with liquor, had robbed him of his gun. Wolf, too, had disappeared, but he might have strayed away after a squirrel or partridge. He whistled after him, and shouted his name, but all in vain; the echoes repeated his whistle and shout, but no dog was to be seen.

He determined to revisit the scene of the last evening's gambol, and, if he met with any of the party, to demand his dog and gun. As he rose to walk he found himself stiff in the joints, and wanting in his usual activity. "These mountain beds do not agree with me," thought Rip; "and if this frolic should lay me up with a fit of the rheumatism, I shall have a blessed time with Dame Van Winkle." With some difficulty he got down into the glen: he found the gully up which he and his companion had ascended the preceding evening; but, to his astonishment, a mountain stream was now foaming down it—leaping from rock to rock, and filling the glen with babbling murmurs. He, however, made shift to scramble up its sides, working his toilsome way through thickets of birch, sassafras, and witch-hazel, and sometimes tripped up or entangled by the wild grape-vines that twisted their coils or tendrils from tree to tree, and spread a kind of network in his path.

At length he reached to where the ravine had opened through the cliffs to the amphitheatre; but no traces of such opening remained. The rocks presented a high impenetrable wall, over which the torrent came tumbling in a sheet of feathery foam, and fell into a broad, deep basin, black from the shadows of the surrounding forest. Here, then, poor Rip was brought to a stand. He again called and whistled after his dog; he was only answered by the cawing of a flock of idle crows, sporting high in air about a dry tree that overhung a sunny precipice; and who, secure in their elevation, seemed to look down and scoff at the poor man's perplexities. What was to be done?—the morning was passing away, and Rip felt famished for want of his breakfast. He grieved to give up his dog and his gun; he dreaded to meet his wife; but it would not do to starve among the mountains. He shook his head, shouldered the rusty firelock, and, with a heart full of trouble and anxiety, turned his steps homeward.

As he approached the village he met a number of people, but none whom he knew, which somewhat surprised him, for he had thought himself acquainted with everyone in the country round. Their dress, too, was of a different fashion from that to which he was accustomed. They all stared at him with equal marks of surprise, and, whenever they cast their eyes upon him, invariably stroked their chins. The constant recurrence of this gesture induced Rip, involuntarily, to do the same—when, to his astonishment, he found his beard had grown a foot long!

He had now entered the skirts of the village. A troop of strange children ran at his heels, hooting after him, and pointing at his gray beard. The dogs, too, not one of which he recognised for an old acquaintance, barked at him as he passed. The very village was altered; it was larger and more populous. There were rows of houses which he had never seen before, and those which had been his familiar haunts had disappeared. Strange names were over the doors—strange faces at the windows—everything was strange. His mind now misgave him; he began to doubt whether both he and the world around him were not bewitched. Surely this was his native village, which he had left but the day before. There stood the Kaatskill mountains—there ran the silver Hudson at a distance—there was every hill and dale precisely as it had always been. Rip was sorely perplexed. "That flagon last night," thought he, "has addled my poor head sadly!"

It was with some difficulty that he found the way to his own house, which he approached with silent awe, expecting every moment to hear the shrill voice of Dame Van Winkle. He found the house gone to decay—the roof fallen in, the windows shattered, and the doors off the hinges. A half-starved dog that looked like Wolf, was skulking about it. Rip called him by name, but the cur snarled, showed his teeth, and passed on. This was an unkind cut indeed—"My very dog," sighed poor Rip, "has forgotten me!"

He entered the house, which, to tell the truth, Dame Van Winkle had always kept in neat order. It was empty, forlorn, and apparently abandoned. The desolateness overcame all his connubial fears—he called loudly for his wife and children—the lonely chambers rang for a moment with his voice, and then all again was silence.

He now hurried forth, and hastened to his old resort, the village inn—but it too was gone. A large, rickety, wooden building stood in its place, with great gaping windows, some of them broken and mended with old hats and petticoats, and over the door was painted, "The Union Hotel, by Jonathan Doolittle." Instead of the great tree that used to shelter the quiet little Dutch inn of yore, there was now reared a tall naked pole, with something on the top that looked like a red nightcap, and from it was fluttering a flag, on which was a singular assemblage of stars and stripes—all this was strange and incomprehensible. He recognised on the sign, however, the ruby face of King George, under which he had smoked so many a peaceful pipe; but even this was singularly metamorphosed. The red coat was changed for one of blue and buff, a sword was held in the hand instead of a sceptre, the head was decorated with a cocked hat, and underneath was painted in large characters, GENERAL WASHINGTON.

There was, as usual, a crowd of folks about the door, but none that Rip recollected. The very character of the people seemed changed. There was a busy, bustling, disputatious tone about it, instead of the accustomed phlegm and drowsy tranquillity. He looked in vain for the sage Nicholas Vedder, with his broad face, double chin, and fair long pipe, uttering clouds of tobacco-smoke instead of idle speeches; or Van Bummel, the schoolmaster, doling forth the contents of an ancient newspaper. In place of these, a lean, bilious-looking fellow, with his pockets full of hand-bills, was haranguing vehemently about rights of citizens—elections—members of Congress—liberty—Bunker's Hill—heroes of seventy-six—and other words, which were a perfect Babylonish jargon to the bewildered Van Winkle.

The appearance of Rip, with his long grizzled beard, his rusty fowling-piece, his uncouth dress, and an army of women and children at his heels, soon attracted the attention of the tavern politicians. They crowded round him, eyeing him from head to foot with great curiosity. The orator bustled up to him, and, drawing him partly aside, inquired "on which side he voted?" Rip stared in vacant stupidity. Another short but busy little fellow pulled him by the arm, and, rising on tiptoe, inquired in his ear, "Whether he was Federal or Democrat?" Rip was equally at a loss to comprehend the question; when a knowing, self-important old gentleman, in a sharp cocked hat, made his way through the crowd, putting them to the right and left with his elbows as he passed, and planting himself before Van Winkle, with one arm akimbo, the other resting on his cane, his keen eyes and sharp hat penetrating, as it were, into his very soul, demanded in an austere tone, "What brought him to the election with a gun on his shoulder, and a mob at his heels, and whether he meant to breed a riot in the village?"—"Alas! gentlemen," cried Rip, somewhat dismayed, "I am a poor quiet man, a native of the place, and a loyal subject of the king, God bless him!"

Here a general shout burst from the bystanders—"A tory! a tory! a spy! a refugee! hustle him! away with him!" It was with great difficulty that the self-important man in the cocked hat restored order; and, having assumed a tenfold austerity of brow, demanded again of the unknown culprit, what he came there for, and whom he was seeking? The poor man humbly assured him that he meant no harm, but merely came there in search of some of his neighbours, who used to keep about the tavern.

"Well—who are they?—name them."

Rip bethought himself a moment, and inquired, "Where's Nicholas Vedder?"

There was a silence for a little while, when an old man replied in a thin piping voice, "Nicholas Vedder! why, he is dead and gone these eighteen years! There was a wooden tombstone in the churchyard that used to tell all about him, but that's rotten and gone too."

"Where's Brom Dutcher?"

"Oh, he went off to the army in the beginning of the war; some say he was killed at the storming of Stony Point—others say he was drowned in a squall at the foot of Antony's Nose. I don't know—he never came back again."

"Where's Van Bummel, the schoolmaster?"

"He went off to the wars too, was a great militia general, and is now in Congress."

Rip's heart died away at hearing of these sad changes in his home and friends, and finding himself thus alone in the world. Every answer puzzled him too, by treating of such enormous lapses of time, and of matters which he could not understand; war—Congress—Stony Point;—he had no courage to ask after any more friends, but cried out in despair, "Does nobody here know Rip Van Winkle?"

"Oh, Rip Van Winkle!" exclaimed two or three. "Oh, to be sure! that's Rip Van Winkle yonder, leaning against the tree."

Rip looked, and beheld a precise counterpart of himself, as he went up the mountain: apparently as lazy, and certainly as ragged. The poor fellow was now completely confounded. He doubted his own identity, and whether he was himself or another man. In the midst of his bewilderment, the man in the cocked hat demanded who he was, and what was his name?

"God knows," exclaimed he, at his wits' end; "I'm not myself—I'm somebody else—that's me yonder—no—that's somebody else got into my shoes—I was myself last night, but I fell asleep on the mountain, and they've changed my gun, and everything's changed, and I'm changed, and I can't tell what's my name, or who I am!"

The bystanders began now to look at each other, nod, wink significantly, and tap their fingers against their foreheads. There was a whisper, also, about securing the gun, and keeping the old fellow from doing mischief, at the very suggestion of which the self-important man in the cocked hat retired with some precipitation. At this critical moment a fresh, comely woman pressed through the throng to get a peep at the gray-bearded man. She had a chubby child in her arms, which, frightened at his looks, began to cry. "Hush, Rip," cried she, "hush, you little fool; the old man won't hurt you." The name of the child, the air of the mother, the tone of her voice, all awakened a train of recollections in his mind.

"What is your name, my good woman?" asked he.

"Judith Gardenier."

"And your father's name?"

"Ah, poor man, Rip Van Winkle was his name, but it's twenty years since he went away from home with his gun, and never has been heard of since—his dog came home without him; but whether he shot himself, or was carried away by the Indians, nobody can tell. I was then but a little girl."

Rip had but one question more to ask; but he put it with a faltering voice,— "Where's your mother?"

"Oh, she too had died but a short time since; she broke a blood-vessel in a fit of passion at a New-England pedlar."

There was a drop of comfort, at least, in this intelligence. The honest man could contain himself no longer. He caught his daughter and her child in his arms. "I am your father!" cried he—"Young Rip Van Winkle once—old Rip Van Winkle now!—Does nobody know poor Rip Van Winkle?"

All stood amazed, until an old woman, tottering out from among the crowd, put her hand to her brow, and peering under it in his face for a moment, exclaimed, "Sure enough! it is Rip Van Winkle—it is himself! Welcome home again, old neighbour—Why, where have you been these twenty long years?"

Rip's story was soon told, for the whole twenty years had been to him but as one night. The neighbours stared when they heard it; some were seen to wink at each other, and put their tongues in their cheeks: and the self-important man in the cocked hat, who, when the alarm was over, had returned to the field, screwed down the corners of his mouth, and shook his head—upon which there was a general shaking of the head throughout the assemblage.

It was determined, however, to take the opinion of old Peter Vanderdonk, who was seen slowly advancing up the road. He was a descendant of the historian of that name, who wrote one of the earliest accounts of the province. Peter was the most ancient inhabitant of the village, and well versed in all the wonderful events and traditions of the neighbourhood. He recollected Rip at once, and corroborated his story in the most satisfactory manner. He assured the company that it was a fact, handed down from his ancestor the historian, that the Kaatskill mountains had always been haunted by strange beings. That it was affirmed that the great Hendrick Hudson, the first discoverer of the river and country, kept a kind of vigil there every twenty years, with his crew of the *Half-moon;* being permitted in this way to revisit the scenes of his enterprise, and keep a guardian eye upon the river, and the great city called by his name. That his father had once seen them in their old Dutch dresses playing at nine-pins in a hollow of the mountain; and that he himself had heard, one summer afternoon, the sound of their balls, like distant peals of thunder.

To make a long story short, the company broke up, and returned to the more important concerns of the election. Rip's daughter took him home to live with her; she had a snug, well-furnished house, and a stout cheery farmer for her husband, whom Rip recollected for one of the urchins that used to climb upon his back. As to Rip's son and heir, who was the ditto of himself, seen leaning against the tree, he was employed to work on the farm; but evinced an hereditary disposition to attend to anything else but his business.

Rip now resumed his old walks and habits; he soon found many of his former cronies, though all rather the worse for the wear and tear of time; and preferred making friends among the rising generation, with whom he soon grew into great favour.

Having nothing to do at home, and being arrived at that happy age when a man can be idle with impunity, he took his place once more on the bench at the inn door, and was reverenced as one of the patriarchs of the village, and a chronicle of the old times "before the war." It was some time before he could get into the regular track of gossip, or could be made to comprehend the strange events that had taken place during his torpor. How that there had been a revolutionary war—that the country had thrown off the yoke of Old England—and that, instead of being a subject of His Majesty George the Third, he was now a free citizen of the United States. Rip, in fact, was no politician; the changes of states and empires made but little impression on him; but there was one species of despotism under which he had long groaned, and that was—petticoat government. Happily that was at an end; he had got his neck out of the yoke of matrimony, and could go in and out whenever he pleased without dreading the tyranny of Dame Van Winkle. Whenever her name was mentioned, however, he shook his head, shrugged his shoulders, and cast up his eyes; which might pass either for an expression of resignation to his fate, or joy at his deliverance.

He used to tell his story to every stranger that arrived at Mr. Doolittle's hotel. He was observed at first to vary on some points every time he told it, which was, doubtless, owing to his having so recently awaked. It at last settled down precisely to the tale I have related, and not a man, woman, or child in the neighbourhood but knew it by heart. Some always pretended to doubt the reality of it, and insisted that Rip had been out of his head, and that this was one point on which he always remained flighty. The old Dutch inhabitants, however, almost universally gave it full credit. Even to this day they never hear a thunder-storm of a summer afternoon about the Kaatskill, but they say Hendrick Hudson and his crew are at their game of nine-pins; and it is a common wish of all henpecked husbands in the neighbourhood, when life hangs heavy on their hands, that they might have a quieting draught out of Rip Van Winkle's flagon.

NOTE.—The foregoing tale, one would suspect, had been suggested to Mr. Knickerbocker by a little German superstition about the Emperor Frederick *der Rothbart*, and the Kypphaüser mountain; the subjoined note, however, which he had appended to the tale, shows that it is an absolute fact, narrated with his usual fidelity:—

"The story of Rip Van Winkle may seem incredible to many, but nevertheless I give it my full belief, for I know the vicinity of our old Dutch settlements to have been very subject to marvellous events and appearances. Indeed, I have heard many stranger stories than this in the villages along the Hudson, all of which were too well authenticated to admit of a doubt. I have even talked with Rip Van Winkle myself, who, when I last saw him, was a very venerable old man, and so perfectly rational and consistent on every other point, that I think no conscientious person could refuse to take this into the bargain; nay, I have seen a certificate on the subject, taken before a country justice, and signed with a cross, in the justice's own handwriting. The story, therefore, is beyond the possibility of doubt.   D. K."

POSTSCRIPT.—The following are travelling notes from a memorandum-book of Mr. Knickerbocker:—

"The Kaatsberg, or Catskill Mountains, have always been a region full of fable. The Indians considered them the abode of spirits, who influenced the weather, spreading sunshine or clouds over the landscape, and sending good or bad hunting seasons. They were ruled by an old squaw spirit, said to be their mother. She dwelt on the highest peak of the Catskills, and had charge of the doors of day and night, to open and shut them at the proper hour. She hung up the new moons in the skies, and cut up the old ones into stars. In times of drought, if properly propitiated, she would spin light summer clouds out of cobwebs and morning dew, and send them off from the crest of the mountain, flake after flake, like flakes of carded cotton, to float in the air, until, dissolved by the heat of the sun, they would fall in gentle showers, causing the grass to spring, the fruits to ripen, and the corn to grow an inch an hour. If displeased, however, she would brew up clouds black as ink, sitting in the midst of them like a bottle-bellied spider in the midst of its web; and when these clouds broke, woe betide the valleys!

"In old times, say the Indian traditions, there was a kind of Manitou or Spirit, who kept about the wildest recesses of the Catskill Mountains, and took a mischievous pleasure in wreaking all kinds of evils and vexations upon the red men. Sometimes he would assume the form of a bear, a panther, or a deer, lead the bewildered hunter a weary chase through tangled forests and among ragged rocks, and then spring off with a loud ho! ho! leaving him aghast on the brink of a beetling precipice or raging torrent.

"The favourite abode of this Manitou is still shown. It is a great rock or cliff on the loneliest part of the mountains, and, from the flowering vines which clamber about it, and the wild flowers which abound in its neighbourhood, is known by the name of the Garden Rock. Near the foot of it is a small lake, the haunt of the solitary bittern, with water-snakes basking in the sun on the leaves of the pond-lilies which lie on the surface. This place was held in great awe by the Indians, insomuch that the boldest hunter would not pursue his game within its precincts. Once upon a time, however, a hunter who had lost his way penetrated to the Garden Rock, where he beheld a number of gourds placed in the crotches of trees. One of these he seized and made off with, but in the hurry of his retreat he let it fall among the rocks, when a great stream gushed forth, which washed him away and swept him down precipices, where he was dashed to pieces, and the stream made its way to the Hudson, and continues to flow to the present day, being the identical stream known by the name of the Kaaters-kill."

ENGLISH WRITERS ON AMERICA

Methinks I see in my mind a noble and puissant nation, rousing herself like a strong man after sleep, and shaking her invincible locks: methinks I see her as an eagle, mewing her mighty youth, and kindling her endazzled eyes at the full mid-day beam.—MILTON ON "THE LIBERTY OF THE PRESS."

IT IS with feelings of deep regret that I observe the literary animosity daily growing up between England and America. Great curiosity has been awakened of late with respect to the United States, and the London press has teemed with volumes of travels through the Republic; but they seem intended to diffuse error rather than knowledge; and so successful have they been that, notwithstanding the constant intercourse between the nations, there is no people concerning whom the great mass of the British public have less pure information, or entertain more numerous prejudices.

English travellers are the best and the worst in the world. Where no motives of pride or interest intervene, none can equal them for profound and philosophical views of society, or faithful and graphical descriptions of external objects; but when either the interest or reputation of their own country comes in collision with that of another, they go to the opposite extreme, and forget their usual probity and candour in the indulgence of splenetic remark, and an illiberal spirit of ridicule.

Hence, their travels are more honest and accurate the more remote the country described. I would place implicit confidence in an Englishman's description of the regions beyond the cataracts of the Nile; of unknown islands in the Yellow Sea; of the interior of India; or of any other tract which other travellers might be apt to picture out with the illusions of their fancies, but I would cautiously receive his account of his immediate neighbours, and of those nations with which he is in habits of most frequent intercourse. However I might be disposed to trust his probity, I dare not trust his prejudices.

It has also been the peculiar lot of our country to be visited by the worst kind of English travellers. While men of philosophical spirit and cultivated minds have been sent from England to ransack the poles, to penetrate the deserts, and to study the manners and customs of barbarous nations, with which she can have no permanent intercourse of profit or pleasure, it has been left to the broken-down tradesman, the scheming adventurer, the wandering mechanic, the Manchester and Birmingham agent, to be her oracles respecting America. From such sources she is content to receive her information respecting a country in a singular state of moral and physical development; a country in which one of the greatest political experiments in the history of the world is now performing, and which presents the most profound and momentous studies to the statesman and the philosopher.

That such men should give prejudicial accounts of America is not a matter of surprise. The themes it offers for contemplation are too vast and elevated for their capacities. The national character is yet in a state of fermentation; it may have its frothiness and sediment, but its ingredients are sound and wholesome; it has already given proofs of powerful and generous qualities; and the whole promises to settle down into something substantially excellent. But the causes which are operating to strengthen and ennoble it, and its daily indication of admirable properties, are all lost upon these purblind observers, who are only affected by the little asperities incident to its present situation. They are capable of judging only of the surface of things; of those matters which come in contact with their private interests and personal gratifications. They miss some of the snug conveniences and petty comforts which belong to an old, highly-finished, and over-populous state of society; where the ranks of useful labour are crowded, and many earn a painful and servile subsistence by studying the very caprices of appetite and self-indulgence. These minor comforts, however, are all-important in the estimation of narrow minds, which either do not perceive, or will not acknowledge, that they are more than counterbalanced among us by great and generally diffused blessings.

They may, perhaps, have been disappointed in some unreasonable expectation of sudden gain. They may have pictured America to themselves an El Dorado, where gold and silver abounded, and the natives were lacking in sagacity; and where they were to become strangely and suddenly rich, in some unforeseen but easy manner. The same weakness of mind that indulges absurd expectations produces petulance in disappointment. Such persons become embittered against the country on finding that there, as everywhere else, a man must sow before he can reap; must win wealth by industry and talent; and must contend with the common difficulties of nature, and the shrewdness of an intelligent and enterprising people.

Perhaps, through mistaken or ill-directed hospitality, or from the prompt disposition to cheer and countenance the stranger, prevalent among my countrymen, they may have been treated with unwonted respect in America;

and having been accustomed all their lives to consider themselves below the surface of good society, and brought up in a servile feeling of inferiority, they become arrogant on the common boon of civility; they attribute to the lowliness of others their own elevation; and underrate a society where there are no artificial distinctions, and where, by any chance, such individuals as themselves can rise to consequence.

One would suppose, however, that information coming from such sources, on a subject where the truth is so desirable, would be received with caution by the censors of the press; that the motives of these men, their veracity, their opportunities of inquiry and observation, and their capacities for judging correctly, would be rigorously scrutinised before their evidence was admitted in such sweeping extent against a kindred nation. The very reverse, however, is the case, and it furnishes a striking instance of human inconsistency. Nothing can surpass the vigilance with which English critics will examine the credibility of the traveller who publishes an account of some distant and comparatively unimportant country. How warily will they compare the measurements of a pyramid, or the descriptions of a ruin; and how sternly will they censure any inaccuracy in these contributions of merely curious knowledge; while they will receive with eagerness and unhesitating faith the gross misrepresentations of coarse and obscure writers, concerning a country with which their own is placed in the most important and delicate relations. Nay, they will even make these apocryphal volumes text-books on which to enlarge with a zeal and an ability worthy of a more generous cause.

I shall not, however, dwell on this irksome and hackneyed topic; nor should I have adverted to it, but for the undue interest apparently taken in it by my countrymen, and certain injurious effects which I apprehend it might produce upon the national feeling. We attach too much consequence to these attacks. They cannot do us any essential injury. The tissue of misrepresentation attempted to be woven round us are like cobwebs woven round the limbs of an infant giant. Our country continually outgrows them. One falsehood after another falls off of itself. We have but to live on, and every day we live a whole volume of refutation. All the writers of England united, if we could for a moment suppose their great minds stooping to so unworthy a combination, could not conceal our rapidly-growing importance and matchless prosperity. They could not conceal that these are owing, not merely to physical and local, but also to moral causes—to the political liberty, the general diffusion of knowledge, the prevalence of sound moral and religious principles, which give force and sustained energy to the character of a people, and which, in fact, have been the acknowledged and wonderful supporters of their own national power and glory.

But why are we so exquisitely alive to the aspersions of England? Why do we suffer ourselves to be so affected by the contumely she has endeavoured to cast upon us? It is not in the opinion of England alone that honour lives, and reputation has its being. The world at large is the arbiter of a nation's fame; with its thousand eyes it witnesses a nation's deeds, and from their collective testimony is national glory or national disgrace established.

For ourselves, therefore, it is comparatively of but little importance whether England does us justice or not; it is, perhaps, of far more importance to herself. She is instilling anger and resentment into the bosom of a youthful nation, to grow with its growth and strengthen with its strength. If in America, as some of her writers are labouring to convince her, she is hereafter to find an invidious rival and a gigantic foe, she may thank those very writers for having provoked rivalship and irritated hostility. Everyone knows the all-pervading influence of literature at the present day, and how much the opinions and passions of mankind are under its control. The mere contests of the sword are temporary; their wounds are but in the flesh, and it is the pride of the generous to forgive and forget them; but the slanders of the pen pierce to the heart; they rankle longest in the noblest spirits; they dwell ever present in the mind, and render it morbidly sensitive to the most trifling collision. It is but seldom that any one overt act produces hostilities between two nations; there exists, most commonly, a previous jealousy and ill-will; a predisposition to take offence. Trace these to their cause, and how often will they be found to originate in the mischievous effusions of mercenary writers; who, secure in their closets, and for ignominious bread, concoct and circulate the venom that is to inflame the generous and the brave.

I am not laying too much stress upon this point; for it applies most emphatically to our particular case. Over no nation does the press hold a more absolute control than over the people of America; for the universal education of the poorest classes makes every individual a reader. There is nothing published in England on the subject of our country that does not circulate through every part of it. There is not a calumny dropped from English pen, nor an unworthy sarcasm uttered by an English statesman, that does not go to blight good-will, and add to the mass of latent resentment. Possessing, then, as England does, the fountain-head whence the literature of the language flows, how completely is it in her power, and how truly is it her duty, to make it the medium of amiable and magnanimous feeling—a stream where the two nations might meet together and drink in peace and kindness. Should she, however, persist in turning it to waters of bitterness, the time may come when she may repent her folly. The present friendship of America may be of but little moment to her, but the future destinies of that country do not admit of a doubt; over those of England there lower some shadows of uncertainty. Should, then, a day of gloom arrive; should those reverses overtake her from which the proudest empires have not been exempt, she may look back with regret at her infatuation, in repulsing from her side a nation she might have grappled to her bosom, and thus destroying her only chance for real friendship beyond the boundaries of her own dominions.

There is a general impression in England, that the people of the United States are inimical to the parent country. It is one of the errors which have been diligently propagated by designing writers. There is, doubtless, considerable political hostility, and a general soreness at the illiberality of the English press; but, generally speaking, the prepossessions of the people are strongly in favour of England. Indeed, at one time, they amounted, in many parts of the Union, to an absurd degree of bigotry. The bare name of Englishman was a passport to the confidence and hospitality of every family, and too often gave a transient currency to the worthless and the ungrateful. Throughout the country there was something of enthusiasm connected with the idea of England. We looked to it with a hallowed feeling of tenderness and veneration, as the land of our forefathers—the august repository of the monuments and antiquities of our race—the birthplace and mausoleum of the sages and heroes of our paternal history. After our own country, there was none in whose glory we more delighted—none whose good opinion we were more anxious to possess—none towards which our hearts yearned with such throbbings of warm consanguinity. Even during the late war, whenever there was the least opportunity for kind feelings to spring forth, it was the delight of the generous spirits of our country to show that, in the midst of hostilities, they still kept alive the sparks of future friendship.

Is all this to be at an end? Is this golden band of kindred sympathies, so rare between nations, to be broken for ever? Perhaps it is for the best—it may dispel an illusion which might have kept us in mental vasselage; which might have interfered occasionally with our true interests, and prevented the growth of proper national pride. But it is hard to give up the kindred tie! and there are feelings dearer than interest—closer to the heart than pride—that will still make us cast back a look of regret, as we wander farther and farther from the paternal roof, and lament the waywardness of the parent that would repel the affections of the child.

Short-sighted and injudicious, however, as the conduct of England may be in this system of aspersion, recrimination on our part would be equally ill-judged. I speak not of a prompt and spirited vindication of our country, nor the keenest castigation of her slanderers—but I allude to a disposition to retaliate in kind; to retort sarcasm, and inspire prejudice; which seems to be spreading widely among our writers. Let us guard particularly against such a temper, for it would double the evil instead of redressing the wrong. Nothing is so easy and inviting as the retort of abuse and sarcasm; but it is a paltry and an unprofitable contest. It is the alternative of a morbid mind, fretted into petulance, rather than warmed into indignation. If England is willing to permit the mean jealousies of trade, or the rancorous animosities of politics, to deprave the integrity of her press, and poison the fountain of public opinion, let us beware of her example. She may deem it her interest to diffuse error, and engender antipathy, for the purpose of checking emigration; we have no purpose of the kind to serve. Neither have we any spirit of national jealousy to gratify—for as yet, in all our rivalships with England, we are the rising and the gaining party. There can be no end to answer, therefore, but the gratification of resentment—a mere spirit of retaliation; and even that is impotent. Our retorts are never republished in England; they fall short, therefore, of their aim; but they foster a querulous and peevish temper among our writers; they sour the sweet flow of our early literature, and sow thorns and brambles among its blossoms. What is still worse, they circulate through our own country, and, as far as they have effect, excite

virulent national prejudices. This last is the evil most especially to be depre-
cated. Governed, as we are, entirely by public opinion, the utmost care should
be taken to preserve the purity of the public mind. Knowledge is power, and
truth is knowledge; whoever, therefore, knowingly propagates a prejudice,
wilfully saps the foundation of his country's strength.

The members of a republic, above all other men, should be candid and
dispassionate. They are, individually, portions of the sovereign mind and
sovereign will, and should be enabled to come to all questions of national
concern with calm and unbiassed judgments. From the peculiar nature of
our relations with England, we must have more frequent questions of a
difficult and delicate character with her than with any other nation; questions
that affect the most acute and excitable feelings; and as, in the adjusting of
these, our national measures must ultimately be determined by popular sentiment, we cannot be too anxiously attentive to purify it from all latent passion
or prepossession.

Opening, too, as we do, an asylum for strangers from every portion of the
earth, we should receive all with impartiality. It should be our pride to
exhibit an example of one nation, at least, destitute of national antipathies, and
exercising not merely the overt acts of hospitality, but those more rare and
noble courtesies which spring from liberality of opinion.

What have we to do with national prejudices? They are the inveterate
diseases of old countries, contracted in rude and ignorant ages, when nations
knew but little of each other, and looked beyond their own boundaries with
distrust and hostility. We, on the contrary, have sprung into national existence
in an enlightened and philosophic age, when the different parts of the habitable
world, and the various branches of the human family, have been indefatigably
studied and made known to each other; and we forego the advantages of
our birth, if we do not shake off the national prejudices, as we would the
local superstitions of the old world.

But, above all, let us not be influenced by any angry feelings, so far as to
shut our eyes to the perception of what is really excellent and amiable in
the English character. We are a young people, necessarily an imitative one,
and must take our examples and models, in a great degree, from the existing
nations of Europe. There is no country more worthy of our study than
England. The spirit of her constitution is most analagous to ours. The manners
of her people—their intellectual activity—their freedom of opinion—their habits
of thinking on those subjects which concern the dearest interests and most
sacred charities of private life, are all congenial to the American character; and,
in fact, are all intrinsically excellent; for it is in the moral feeling of the people
that the deep foundations of British prosperity are laid; and however the superstructure may be timeworn, or overrun by abuses, there must be something
solid in the basis, admirable in the materials, and stable in the structure of an
edifice, that so long has towered unshaken amidst the tempests of the world.

Let it be the pride of our writers, therefore, discarding all feelings of irritation, and disdaining to retaliate the illiberality of British authors, to speak of
the English nation without prejudice, and with determined candour. While

they rebuke the indiscriminating bigotry with which some of our countrymen admire and imitate everything English, merely because it is English, let them frankly point out what is really worthy of approbation. We may thus place England before us as a perpetual volume of reference, wherein are recorded sound deductions from ages of experience; and while we avoid the errors and absurdities which may have crept into the page, we may draw thence golden maxims of practical wisdom, wherewith to strengthen and to embellish our national character.

RURAL LIFE IN ENGLAND

Oh! friendly to the best pursuits of man,
Friendly to thought, to virtue, and to peace,
*Domestic life in rural pleasures past!—*COWPER.

THE STRANGER who would form a correct opinion of the English character, must not confine his observations to the Metropolis. He must go forth into the country; he must sojourn in villages and hamlets; he must visit castles, villas, farm-houses, cottages; he must wander through parks and gardens; along hedges and green lanes; he must loiter about country churches; attend wakes and fairs, and other rural festivals; and cope with the people in all their conditions, and all their habits and humours.

In some countries the large cities absorb the wealth and fashion of the nation; they are the only fixed abodes of elegant and intelligent society, and the country is inhabited almost entirely by boorish peasantry. In England, on the contrary, the Metropolis is a mere gathering-place, or general rendez-vous of the polite classes, where they devote a small portion of the year to a hurry of gaiety and dissipation, and having indulged this kind of carnival, return again to the apparently more congenial habits of rural life. The various orders of society are therefore diffused over the whole surface of the kingdom, and the most retired neighbourhoods afford specimens of the different ranks.

The English, in fact, are strongly gifted with the rural feeling. They possess a quick sensibility to the beauties of nature, and a keen relish for the pleasures and employments of the country. This passion seems inherent in them. Even the inhabitants of cities, born and brought up among brick walls and bustling streets, enter with facility into rural habits, and evince a tact for rural occupation. The merchant has his snug retreat in the vicinity of the Metropolis, where he often displays as much pride and zeal in the cultivation of his flower-garden, and the maturing of his fruits, as he does in the conduct of his business and the success of a commercial enterprise. Even those less fortunate individuals, who are doomed to pass their lives in the midst of din and traffic, contrive to have something that shall remind them of the green aspect of nature. In the most dark and dingy quarters of the city, the drawing-room window resembles frequently a bank of flowers; every spot capable of vegetation has its grass-plot and flower-bed; and every square its mimic park, laid out with picturesque taste, and gleaming with refreshing verdure.

Those who see the Englishman only in town are apt to form an unfavourable opinion of his social character. He is either absorbed in business, or distracted by the thousand engagements that dissipate time, thought, and feeling, in this huge metropolis. He has, therefore, too commonly a look of hurry and abstraction. Wherever he happens to be, he is on the point of going somewhere else; at the moment he is talking on one subject, his mind is wandering to another; and while paying a friendly visit, he is calculating how he shall economise time so as to pay the other visits allotted in the morning. An immense metropolis, like London, is calculated to make men selfish and uninteresting. In their casual and transient meetings they can but deal briefly in commonplaces. They present but the cold superficies of character—its rich and genial qualities have no time to be warmed into a flow.

It is in the country that the Englishman gives scope to his natural feelings. He breaks loose gladly from the cold formalities and negative civilities of town; throws off his habits of shy reserve, and becomes joyous and free-hearted. He manages to collect round him all the conveniences and elegancies of polite life, and to banish its restraints. His country-seat abounds with every requisite, either for studious retirement, tasteful gratification, or rural exercise. Books, paintings, music, horses, dogs, and sporting implements of all kinds, are at hand. He puts no constraint either upon his guests or himself, but in the true spirit of hospitality provides the means of enjoyment, and leaves every one to partake according to his inclination.

The taste of the English in the cultivation of land, and in what is called landscape gardening, is unrivalled. They have studied nature intently, and discover an exquisite sense of her beautiful forms and harmonious combinations. Those charms, which in other countries she lavishes in wild solitudes, are here assembled round the haunts of domestic life. They seem to have caught her coy and furtive graces, and spread them, like witchery, about their rural abodes.

Nothing can be more imposing than the magnificence of English park scenery. Vast lawns that extend like sheets of vivid green, with here and there clumps of gigantic trees, heaping up rich piles of foliage: the solemn pomp of groves and woodland glades, with the deer trooping in silent herds across them; the hare, bounding away to the covert; or the pheasant, suddenly bursting upon the wing: the brook, taught to wind in natural meanderings, or expand into a glassy lake: the sequestered pool, reflecting the quivering trees, with the yellow leaf sleeping on its bosom, and the trout roaming fearlessly about its limpid waters, while some rustic temple or sylvan statue, grown green and dank with age, gives an air of classic sanctity to the seclusion.

These are but a few of the features of park scenery; but what most delights me, is the creative talent with which the English decorate the unostentatious abodes of middle life. The rudest habitation, the most unpromising and scanty portion of land, in the hands of an Englishman of taste, becomes a little paradise. With a nicely discriminating eye, he seizes at once upon its capabilities, and pictures in his mind the future landscape. The sterile spot grows into loveliness under his hand; and yet the operations of art which produce the effect are scarcely to be perceived. The cherishing and training of some trees; the cautious pruning of others; the nice distribution of flowers and plants of tender and graceful foliage; the introduction of a green slope of velvet turf; the partial opening to a peep of blue distance, or silver gleam of water: all these are managed with a delicate tact, a pervading yet quiet assiduity, like the magic touchings with which a painter finishes up a favourite picture.

The residence of people of fortune and refinement in the country has diffused a degree of taste and elegance in rural economy, that descends to the lowest class. The very labourer, with his thatched cottage and narrow slip of ground, attends to their embellishment. The trim hedge, the grass-plot before the door, the little flower-bed bordered with snug box, the woodbine trained up against the wall, and hanging its blossoms about the lattice, the pot of flowers in the window, the holly, providentially planted about the house, to cheat winter of its dreariness, and to throw in a semblance of green summer to cheer the fireside: all these bespeak the influence of taste, flowing down from high sources, and pervading the lowest levels of the public mind. If ever Love, as poets sing, delights to visit a cottage, it must be the cottage of an English peasant.

The fondness for rural life among the higher classes of the English has had a great and salutary effect upon the national character. I do not know a finer race of men than the English gentlemen. Instead of the softness and effeminacy which characterise the men of rank in most countries, they exhibit a union of elegance and strength, a robustness of frame and freshness of complexion, which I am inclined to attribute to their living so much in the open air, and pursuing so eagerly the invigorating recreations of the country. These hardy exercises produce also a healthful tone of mind and spirits, and a manliness and simplicity of manners, which even the follies and dissipations of the town cannot easily pervert, and can never entirely destroy. In the country, too, the different orders of society seem to approach more freely, to be more disposed to blend and operate favourably upon each other. The distinctions between them do not appear to be so marked and impassable as in the cities. The manner in which property has been distributed into small estates and farms has established a regular gradation from the nobleman, through the classes of gentry, small landed proprietors, and substantial farmers, down to the labouring peasantry, and while it has thus banded the extremes of society together, has infused into each intermediate rank a spirit of independence. This, it must be confessed, is not so universally the case at present as it was formerly; the larger estates having, in late years of distress, absorbed the smaller; and, in some parts of the country, almost annihilated the sturdy race of small farmers. These, however, I believe, are but casual breaks in the general system I have mentioned.

In rural occupation there is nothing mean and debasing. It leads a man forth among scenes of natural grandeur and beauty; it leaves him to the workings of his own mind, operated upon by the purest and most elevating of external influences. Such a man may be simple and rough, but he cannot be vulgar. The man of refinement, therefore, finds nothing revolting in an intercourse with the lower orders in rural life, as he does when he casually mingles with the lower orders of cities. He lays aside his distance and reserve, and is glad to waive the distinctions of rank, and to enter into the honest, heartfelt enjoyments of common life. Indeed, the very amusements of the country bring men more and more together; and the sound of hound and horn blend all feelings into harmony. I believe this is one great reason why the nobility and gentry are more popular among the inferior orders in England than they are in any other country; and why the latter have endured so many excessive pressures and extremities, without repining more generally at the unequal distribution of fortune and privilege.

To this mingling of cultivated and rustic society may also be attributed the rural feeling that runs through British literature; the frequent use of illustrations from rural life; those incomparable descriptions of nature that abound in the British poets, that have continued down from *The Flower and the Leaf* of Chaucer, and have brought into our closets all the freshness and fragrance of the dewy landscape. The pastoral writers of other countries appear as if they had paid Nature an occasional visit, and become acquainted with her general charms; but the British poets have lived and revelled with her—they have wooed her in her most secret haunts—they have watched her minutest caprices. A spray could not tremble in the breeze—a leaf could not rustle to the ground—a diamond drop could not patter in the stream—a fragrance could not exhale from the humble violet, nor a daisy unfold its crimson tints to the morning, but it has been noticed by these impassioned and delicate observers, and wrought up into some beautiful morality.

The effect of this devotion of elegant minds to rural occupations has been wonderful on the face of the country. A great part of the island is rather level, and would be monotonous, were it not for the charms of culture: but it is studded and gemmed, as it were, with castles and palaces, and embroidered with parks and gardens. It does not abound in grand and sublime prospects, but rather in little home scenes of rural repose and sheltered quiet. Every antique farm-house and moss-grown cottage is a picture; and as the roads are continually winding, and the view is shut in by groves and hedges, the eye is delighted by a continual succession of small landscapes of captivating loveliness.

The great charm, however, of English scenery is the moral feeling that seems to pervade it. It is associated in the mind with ideas of order, of quiet, of sober, well-established principles, of hoary usage and reverend custom. Everything seems to be the growth of ages of regular and peaceful existence. The old church of remote architecture, with its low, massive portal, its Gothic tower, its windows rich with tracery and painted glass, in scrupulous preservation, its stately monuments of warriors and worthies of the olden time, ancestors of the present lords of the soil; its tombstones, recording successive generations of sturdy yeomanry, whose progeny still plough the same fields, and kneel at the same altar—the parsonage, a quaint, irregular pile, partly antiquated, but repaired and altered in the tastes of various ages and occupants

—the stile and footpath leading from the churchyard, across pleasant fields, and along shady hedge-rows, according to an immemorial right of way— the neighbouring village, with its venerable cottages, its public green sheltered by trees, under which the forefathers of the present race have sported— the antique family mansion, standing apart in some little rural domain, but looking down with a protecting air on the surrounding scene: all these common features of English landscape evince a calm and settled security, and hereditary transmission of home-bred virtues and local attachments, that speak deeply and touchingly for the moral character of the nation.

It is a pleasing sight of a Sunday morning, when the bell is sending its sober melody across the quiet fields, to behold the peasantry in their best finery, with ruddy faces and modest cheerfulness, thronging tranquilly along the green lanes to church; but it is still more pleasing to see them in the evenings, gathering about their cottage doors, and appearing to exult in the humble comforts and embellishments which their own hands have spread around them.

It is this sweet home-feeling, this settled repose of affection in the domestic scene, that is, after all, the parent of the steadiest virtues and purest enjoyments; and I cannot close these desultory remarks better than by quoting the words of a modern English poet, who has depicted it with remarkable felicity,—

> Through each gradation, from the castled hall,
> The city dome, the villa crowned with shade,
> But chief from modest mansions numberless,
> In town or hamlet, shelt'ring middle life
> Down to the cottaged vale, and straw-roof'd shed;
> This western isle hath long been famed for scenes
> Where bliss domestic finds a dwelling-place;
> Domestic bliss, that, like a harmless dove,
> (Honour and sweet endearment keeping guard),
> Can centre in a little quiet nest
> All that desire would fly for through the earth;
> That can, the world eluding, be itself
> A world enjoyed; that wants no witnesses
> But its own sharers, and approving heaven;
> That, like a flower deep hid in rocky cleft,
> Smiles, though 'tis looking only at the sky.[1]

THE ART OF BOOK-MAKING

If that severe doom of Synesius be true—"It is a greater offence to steal dead men's labour than their clothes,"—what shall become of most writers?—BURTON'S "ANATOMY OF MELANCHOLY."

I HAVE often wondered at the extreme fecundity of the press, and how it comes to pass that so many heads, on which Nature seemed to have inflicted

[1] From a Poem on the Death of the Princess Charlotte, by the Reverend Rann Kennedy, A.M.

the curse of barrenness, should teem with voluminous productions. As a man travels on, however, in the journey of life, his objects of wonder daily diminish, and he is continually finding out some very simple cause for some great matter of marvel. Thus have I chanced, in my peregrinations about this great metropolis, to blunder upon a scene which unfolded to me some of the mysteries of the book-making craft, and at once put an end to my astonishment.

I was one summer's day loitering through the great saloons of the British Museum, with that listlessness with which one is apt to saunter about a museum in warm weather; sometimes lolling over the glass cases of minerals, sometimes studying the hieroglyphics on an Egyptian mummy, and sometimes trying, with nearly equal success, to comprehend the allegorical paintings on the lofty ceilings. Whilst I was gazing about in this idle way, my attention was attracted to a distant door, at the end of a suite of apartments. It was closed, but every now and then it would open, and some strange-favoured being, generally clothed in black, would steal forth, and glide through the rooms, without noticing any of the surrounding objects. There was an air of mystery about this that piqued my languid curiosity, and I determined to attempt the passage of that strait, and to explore the unknown regions beyond. The door yielded to my hand, with that facility with which the portals of enchanted castles yield to the adventurous knight-errant. I found myself in a spacious chamber, surrounded with great cases of venerable books. Above the cases, and just under the cornice, were arranged a great number of black-looking portraits of ancient authors. About the room were placed long tables, with stands for reading and writing, at which sat many pale, studious personages, poring intently over dusty volumes, rummaging among mouldy manuscripts, and taking copious notes of their contents. A hushed stillness reigned through this mysterious apartment, excepting that you might hear the racing of pens over sheets of paper, or occasionally, the deep sigh of one of these sages, as he shifted his position to turn over the page of an old folio; doubtless arising from that hollowness and flatulency incident to learned research.

Now and then one of these personages would write something on a small slip of paper, and ring a bell, whereupon a familiar would appear, take the paper in profound silence, glide out of the room, and return shortly loaded with ponderous tomes, upon which the other would fall tooth and nail with famished voracity. I had no longer a doubt that I had happened upon a body of magi, deeply engaged in the study of occult sciences. The scene reminded me of an old Arabian tale, of a philosopher shut up in an enchanted library, in the bosom of a mountain, which opened only once a year; where he made the spirits of the place bring him books of all kinds of dark knowledge, so that at the end of the year, when the magic portal once more swung open on its hinges, he issued forth so versed in forbidden lore, as to be able to soar above the heads of the multitude, and to control the powers of nature.

My curiosity being now fully aroused, I whispered to one of the familiars, as he was about to leave the room, and begged an interpretation of the strange scene before me. A few words were sufficient for the purpose. I found that these mysterious personages, whom I had mistaken for magi, were principally authors, and in the very act of manufacturing books. I was, in fact, in the reading-room of the great British Library—an immense collection of volumes of all ages and languages, many of which are now forgotten, and most of which are seldom read: one of these sequestered pools of obsolete literature, to which modern authors repair, and draw buckets full of classic lore, or "pure English, undefiled," wherewith to swell their own scanty rills of thought.

Being now in possession of the secret, I sat down in a corner, and watched the process of this book manufactory. I noticed one lean, bilious-looking wight, who sought none but the most worm-eaten volumes, printed in black-letter. He was evidently constructing some work of profound erudition, that would be purchased by every man who wished to be thought learned, placed upon a conspicuous shelf of his library, or laid open upon his table, but never read. I observed him, now and then, draw a large fragment of biscuit out of his pocket, and gnaw; whether it was dinner, or whether he was endeavouring to keep off that exhaustion of the stomach produced by much pondering over dry works, I leave to harder students than myself to determine.

There was one dapper little gentleman in bright-coloured clothes, with a chirping, gossiping expression of countenance, who had all the appearance of an author on good terms with his bookseller. After considering him attentively, I recognised in him a diligent getter-up of miscellaneous works, which bustled off well with the trade. I was curious to see how he manu-factured his wares. He made more stir and show of business than any of the others; dipping into various books, fluttering over the leaves of manuscripts, taking a morsel out of one, a morsel out of another, "line upon line, precept upon precept, here a little and there a little." The contents of his book seemed to be as heterogeneous as those of the witches' cauldron in *Macbeth*. It was here a finger and there a thumb, toe of frog and blind-worm's sting, with his own gossip poured in like "baboon's blood," to make the medley "slab and good."

After all, thought I, may not this pilfering disposition be implanted in authors for wise purposes; may it not be the way in which Providence has taken care that the seeds of knowledge and wisdom shall be preserved from age to age, in spite of the inevitable decay of the works in which they were first produced? We see that nature has wisely, though whimsically, provided for the conveyance of seeds from clime to clime, in the maws of certain birds; so that animals which, in themselves, are little better than carrion, and apparently the lawless plunderers of the orchard and the cornfield, are, in fact, Nature's carriers, to disperse and perpetuate her blessings. In like manner, the beauties and fine thoughts of ancient and obsolete authors are caught up by these flights of predatory writers, and cast forth again to flourish and bear fruit in a remote and distant tract of time. Many of their works, also, undergo a kind of metempsychosis, and spring up under new forms. What was formerly a ponderous history, revives in the shape of a romance—an old legend changes into a modern play—and a sober philosophical treatise furnishes the body for a whole series of bouncing and sparkling essays. Thus it is in the clearing of our American woodlands; where we burn down a forest of stately pines, a progeny of dwarf oaks start up in their place; and we never see the prostrate trunk of a tree mouldering into soil, but it gives birth to a whole tribe of fungi.

Let us not, then, lament over the decay and oblivion into which ancient writers descend; they do but submit to the great law of nature, which declares that all sublunary shapes of matter shall be limited in their duration, but which decrees, also, that their elements shall never perish. Generation after generation, both in animal and vegetable life, passes away, but the vital principle is transmitted to posterity, and the species continue to flourish. Thus, also, do authors beget authors, and having produced a numerous progeny, in a good old age they sleep with their fathers, that is to say, with the authors who preceded them, and from whom they had stolen.

Whilst I was indulging in these rambling fancies, I had leaned my head against a pile of reverend folios. Whether it was owing to the soporific emanations from these works; or to the profound quiet of the room; or to the lassitude arising from much wandering; or to an unlucky habit of napping at improper times and places, with which I am grievously afflicted—so it was, that I fell into a doze. Still, however, my imagination continued busy, and indeed the same scene remained before my mind's eye, only a little changed in some of the details. I dreamt that the chamber was still decorated with the portraits of ancient authors, but that the number was increased. The long tables had disappeared, and, in place of the sage magi, I beheld a ragged, threadbare throng, such as may be seen plying about the great repository of cast-off clothes, Monmouth Street. Whenever they seized upon a book, by one of those incongruities common to dreams, methought it turned into a garment of foreign or antique fashion, with which they proceeded to equip themselves. I noticed, however, that no one pretended to clothe himself from any particular suit, but took a sleeve from one, a cape from another, a skirt from a third, thus decking himself out piecemeal, while some of his original rags would peep out from among his borrowed finery.

There was a portly, rosy, well-fed parson, whom I observed ogling several mouldy polemical writers through an eye-glass. He soon contrived to slip on the voluminous mantle of one of the old fathers, and, having purloined the gray beard of another, endeavoured to look exceedingly wise; but the smirking commonplace of his countenance set at naught all the trappings of wisdom. One sickly-looking gentleman was busied embroidering a very flimsy garment with gold thread, drawn out of several old court-dresses of the reign of Queen Elizabeth. Another had trimmed himself magnificently from an illuminated manuscript, had stuck a nosegay in his bosom, culled from *The Paradise of Daintie Devices*, and, having put Sir Philip Sidney's hat on one side of his head, strutted off with an exquisite air of vulgar elegance. A third, who was but puny dimensions, had bolstered himself out bravely with the spoils from several obscure tracts of philosophy, so that he had a very imposing front; but he was lamentably tattered in rear, and I perceived that he had patched his small-clothes with scraps of parchment from a Latin author.

There were some well-dressed gentlemen, it is true, who only helped themselves to a gem or so, which sparkled among their own ornaments, without eclipsing them. Some, too, seemed to contemplate the costumes of the old writers, merely to imbibe their principles of taste, and to catch their air and spirit; but I grieve to say, that too many were apt to array themselves from top to toe, in the patchwork manner I have mentioned. I shall not omit to speak of one genius, in drab breeches and gaiters, and an Arcadian hat, who had a violent propensity to the pastoral, but whose rural wanderings had been confined to the classic haunts of Primrose Hill, and the solitudes of the Regent's Park. He had decked himself in wreaths and ribands from all the old pastoral poets, and, hanging his head on one side, went about with a fantastical lackadaisical air, "babbling about green fields." But the personage that most struck my attention was a pragmatical old gentleman, in clerical robes, with a remarkably large and square, but bald head. He entered the room wheezing and puffing, elbowed his way through the throng, with a look of sturdy self-confidence, and, having laid hands upon a thick Greek quarto, clapped it upon his head, and swept majestically away in a formidable frizzled wig.

In the height of this literary masquerade, a cry suddenly resounded from every side, of "Thieves! thieves!" I looked, and lo! the portraits about the wall became animated! The old authors thrust out, first a head, then a shoulder, from the canvas, looked down curiously, for an instant, upon the motley throng, and then descended, with fury in their eyes, to claim their rifled property. The scene of scampering and hubbub that ensued baffles all description. The unhappy culprits endeavoured in vain to escape with plunder. On one side might be seen half a dozen old monks, stripping a modern professor; on another, there was sad devastation carried into the ranks of modern dramatic writers. Beaumont and Fletcher, side by side, raged round the field like Castor and Pollux; and sturdy Ben Jonson enacted more wonders than when a volunteer with the army in Flanders. As to the dapper little compiler of farragos, mentioned some time since, he had arrayed himself in as many patches and colours as Harlequin, and there was as fierce a contention of claimants about him, as about the dead body of Patroclus. I was grieved to see many men, to whom I had been accustomed to look up with awe and reverence, fain to steal off with scarce a rag to cover their nakedness. Just then my eye was caught by the pragmatical old gentleman in the Greek grizzled wig, who was scrambling away in sore affright with half a score of authors in full cry after him! They were close upon his haunches: in a twinkling off went his wig; at every turn some strip of raiment was peeled away; until in a few moments, from his domineering pomp, he shrunk into a little, pursy, "chopped bald shot," and made his exit with only a few tags and rags fluttering at his back.

There was something so ludicrous in the catastrophe of this learned Theban, that I burst into an immoderate fit of laughter, which broke the whole illusion. The tumult and the scuffle were at an end. The chamber resumed its usual appearance. The old authors shrunk back into their picture-frames, and hung in shadowy solemnity along the walls. In short, I found myself wide awake in my corner, with the whole assemblage of book-worms gazing at me with astonishment. Nothing of the dream had been real but my burst of laughter, a sound never before heard in that grave sanctuary, and so abhorrent to the ears of wisdom, as to electrify the fraternity.

The librarian now stepped up to me, and demanded whether I had a card of admission. At first I did not comprehend him, but I soon found that the library was a kind of literary "preserve," subject to game-laws, and that no one must presume to hunt there without special license and permission. In a word, I stood convicted of being an arrant poacher, and was glad to make a precipitate retreat, lest I should have a whole pack of authors let loose upon me.

A ROYAL POET

> *Though your body be confined,*
> *And soft love a prisoner bound,*
> *Yet the beauty of your mind*
> *Neither check nor chain hath found.*
> *Look out nobly, then, and dare*
> *Even the fetters that you wear.*—FLETCHER.

ON A SOFT SUNNY MORNING, in the genial month of May, I made an excursion to Windsor Castle. It is a place full of storied and poetical associations. The very external aspect of the proud old pile is enough to inspire high thought. It rears its irregular walls and massive towers, like a mural crown, round the brow of a lofty ridge, waves its royal banner in the clouds, and looks down with a lordly air upon the surrounding world.

On this morning the weather was of that voluptuous vernal kind which calls forth all the latent romance of a man's temperament, filling his mind with music, and disposing him to quote poetry and dream of beauty. In wandering through the magnificent saloons and long echoing galleries of the castle, I passed with indifference by whole rows of portraits of warriors and statesmen, but lingered in the chamber where hang the likenesses of the beauties which graced the gay court of Charles the Second, and as I gazed upon them, depicted with amorous half-dishevelled tresses, and the sleepy eye of love, I blessed the pencil of Sir Peter Lely, which had thus enabled me to bask in the reflected rays of beauty. In traversing also the "large green courts," with sunshine beaming on the gray walls, and glancing along the velvet turf, my mind was engrossed with the image of the tender, the gallant, but hapless Surrey, and his account of his loiterings about them in his stripling days, when enamoured of the Lady Geraldine,—

> *"With eyes cast up unto the maiden's tower,*
> *With easie sighs, such as men draw in love."*

In this mood of mere poetical susceptibility, I visited the ancient Keep of the Castle, where James the First of Scotland, the pride and theme of Scottish poets and historians, was for many years of his youth detained a prisoner of state. It is a large gray tower, that has stood the brunt of ages, and is still in good preservation. It stands on a mound which elevates it above the other parts of the castle, and a great flight of steps leads to the interior. In the armoury, a Gothic hall, furnished with weapons of various kinds and ages, I was shown a coat of armour hanging against the wall which had once belonged to James. Hence I was conducted up a staircase to a suite of apartments of faded magnificence, hung with storied tapestry, which formed his prison, and the scene of that passionate and fanciful amour which has woven into the web of his story the magical hues of poetry and fiction.

The whole history of this amiable but unfortunate prince is highly romantic. At the tender age of eleven he was sent from home by his father, Robert III., and destined for the French court, to be reared under the eye of the French monarch, secure from the treachery and danger that surrounded the royal house of Scotland. It was his mishap in the course of his voyage to fall into the hands of the English, and he was detained prisoner by Henry IV., notwithstanding that a truce existed between the two countries.

The intelligence of his capture, coming in the train of many sorrows and disasters, proved fatal to his unhappy father. "The news," we are told, "was brought to him while at supper, and did so overwhelm him with grief, that he was almost ready to give up the ghost into the hands of the servant that attended him. But being carried to his bed-chamber, he abstained from all food, and in three days died of hunger and grief, at Rothesay."[1]

James was detained in captivity above eighteen years; but though deprived of personal liberty, he was treated with the respect due to his rank. Care was taken to instruct him in all the branches of useful knowledge cultivated at that period, and to give him those mental and personal accomplishments deemed proper for a prince. Perhaps, in this respect, his imprisonment was an advantage, as it enabled him to apply himself the more exclusively to his improvement, and quietly to imbibe that rich fund of knowledge, and to cherish those elegant tastes which have given such a lustre to his memory. The picture drawn of him in early life by the Scottish historians is highly captivating, and seems rather the description of a hero of romance, than of a character in real history. He was well learnt, we are told, "to fight with the sword, to joust, to tournay, to wrestle, to sing and dance; he was an expert mediciner, right crafty in playing both of lute and harp, and sundry other instruments of music, and was expert in grammar, oratory, and poetry."[2]

With this combination of manly and delicate accomplishments, fitting him to shine both in active and elegant life, and calculated to give him an intense relish for joyous existence, it must have been a severe trial, in an age of bustle and chivalry, to pass the spring-time of his years in monotonous captivity

[1]Buchanan.
[2]Ballenden's Translation of Hector Boyce.

It was the good fortune of James, however, to be gifted with a powerful poetic fancy, and to be visited in his prison by the choicest inspirations of the muse. Some minds corrode and grow inactive under the loss of personal liberty; others grow morbid and irritable; but it is the nature of the poet to become tender and imaginative in the loneliness of confinement. He banquets upon the honey of his own thoughts, and, like the captive bird, pours forth his soul in melody.

> Have you not seen the nightingale,
> A pilgrim coop'd into a cage,
> How doth she chant her wonted tale,
> In that her lonely hermitage!
> Even there her charming melody doth prove
> That all her boughs are trees, her cage a grove.[3]

Indeed, it is the divine attribute of the imagination, that it is irrepressible, unconfinable; that when the real world is shut out, it can create a world for itself, and with a necromantic power, can conjure up glorious shapes and forms, and brilliant visions, to make solitude populous, and irradiate the gloom of the dungeon. Such was the world of pomp and pageant that lived round Tasso in his dismal cell at Ferrara, when he conceived the splendid scenes of his "Jerusalem;" and we may consider the "King's Quair," composed by James during his captivity at Windsor, as another of those beautiful breakings-forth of the soul from the restraint and gloom of the prison-house.

The subject of the poem is his love for the Lady Jane Beaufort, daughter of the Earl of Somerset, and a princess of the blood royal of England, of whom he became enamoured in the course of his captivity. What gives it a peculiar value is, that it may be considered a transcript of the royal bard's true feelings, and the story of his real loves and fortunes. It is not often that sovereigns write poetry, or that poets deal in fact. It is gratifying to the pride of a common man to find a monarch thus suing, as it were, for admission into his closet, and seeking to win his favour by administering to his pleasures. It is a proof of the honest equality of intellectual competition, which strips off all the trappings of factitious dignity, brings the candidate down to a level with his fellow-men, and obliges him to depend on his own native powers for distinction. It is curious, too, to get at the history of a monarch's heart, and to find the simple affections of human nature throbbing under the ermine. But James had learnt to be a poet before he was a king; he was schooled in adversity, and reared in the company of his own thoughts. Monarchs have seldom time to parley with their hearts, or to meditate their minds into poetry; and had James been brought up amidst the adulation and gaiety of a court, we should never, in all probability, have had such a poem as the "Quair."

I have been particularly interested by those parts of the poem which breathe his immediate thoughts concerning his situation, or which are con-

[3]Roger l'Estrange.

nected with the apartment in the tower. They have thus a personal and local charm, and are given with such circumstantial truth, as to make the reader present with the captive in his prison, and the companion of his meditations.

Such is the account which he gives of his weariness of spirit, and of the incident which first suggested the idea of writing the poem. It was the still mid-watch of a clear moonlight night; the stars, he says, were twinkling as fire in the high vault of heaven, and "Cynthia rinsing her golden locks in Aquarius." He lay in bed wakeful and restless, and took a book to beguile the tedious hours. The book he chose was Boetius's *Consolations of Philosophy*, a work popular among the writers of that day, and which had been translated by his great prototype Chaucer. From the high eulogium in which he indulges, it is evident this was one of his favourite volumes while in prison; and indeed it is an admirable text-book for meditation under adversity. It is the legacy of a noble and enduring spirit, purified by sorrow and suffering, bequeathing to its successors in calamity the maxims of sweet morality, and the trains of eloquent but simple reasoning by which it was enabled to bear up against the various ills of life. It is a talisman which the unfortunate may treasure up in his bosom, or, like the good King James, lay upon his nightly pillow.

After closing the volume, he turns its contents over in his mind, and gradually falls into a fit of musing on the fickleness of fortune, the vicissitudes of his own life, and the evils that had overtaken him even in his tender youth. Suddenly he hears the bell ringing to matins; but its sound, chiming in with his melancholy fancies, seems to him like a voice exhorting him to write his story. In the spirit of poetic errantry he determines to comply with this intimation; he therefore takes pen in hand, makes with it a sign of the cross to implore a benediction, and sallies forth into the fairy land of poetry. There is something extremely fanciful in all this, and it is interesting as furnishing a striking and beautiful instance of the simple manner in which whole trains of poetical thought are sometimes awakened, and literary enterprises suggested to the mind.

In the course of his poem he more than once bewails the peculiar hardness of his fate; thus doomed to lonely and inactive life, and shut up from the freedom and pleasure of the world, in which the meanest animal indulges unrestrained. There is a sweetness, however, in his very complaints; they are the lamentations of an amiable and social spirit at being denied the indulgence of its kind and generous propensities; there is nothing in them harsh nor exaggerated; they flow with a natural and touching pathos, and are perhaps rendered more touching by their simple brevity. They contrast finely with those elaborate and iterated repinings, which we sometimes meet with in poetry;—the effusions of morbid minds sickening under miseries of their own creating, and venting their bitterness upon an unoffending world. James speaks of his privations with acute sensibility, but having mentioned them, passes on, as if his manly mind disdained to brood over unavoidable calamities. When such a spirit breaks forth into complaint, however brief, we are aware how great must be the suffering that extorts the murmur. We sympathise with

James, a romantic, active, and accomplished prince, cut off in the lustihood of youth from all the enterprise, the noble uses, and vigorous delights of life; as we do with Milton, alive to all the beauties of nature and glories of art, when he breathes forth brief, but deep-toned lamentations over his perpetual blindness.

Had not James evinced a deficiency of poetic artifice, we might almost have suspected that these lowerings of gloomy reflection were meant as preparative to the brightest scene of his story; and so contrast with that refulgence of light and loveliness, that exhilarating accompaniment of bird and song, and foliage and flower, and all the revel of the year, with which he ushers in the lady of his heart. It is this scene, in particular, which throws all the magic of romance about the old castle keep. He had risen, he says, at daybreak, according to custom, to escape from the dreary meditations of a sleepless pillow. "Bewailing in his chamber thus alone," despairing of all joy and remedy, "fortired of thought and wobegone," he had wandered to the window, to indulge the captive's miserable solace of gazing wistfully upon the world from which he is excluded. The window looked forth upon a small garden which lay at the foot of the tower. It was a quiet, sheltered spot, adorned with arbours and green alleys, and protected from the passing gaze by trees and hawthorn hedges.

> Now was there made, fast by the tower's wall,
>   A garden faire, and in the corners set
> An arbour green, with wandis long and small
>   Railed about, and so with leaves beset
> Was all the place, and hawthorn hedges knet,
>   That lyf[4] was none, walkyng there forbye
>   That might within scarce any wight espye.
>
> So thick the branches and the leves grene,
>   Beshaded all the alleys that there were,
> And midst of every arbour might be sene
>   The sharpe, grene, swete juniper,
> Growing so fair, with branches here and there,
>   That as it seemed to a lyf without,
>   The boughs did spread the arbour all about.
>
> And on the small grene twistis[5] set
>   The lytel swete nightingales, and sung
> So loud and clear, the hymnis consecrate
>   Of lovis use, now soft, now loud among,
> That all the garden and the wallis rung
>   Right of their song——

[4]Lyf, person.

[5]Twistis, small boughs or twigs.

NOTE.—The language of the quotations is generally modernised.

It was the month of May, when everything was in bloom, and he interprets the song of the nightingale into the language of his enamoured feeling.

> *Worship, all ye that lovers be, this May,*
> *For of your bliss the kalends are begun,*
> *And sing with us, away, winter, away,*
> *Come, summer, come, the sweet season and sun.*

As he gazes on the scene, and listens to the notes of the birds, he gradually relapses into one of those tender and undefinable reveries, which fill the youthful bosom in this delicious season. He wonders what this love may be, of which he has so often read, and which thus seems breathed forth in the quickening breath of May, and melting all nature into ecstasy and song. If it really be so great a felicity, and if it be a boon thus generally dispensed to the most insignificant beings, why is he alone cut off from its enjoyments?

> *Oft would I think, O Lord, what may this be,*
> *That love is of such noble myght and kynde?*
> *Loving his folke, and such prosperitee*
> *Is it of him, as we in books do find:*
> *May he oure hertes setten*⁶ *and unbynd:*
> *Hath he upon our hertes such maistrye?*
> *Or is all this but feynit fantasye?*
> *For giff he be of so grete excellence,*
> *That he of every wight hath care and charge,*
> *What have I gilt*⁷ *to him, or done offense,*
> *That I am thral'd, and birdis go at large?*

In the midst of his musing, as he casts his eye downward, he beholds "the fairest and the freshest young floure" that ever he had seen. It is the lovely Lady Jane, walking in the garden to enjoy the beauty of that "fresh May morrowe." Breaking thus suddenly upon his sight, in the moment of loneliness and excited susceptibility, she at once captivates the fancy of the romantic prince, and becomes the object of his wandering wishes, the sovereign of his ideal world.

There is, in this charming scene, an evident resemblance to the early part of Chaucer's *Knight's Tale;* where Palamon and Arcite fall in love with Emilia, whom they see walking in the garden of their prison. Perhaps the similarity of the actual fact to the incident which he had read in Chaucer may have induced James to dwell on it in his poem. His description of the Lady Jane is given in the picturesque and minute manner of his master; and being doubtless taken from the life, is a perfect portrait of a beauty of that day. He dwells, with the fondness of a lover, on every article of her apparel, from the net of pearl, splendent with emeralds and sapphires, that confined her golden hair,

---

⁶*Setten*, incline.

⁷*Gilt*, what injury have I done, &c.

even to the "goodly chaine of small orfeverye"[8] about her neck, whereby there
hung a ruby in shape of a heart, that seemed, he says, like a spark of fire burning
upon her white bosom. Her dress of white tissue was looped up to enable her
to walk with more freedom. She was accompanied by two female attendants,
and about her sported a little hound decorated with bells; probably the small
Italian hound of exquisite symmetry, which was a parlour favourite and a pet
among the fashionable dames of ancient times. James closes his description by
a burst of general eulogium,—

> In her was youth, beauty, with humble port,
> Bounty, richesse, and womanly feature;
> God better knows than my pen can report,
> Wisdom, largesse,[9] estate,[10] cunning[11] sure,
> In every point so guided her measure,
> In word, in deed, in shape, in countenance,
> That Nature·might no more her child advance.

The departure of the Lady Jane from the garden puts an end to this transient
riot of the heart. With her departs the amorous illusion that had shed a temporary charm over the scene of his captivity, and he relapses into loneliness,
now rendered tenfold more intolerable by this passing beam of unattainable
beauty. Through the long and weary day he repines at his unhappy lot, and
when evening approaches, and Phœbus, as he beautifully expresses it, had "bade
farewell to every leaf and flower," he still lingers at the window, and, laying
his head upon the cold stone, gives vent to a mingled flow of love and sorrow,
until, gradually lulled by the mute melancholy of the twilight hour, he lapses,
"half sleeping, half swoon," into a vision, which occupies the remainder of the
poem, and in which is allegorically shadowed out the history of his passion.

When he wakes from his trance, he rises from his stony pillow, and, pacing
his apartment, full of dreary reflections, questions his spirit whither it has been
wandering; whether, indeed, all that has passed before his dreaming fancy has
been conjured up by preceding circumstances; or whether it is a vision, intended to comfort and assure him in his despondency. If the latter, he prays
that some token may be sent to confirm the promise of happier days, given him
in his slumbers. Suddenly, a turtle-dove, of the purest whiteness, comes flying
in at the window, and alights upon his hand, bearing in her bill a branch of
red gilliflower, on the leaves of which is written, in letters of gold, the following sentence:—

> Awake! awake! I bring, lover, I bring
> The newis glad that blissful is, and sure
> Of thy comfort; now laugh, and play, and sing,
> For in the heaven decretit is thy cure.

[8]Wrought gold.
[9]*Largesse*, bounty.
[10]*Estate*, dignity.
[11]*Cunning*, discretion.

He receives the branch with mingled hope and dread; reads it with rapture: and this, he says, was the first token of his succeeding happiness. Whether this is a mere poetic fiction, or whether the Lady Jane did actually send him a token of her favour in this romantic way, remains to be determined according to the faith or fancy of the reader. He concludes his poem by intimating that the promise conveyed in the vision and by the flower is fulfilled, by his being restored to liberty, and made happy in the possession of the sovereign of his heart.

Such is the poetical account given by James of his love-adventures in Windsor Castle. How much of it is absolute fact, and how much the embellishment of fancy, it is fruitless to conjecture: let us not, however, reject every romantic incident as incompatible with real life; but let us sometimes take a poet at his word. I have noticed merely those parts of the poem immediately connected with the tower, and have passed over a large part, written in the allegorical vein, so much cultivated at that day. The language, of course, is quaint and antiquated, so that the beauty of many of its golden phrases will scarcely be perceived at the present day; but it is impossible not to be charmed with the genuine sentiment, the delightful artlessness and urbanity, which prevail throughout it. The descriptions of nature, too, with which it is embellished, are given with a truth, a discrimination, and a freshness, worthy of the most cultivated periods of the art.

As an amatory poem, it is edifying in these days of courser thinking, to notice the nature, refinement, and exquisite delicacy which pervade it; banishing every gross thought or immodest expression, and presenting female loveliness, clothed in all its chivalrous attributes of almost supernatural purity and grace.

James flourished nearly about the time of Chaucer and Gower, and was evidently an admirer and studier of their writings. Indeed, in one of his stanzas he acknowledges them as his masters, and in some parts of his poem we find traces of similarity to their productions, more especially to those of Chaucer. There are always, however, general features of resemblance in the works of contemporary authors, which are not so much borrowed from each other as from the times. Writers, like bees, toll their sweets in the wide world; they incorporate with their own conceptions the anecdotes and thoughts current in society; and thus each generation has some features in common, characteristic of the age in which it lived.

James belongs to one of the most brilliant eras of our literary history, and establishes the claims of his country to a participation in its primitive honours. Whilst a small cluster of English writers are constantly cited as the fathers of our verse, the name of their great Scottish compeer is apt to be passed over in silence; but he is evidently worthy of being enrolled in that little constellation of remote but never-failing luminaries, who shine in the highest firmament of literature, and who, like morning-stars, sang together at the bright dawning of British poesy.

Such of my readers as may not be familiar with Scottish history (though the manner in which it has of late been woven with captivating fiction has made it a universal study) may be curious to learn something of the subsequent history of James, and the fortunes of his love. His passion for the Lady Jane, as it was the solace of his captivity, so it facilitated his release, it being imagined by the court that a connection with the blood royal of England would attach him to its own interests. He was ultimately restored to his liberty and crown, having previously espoused the Lady Jane, who accompanied him to Scotland, and made him a most tender and devoted wife.

He found his kingdom in great confusion, the feudal chieftains having taken advantage of the troubles and irregularities of a long interregnum to strengthen themselves in their possessions, and place themselves above the power of the laws. James sought to found the basis of his power in the affections of his people. He attached the lower orders to him by the reformation of abuses, the temperate and equable administration of justice, the encouragement of the arts of peace, and the promotion of everything that could diffuse comfort, competency, and innocent enjoyment through the humblest ranks of society. He mingled occasionally among the common people in disguise; visited their firesides; entered into their cares, their pursuits, and their amusements; informed himself of the mechanical arts, and how they could best be patronised and improved; and was thus an all-pervading spirit, watching with a benevolent eye over the meanest of his subjects. Having in this generous manner made himself strong in the hearts of the common people, he turned himself to curb the power of the factious nobility; to strip them of those dangerous immunities which they had usurped; to punish such as had been guilty of flagrant offences; and to bring the whole into proper obedience to the crown. For some time they bore this with outward submission, but with secret impatience and brooding resentment. A conspiracy was at length formed against his life, at the head of which was his own uncle, Robert Stewart, Earl of Athol, who, being too old himself for the perpetration of the deed of blood, instigated his grandson, Sir Robert Stewart, together with Sir Robert Graham, and others of less note, to commit the deed. They broke into his bedchamber at the Dominican Convent, near Perth, where he was residing, and barbarously murdered him by oft-repeated wounds. His faithful queen, rushing to throw her tender body between him and the sword, was twice wounded in the ineffectual attempt to shield him from the assassin; and it was not until she had been forcibly torn from his person, that the murder was accomplished.

It was the recollection of this romantic tale of former times, and of the golden little poem which had its birthplace in this tower, that made me visit the old pile with more than common interest. The suit of armour hanging up in the hall, richly gilt and embellished, as if to figure in the tournay, brought the image of the gallant and romantic prince vividly before my imagination. I paced the deserted chambers where he had composed his poem; I leaned upon the window, and endeavoured to persuade myself it was the very one where he had been visited by his vision; I looked out upon the spot where he had first seen the Lady Jane. It was the same genial and joyous month; the birds were again vying with each other in strains of liquid melody; everything was bursting into vegetation, and budding forth the tender promise of the year. Time, which delights to obliterate the sterner memorials of human pride, seems to have passed lightly over this little scene of poetry and love, and to have withheld his desolating hand. Several centuries have gone by, yet the garden still flourishes at the foot of the tower. It occupies what was once the moat of the keep; and though some parts have been separated by dividing walls, yet others have still their arbours and shaded walks, as in the days of James, and the whole is sheltered, blooming, and retired. There is a charm about a spot that has been printed by the footsteps of departed beauty, and consecrated by the inspirations of the poet, which is heightened, rather than impaired, by the lapse of ages. It is, indeed, the gift of poetry to hallow every place in which it moves; to breathe around nature an odour more exquisite than the perfume of the rose, and to shed over it a tint more magical than the blush of morning.

Others may dwell on the illustrious deeds of James as a warrior and a legislator; but I have delighted to view him merely as the companion of his fellowmen, the benefactor of the human heart, stooping from his high estate to sow the sweet flowers of poetry and song in the paths of common life. He was the first to cultivate the vigorous and hardy plant of Scottish genius, which has since become so prolific of the most wholesome and highly-flavoured fruit. He carried with him into the sterner regions of the north all the fertilising arts of southern refinement. He did everything in his power to win his countrymen to the gay, the elegant, and gentle arts, which soften and refine the character of a people, and wreathe a grace round the loftiness of a proud and warlike spirit. He wrote many poems, which, unfortunately for the fulness of his fame, are now lost to the world; one, which is still preserved, called "Christ's Kirk of the Green," shows how diligently he had made himself acquainted with the rustic sports and pastimes which constitute such a source of kind and social feeling among the Scottish peasantry; and with what simple and happy humour he could enter into their enjoyments. He contributed greatly to improve the national music; and traces of his tender sentiment and elegant taste are said to exist in those witching airs still piped among the wild mountains and lonely glens of Scotland. He has thus connected his image with whatever is most gracious and endearing in the national character; he has embalmed his memory in song, and floated his name to after-ages in the rich streams of Scottish melody. The recollection of these things was kindling at my heart as I paced the silent scene of his imprisonment. I have visited Vaucluse with as much enthusiasm as a pilgrim would visit the shrine at Loretto; but I have never felt more poetical devotion than when contemplating the old tower and the little garden at Windsor, and musing over the romantic loves of the Lady Jane and the Royal Poet of Scotland.

A SUNDAY IN LONDON[1]

IN A PRECEDING PAPER I have spoken of an English Sunday in the country, and its tranquillising effect upon the landscape; but where is its sacred influence more strikingly apparent than in the very heart of that great Babel, London? On this sacred day, the gigantic monster is charmed into repose. The intolerable

[1]Part of a sketch omitted in the preceding editions.

din and struggle of the week are at an end. The shops are shut. The fires of forges and manufactories are extinguished; and the sun, no longer obscured by murky clouds of smoke, pours down a sober, yellow radiance into the quiet streets.

The few pedestrians we meet, instead of hurrying forward with anxious countenances, move leisurely along; their brows are smoothed from the wrinkles of business and care; they have put on their Sunday looks, and Sunday manners, with their Sunday clothes, and are cleansed in mind as well as in person.

And now the melodious clangour of bells from church towers summons their several flocks to the fold. Forth issues from his mansion the family of the decent tradesman, the small children in the advance; then the citizen and his comely spouse, followed by the grown-up daughters, with small morocco-bound prayer-books laid in the folds of their pocket-handkerchiefs. The house-maid looks after them from the window, admiring the finery of the family, and receiving, perhaps, a nod and smile from her young mistresses, at whose toilet she has assisted.

Now rumbles along the carriage of some magnate of the city, peradventure an alderman or a sheriff, and now the patter of many feet announces a procession of charity scholars, in uniforms of antique cut, and each with a prayer-book under his arm.

The ringing of bells is at an end; the rumbling of the carriage has ceased; the pattering of feet is heard no more; the flocks are folded in ancient churches, cramped up in by-lanes and corners of the crowded city, where the vigilant beadle keeps watch, like a shepherd's dog, round the threshold of the sanctuary. For a time everything is hushed; but soon is heard the deep pervading sound of the organ, rolling and vibrating through the empty lanes and courts; and the sweet chanting of the choir making them resound with melody and praise. Never have I been more sensible of the sanctifying effect of church music, than when I have heard it thus poured forth, like a river of joy through the inmost recesses of this great metropolis, elevating it, as it were, from all the sordid pollutions of the week; and bearing the poor world-worn soul on a tide of triumphant harmony to heaven.

The morning service is at an end. The streets are again alive with the congregations returning to their homes, but soon again relapse into silence. Now comes on the Sunday dinner, which, to the city tradesman, is a meal of some importance. There is more leisure for social enjoyment at the board. Members of the family can now gather together, who are separated by the laborious occupations of the week. A school-boy may be permitted on that day to come to the paternal home; an old friend of the family takes his accustomed Sunday seat at the board, tells over his well-known stories, and rejoices young and old with his well-known jokes.

On Sunday afternoon the city pours forth its legions to breathe the fresh air and enjoy the sunshine of the parks and rural environs. Satirists may say what they please about the rural enjoyments of a London citizen on Sunday, but to me there is something delightful in beholding the poor prisoner of the crowded and dusty city enabled thus to come forth once a week and throw himself upon the green bosom of nature. He is like a child restored to the mother's breast; and they who first spread out these noble parks and magnificent pleasure-grounds which surround this huge metropolis, have done at least as much for its health and morality, as if they had expended the amount of cost, in hospitals, prisons, and penitentiaries.

THE INN KITCHEN

Shall I not take mine ease in mine inn?—FALSTAFF.

DURING a journey that I once made through the Netherlands, I had arrived one evening at the *Pomme d'Or*, the principal inn of a small Flemish village. It was after the hour of the *table d'hote*, so that I was obliged to make a solitary supper from the relics of its ampler board. The weather was chilly; I was seated alone in one end of a great gloomy dining-room, and, my repast being over, I had the prospect before me of a long dull evening, without any visible means of enlivening it. I summoned mine host, and requested something to read; he brought me the whole literary stock of his household, a Dutch family Bible, an almanac in the same language, and a number of old Paris newspapers. As I sat dozing over one of the latter, reading old news and stale criticisms, my ear was now and then struck with bursts of laughter which seemed to proceed from the kitchen. Every one that has travelled on the continent must know how favourite a resort the kitchen of a country inn is to the middle and inferior order of travellers; particularly in that equivocal kind of weather, when a fire becomes agreeable toward evening. I threw aside the newspaper, and explored my way to the kitchen, to take a peep at the group that appeared to be so merry. It was composed partly of travellers who had arrived some hours before in a diligence, and partly of the usual attendants and hangers-on of inns. They were seated round a great burnished stove, that might have been mistaken for an altar, at which they were worshipping. It was covered with various kitchen vessels of resplendent brightness; among which steamed and hissed a huge copper tea-kettle. A large lamp threw a strong mass of light upon the group, bringing out many odd features in strong relief. Its yellow rays partially illumined the spacious kitchen, dying duskily away into remote corners; except where they settled in mellow radiance on the broad side of a flitch of bacon, or were reflected back from well-scoured utensils that gleamed from the midst of obscurity. A strapping Flemish lass, with long golden pendants in her ears, and a necklace with a golden heart suspended to it, was the presiding priestess of the temple.

Many of the company were furnished with pipes, and most of them with some kind of evening potation. I found their mirth was occasioned by anecdotes, which a little swarthy Frenchman, with a dry weazen face and large whiskers, was giving of his love adventures; at the end of each of which there was one of those bursts of honest unceremonious laughter, in which a man indulges in that temple of true liberty, an inn.

As I had no better mode of getting through a tedious blustering evening, I took my seat near the stove, and listened to a variety of travellers' tales, some very extravagant, and most very dull. All of them, however, have faded from my treacherous memory except one, which I will endeavour to relate. I fear, however, it derived its chief zest from the manner in which it was told, and the peculiar air and appearance of the narrator. He was a corpulent old Swiss, who had the look of a veteran traveller. He was dressed in a tarnished green travelling-jacket, with a broad belt round his waist, and a pair of overalls, with buttons from the hips to the ankles. He was of a full rubicund countenance, with a double chin, aquiline nose, and a pleasant twinkling eye. His hair was light, and curled from under an old green velvet travelling-cap stuck on one side of his head. He was interrupted more than once by the arrival of guests, or the remarks of his auditors; and paused now and then to replenish his pipe; at which times he had generally a roguish leer, and a sly joke for the buxom kitchen-maid.

I wish my readers could imagine the old fellow lolling in a huge arm-chair, one arm akimbo, the other holding a curiously twisted tobacco-pipe, formed of genuine *écume de mer*, decorated with silver chain and silken tassel—his head cocked on one side, and a whimsical cut of the eye occasionally, as he related the following story.

THE SPECTRE BRIDEGROOM

A TRAVELLER'S TALE[1]

> He that supper for is dight,
> He lyes full cold, I trow, this night!
> Yestreen to chamber I him led,
>   This night Gray-Steel has made his bed.
>   "SIR EGER, SIR GRAHAME, AND SIR GRAY-STEEL."

ON THE SUMMIT of one of the heights of the Odenwald, a wild and romantic tract of Upper Germany, that lies not far from the confluence of the Maine and the Rhine, there stood, many, many years since, the Castle of the Baron Von Landshort. It is now quite fallen to decay, and almost buried among the beech-trees and dark firs; above which, however, its old watch-tower may still be seen struggling, like the former possessor, I have mentioned, to carry a high head, and look down upon the neighbouring country.

The baron was a dry branch of the great family of Katzenellenbogen,[2] and inherited the relics of the property, and all the pride of his ancestors. Though the warlike disposition of his predecessors had much impaired the family pos-

---

[1] The erudite reader, well versed in good-for-nothing lore, will perceive that the above tale must have been suggested to the old Swiss by a little French anecdote, a circumstance said to have taken place at Paris.

[2] *i.e.* CAT'S-ELBOW—the name of a family of those parts very powerful in former times. The appellation, we are told, was given in compliment to a peerless dame of the family, celebrated for her fine arm.

sessions, yet the baron still endeavoured to keep up some show of former state. The times were peaceable, and the German nobles, in general, had abandoned their inconvenient old castles, perched like eagles' nests among the mountains, and had built more convenient residences in the valleys: still the baron remained proudly drawn up in his little fortress, cherishing, with hereditary inveteracy, all the old family feuds; so that he was on ill terms with some of his nearest neighbours, on account of disputes that had happened between their great-great-grandfathers.

The baron had but one child, a daughter; but nature, when she grants one child, always compensates by making it a prodigy; and so it was with the daughter of the baron. All the nurses, gossips, and country cousins, assured her father that she had not her equal for beauty in all Germany; and who should know better than they? She had, moreover, been brought up with great care under the superintendence of two maiden aunts, who had spent some years of their early life at one of the little German courts, and were skilled in all the branches of knowledge necessary to the education of a fine lady. Under their instructions she became a miracle of accomplishments. By the time she was eighteen, she could embroider to admiration, and had worked whole histories of the saints in tapestry, with such strength of expression in their countenances, that they looked like so many souls in purgatory. She could read without great difficulty, and had spelled her way through several church legends, and almost all the chivalric wonders of the Heldenbuch. She had even made considerable proficiency in writing; could sign her own name without missing a letter, and so legibly that her aunts could read it without spectacles. She excelled in making little elegant good-for-nothing lady-like nicknacks of all kinds; was versed in the most abstruse dancing of the day; played a number of airs on the harp and guitar; and knew all the tender ballads of the Minnielieders by heart.

Her aunts, too, having been great flirts and coquettes in their younger days, were admirably calculated to be vigilant guardians and strict censors of the conduct of their niece; for there is no duenna so rigidly prudent, and inexorably decorous, as a superannuated coquette. She was rarely suffered out of their sight; never went beyond the domains of the castle, unless well attended, or rather well watched; had continual lectures read to her about strict decorum and implicit obedience; and, as to the men—pah!—she was taught to hold them at such a distance, and in such absolute distrust, that, unless properly authorised, she would not have cast a glance upon the handsomest cavalier in the world— no, not if he were even dying at her feet.

The good effects of this system were wonderfully apparent. The young lady was a pattern of docility and correctness. While others were wasting their sweetness in the glare of the world, and liable to be plucked and thrown aside by every hand, she was coyly blooming into fresh and lovely womanhood under the protection of those immaculate spinsters, like a rose-bud blushing forth among guardian thorns. Her aunts looked upon her with pride and exultation, and vaunted that though all the other young ladies in the world might go astray, yet, thank Heaven, nothing of the kind could happen to the heiress of Katzenellenbogen.

But, however scantily the Baron Von Landshort might be provided with children, his household was by no means a small one; for Providence had enriched him with abundance of poor relations. They, one and all, possessed the affectionate disposition common to humble relatives; were wonderfully attached to the baron, and took every possible occasion to come in swarms and enliven the castle. All family festivals were commemorated by these good people at the baron's expense; and when they were filled with good cheer, they would declare that there was nothing on earth so delightful as these family meetings, these jubilees of the heart.

The baron, though a small man, had a large soul, and it swelled with satisfaction at the consciousness of being the greatest man in the little world about him. He loved to tell long stories about the stark old warriors whose portraits looked grimly down from the walls around, and he found no listeners equal to those who fed at his expense. He was much given to the marvellous, and a firm believer in all those supernatural tales with which every mountain and valley in Germany abounds. The faith of his guests exceeded even his own; they listened to every tale of wonder with open eyes and mouth, and never failed to be astonished, even though repeated for the hundredth time. Thus lived the Baron Von Landshort, the oracle of his table, the absolute monarch of his little territory, and happy, above all things, in the persuasion that he was the wisest man of the age.

At the time of which my story treats, there was a great family gathering at the castle, on an affair of the utmost importance; it was to receive the destined bridegroom of the baron's daughter. A negotiation had been carried on between the father and an old nobleman of Bavaria, to unite the dignity of their houses by the marriage of their children. The preliminaries had been conducted with proper punctilio. The young people were betrothed without seeing each other, and the time was appointed for the marriage ceremony. The young Count Von Altenburg had been recalled from the army for the purpose, and was actually on his way to the baron's to receive his bride. Missives had even been received from him, from Wurtzburg, where he was accidentally detained, mentioning the day and hour when he might be expected to arrive.

The castle was in a tumult of preparation to give him a suitable welcome. The fair bride had been decked out with uncommon care. The two aunts had superintended her toilet, and quarrelled the whole morning about every article of her dress. The young lady had taken advantage of their contest to follow the bent of her own taste, and fortunately it was a good one. She looked as lovely as youthful bridegroom could desire; and the flutter of expectation heightened the lustre of her charms.

The suffusions that mantled her face and neck, the gentle heaving of the bosom, the eye now and then lost in reverie, all betrayed the soft tumult that was going on in her little heart. The aunts were continually hovering around her; for maiden aunts are apt to take a great interest in affairs of this nature. They were giving her a world of staid counsel how to deport herself, what to say, and in what manner to receive the expected lover.

The baron was no less busied in preparations. He had, in truth, nothing exactly to do; but he was naturally a fuming, bustling little man, and could not remain passive when all the world was in a hurry. He worried from top to bottom of the castle with an air of infinite anxiety; he continually called the servants from their work to exhort them to be diligent; and buzzed about every hall and chamber as idly restless and importunate as a blue-bottle fly on a warm summer's day.

In the meantime the fatted calf had been killed; the forests had rung with the clamour of the huntsmen; the kitchen was crowded with good cheer; the cellars had yielded up whole oceans of Rhein-wein and Ferne-wein; and even the great Heidelburg tun had been laid under contribution. Everything was ready to receive the distinguished guest with Saus and Braus in the true spirit of German hospitality—but the guest delayed to make his appearance. Hour rolled after hour. The sun, that had poured his downward rays upon the rich forest of the Odenwald, now just gleamed along the summits of the mountains. The baron mounted the highest tower, and strained his eyes in hopes of catching a distant sight of the count and his attendants. Once he thought he beheld them; the sound of horns came floating from the valley, prolonged by the mountain echoes. A number of horsemen were seen far below, slowly advancing along the road; but when they had nearly reached the foot of the mountain, they suddenly struck off in a different direction. The last ray of sunshine departed—the bats began to flit by in the twilight—the road grew dimmer and dimmer to the view, and nothing appeared stirring in it, but now and then a peasant lagging homeward from his labour.

While the old castle of Landshort was in this state of perplexity, a very interesting scene was transacting in a different part of the Odenwald.

The young Count Von Altenburg was tranquilly pursuing his route in that sober jog-trot way in which a man travels towards matrimony when his friends have taken all the trouble and uncertainty of courtship off his hands, and a bride is waiting for him as certainly as a dinner at the end of his journey. He had encountered at Wurtzburg a youthful companion-in-arms, with whom he had seen some service on the frontiers; Herman Von Starkenfaust, one of the stoutest hands and worthiest hearts of German chivalry, who was now returning from the army. His father's castle was not far distant from the old fortress of Landshort, although an hereditary feud rendered the families hostile and strangers to each other.

In the warm-hearted moment of recognition, the young friends related all their past adventures and fortunes, and the count gave the whole history of his intended nuptials with a young lady whom he had never seen, but of whose charms he had received the most enrapturing descriptions.

As the route of the friends lay in the same direction, they agreed to perform the rest of their journey together; and, that they might do it the more leisurely, set off from Wurtzburg at an early hour, the count having given directions for his retinue to follow and overtake him.

They beguiled their wayfaring with recollections of their military scenes and adventures; but the count was apt to be a little tedious, now and then, about the reputed charms of his bride, and the felicity that awaited him.

In this way they had entered among the mountains of the Odwenwald, and were traversing one of its most lonely and thickly-wooded passes. It is well known that the forests of Germany have always been as much infested by robbers as its castles by spectres; and, at this time, the former were particularly numerous, from the hordes of disbanded soldiers wandering about the country. It will not appear extraordinary, therefore, that the cavaliers were attacked by a gang of these stragglers, in the midst of the forest. They defended themselves with bravery, but were nearly overpowered, when the count's retinue arrived to their assistance. At sight of them the robbers fled, but not until the count had received a mortal wound. He was slowly and carefully conveyed back to the city of Wurtzburg, and a friar summoned from a neighbouring convent, who was famous for his skill in administering to both soul and body; but half of his skill was superfluous; the moments of the unfortunate count were numbered.

With his dying breath he entreated his friend to repair instantly to the castle of Landshort, and explain the fatal cause of his not keeping his appointment with his bride. Though not the most ardent of lovers, he was one of the most punctilious of men, and appeared earnestly solicitous that his mission should be speedily and courteously executed. "Unless this is done," said he, "I shall not sleep quietly in my grave!" He repeated these last words with peculiar solemnity. A request, at a moment so impressive, admitted of no hesitation. Starkenfaust endeavoured to soothe him to calmness; promised faithfully to execute his wish, and gave him his hand in solemn pledge. The dying man pressed it in acknowledgment, but soon lapsed into delirium—raved about his bride—his engagements—his plighted word; ordered his horse, that he might ride to the castle of Landshort; and expired in the fancied act of vaulting into the saddle.

Starkenfaust bestowed a sigh and a soldier's tear on the untimely fate of his comrade; and then pondered on the awkward mission he had undertaken. His heart was heavy, and his head perplexed; for he was to present himself an unbidden guest among hostile people, and to damp their festivity with tidings fatal to their hopes. Still there were certain whisperings of curiosity in his bosom to see this far-famed beauty of Katzenellenbogen, so cautiously shut up from the world; for he was a passionate admirer of the sex, and there was a dash of eccentricity and enterprise in his character that made him fond of all simple adventure.

Previous to his departure he made all due arrangements with the holy fraternity of the convent for the funeral solemnities of his friend, who was to be buried in the cathedral of Wurtzburg, near some of his illustrious relatives; and the mourning retinue of the count took charge of his remains.

It is now high time that we should return to the ancient family of Katzenellenbogen, who were impatient for their guest, and still more for their dinner; and to the worthy little baron, whom we left airing himself on the watch-tower.

Night closed in, but still no guest arrived. The baron descended from the tower in despair. The banquet, which had been delayed from hour to hour, could no longer be postponed. The meats were already overdone; the cook in an agony; and the whole household had the look of a garrison that had been reduced by famine. The baron was obliged reluctantly to give orders for the feast without the presence of the guest. All were seated at table, and just on the point of commencing, when the sound of a horn from without the gate gave notice of the approach of a stranger. Another long blast filled the old courts of the castle with its echoes, and was answered by the warder from the walls. The baron hastened to receive his future son-in-law.

The drawbridge had been let down, and the stranger was before the gate. He was a tall gallant cavalier, mounted on a black steed. His countenance was pale, but he had a beaming, romantic eye, and an air of stately melancholy. The baron was a little mortified that he should have come in this simple, solitary style. His dignity for a moment was ruffled, and he felt disposed to consider it a want of proper respect for the important occasion, and the important family with which he was to be connected. He pacified himself, however, with the conclusion, that it must have been youthful impatience which had induced him thus to spur on sooner than his attendants.

"I am sorry," said the stranger, "to break in upon you thus unseasonably—"

Here the baron interrupted him with a world of compliments and greetings, for, to tell the truth, he prided himself upon his courtesy and eloquence. The stranger attempted, once or twice, to stem the torrent of words, but in vain; so he bowed his head, and suffered it to flow on. By the time the baron had come to a pause, they had reached the inner court of the castle; and the stranger was again about to speak, when he was once more interrupted by the appearance of the female part of the family, leading forth the shrinking and blushing bride. He gazed on her for a moment as one entranced; it seemed as if his whole soul beamed forth in the gaze, and rested upon that lovely form. One of the maiden aunts whispered something in her ear; she made an effort to speak; her moist blue eye was timidly raised; gave a shy glance of inquiry on the stranger; and was cast again to the ground. The words died away; but there was a sweet smile playing about her lips, and a soft dimpling of the cheek that showed her glance had not been unsatisfactory. It was impossible for a girl of the fond age of eighteen, highly predisposed for love and matrimony, not to be pleased with so gallant a cavalier.

The late hour at which the guest had arrived left no time for parley. The baron was peremptory, and deferred all particular conversation until the morning, and led the way to the untasted banquet.

It was served up in the great hall of the castle. Around the walls hung the hard-favoured portraits of the heroes of the house of Katzenellenbogen, and the trophies which they had gained in the field and in the chase. Hacked corslets, splintered jousting spears, and tattered banners, were mingled with the spoils of sylvan warfare; the jaws of the wolf, and the tusks of the boar, grinned horribly among cross-bows and battle-axes, and a huge pair of antlers branched immediately over the head of the youthful bridegroom.

The cavalier took but little notice of the company, or the entertainment. He scarcely tasted the banquet, but seemed absorbed in admiration of his bride. He conversed in a low tone that could not be overheard—for the language of love is never loud; but where is the female ear so dull that it cannot catch the softest whisper of the lover? There was a mingled tenderness and gravity in his manner, that appeared to have a powerful effect upon the young lady. Her colour came and went as she listened with deep attention. Now and then she made some blushing reply, and when his eye was turned away, she would steal a sidelong glance at his romantic countenance, and heave a gentle sigh of tender happiness. It was evident that the young couple were completely enamoured. The aunts, who were deeply versed in the mysteries of the heart, declared that they had fallen in love with each other at first sight.

The feast went on merrily, or, at least, noisily, for the guests were all blessed with those keen appetites that attend upon light purses and mountain air. The baron told his best and longest stories, and never had he told them so well, or with such great effect. If there was anything marvellous, his auditors were lost in astonishment; and if anything facetious, they were sure to laugh exactly in the right place. The baron, it is true, like most great men, was too dignified to utter any joke but a dull one; it was always enforced, however, by a bumper of excellent Hockheimer; and even a dull joke, at one's own table, served up with jolly old wine, is irresistible. Many good things were said by poorer and keener wits, that would not bear repeating, except on similar occasions; many sly speeches whispered in ladies' ears, that almost convulsed them with suppressed laughter; and a song or two roared out by a poor, but merry and broadfaced cousin of the baron, that absolutely made the maiden aunts hold up their fans.

Amidst all this revelry, the stranger guest maintained a most singular and unseasonable gravity. His countenance assumed a deeper cast of dejection as the evening advanced; and, strange as it may appear, even the baron's jokes seemed only to render him the more melancholy. At times he was lost in thought, and at times there was a perturbed and restless wandering of the eye that bespoke a mind but ill at ease. His conversations with the bride became more and more earnest and mysterious. Lowering clouds began to steal over the fair serenity of her brow, and tremors to run through her tender frame.

All this could not escape the notice of the company. Their gaiety was chilled by the unaccountable gloom of the bridegroom; their spirits were infected; whispers and glances were interchanged, accompanied by shrugs and dubious shakes of the head. The song and the laugh grew less and less frequent; there were dreary pauses in the conversation, which were at length succeeded by wild tales and supernatural legends. One dismal story produced another still more dismal, and the baron nearly frightened some of the ladies into hysterics with the history of the goblin horseman that carried away the fair Leonora; a dreadful story, which has since been put into excellent verse, and is read and believed by all the world.

The bridegroom listened to this tale with profound attention. He kept his eyes steadily fixed on the baron, and, as the story drew to a close, began gradually to rise from his seat, growing taller and taller, until, in the baron's entranced eye, he seemed almost to tower into a giant. The moment the tale was finished he heaved a deep sigh, and took a solemn farewell of the company. They were all amazement. The baron was perfectly thunderstruck.

"What! going to leave the castle at midnight? why, everything was prepared for his reception; a chamber was ready for him if he wished to retire."

The stranger shook his head mournfully and mysteriously; "I must lay my head in a different chamber tonight!"

There was something in this reply, and the tone in which it was uttered, that made the baron's heart misgive him; but he rallied his forces, and repeated his hospitable entreaties.

The stranger shook his head silently, but positively, at every offer; and, waving his farewell to the company, stalked slowly out of the hall. The maiden aunts were absolutely petrified—the bride hung her head, and a tear stole to her eye.

The baron followed the stranger to the great court of the castle, where the black charger stood pawing the earth, and snorting with impatience. When they had reached the portal, whose deep archway was dimly lighted by a cresset, the stranger paused, and addressed the baron in a hollow tone of voice, which the vaulted roof rendered still more sepulchral.

"Now that we are alone," said he, "I will impart to you the reason of my going. I have a solemn, an indispensable engagement—"

"Why," said the baron, "cannot you send someone in your place?"

"It admits of no substitute—I must attend it in person—I must away to Wurtzburg cathedral—"

"Ay," said the baron, plucking up spirit, "but not until to-morrow—to-morrow you shall take your bride there."

"No! no!" replied the stranger, with tenfold solemnity, "my engagement is with no bride—the worms! the worms expect me! I am a dead man—I have been slain by robbers—my body lies at Wurtzburg—at midnight I am to be buried—the grave is waiting for me—I must keep my appointment!"

He sprang on his black charger, dashed over the drawbridge, and the clattering of his horse's hoofs was lost in the whistling of the night-blast.

The baron returned to the hall in the utmost consternation, and related what had passed. Two ladies fainted outright, others sickened at the idea of having banqueted with a spectre. It was the opinion of some, that this might be the wild huntsman, famous in German legend. Some talked of mountain sprites, of wood-demons, and of other supernatural beings, with which the good people of Germany have been so grievously harassed since time immemorial. One of the poor relations ventured to suggest that it might be some sportive evasion of the young cavalier, and that the very gloominess of the caprice seemed to accord with so melancholy a personage. This, however, drew on him the indignation of the whole company, and especially of the baron, who looked upon him as little better than an infidel; so that he was fain to abjure his heresy as speedily as possible and come into the faith of the true believers.

But whatever may have been the doubts entertained, they were completely put to an end by the arrival, next day, of regular missives, confirming the intelligence of the young count's murder, and his interment in Wurtzburg cathedral.

The dismay at the castle may well be imagined. The baron shut himself up in his chamber. The guests, who had come to rejoice with him, could not think of abandoning him in his distress. They wandered about the courts, or collected in groups in the hall, shaking their heads and shrugging their shoulders, at the troubles of so good a man; and sat longer than ever at table, and ate and drank more stoutly than ever, by way of keeping up their spirits. But the situation of the widowed bride was the most pitiable. To have lost a husband before she had even embraced him—and such a husband! if the very spectre could be so gracious and noble, what must have been the living man? She filled the house with lamentations.

On the night of the second day of her widowhood she had retired to her chamber, accompanied by one of her aunts, who insisted on sleeping with her. The aunt, who was one of the best tellers of ghost-stories in all Germany, had just been recounting one of her longest, and had fallen asleep in the very midst of it. The chamber was remote, and overlooked a small garden. The niece lay pensively gazing at the beams of the rising moon, as they trembled on the leaves of an aspen-tree before the lattice. The castle clock had just tolled midnight, when a soft strain of music stole up from the garden. She rose hastily from her bed, and stepped lightly to the window. A tall figure stood among the shadows of the trees. As it raised its head, a beam of moonlight fell upon the countenance. Heaven and earth! she beheld the Spectre Bridegroom! A loud shriek at that moment burst upon her ear, and her aunt, who had been awakened by the music, and had followed her silently to the window, fell into her arms. When she looked again, the spectre had disappeared.

Of the two females, the aunt now required the most soothing, for she was perfectly beside herself with terror. As to the young lady, there was something, even in the spectre of her lover, that seemed endearing. There was still the semblance of manly beauty! and though the shadow of a man is but little calculated to satisfy the affections of a love-sick girl, yet, where the substance is not to be had, even that is consoling. The aunt declared she never would sleep in that chamber again; the niece, for once, was refractory, and declared as strongly that she would sleep in no other in the castle; the consequence was, that she had to sleep in it alone; but she drew a promise from her aunt not to relate the story of the spectre, lest she should be denied the only melancholy pleasure left her on earth—that of inhabiting the chamber over which the guardian shade of her lover kept its nightly vigils.

How long the good old lady would have observed this promise is uncertain, for she dearly loved to talk of the marvellous, and there is a triumph in being the first to tell a frightful story; it is, however, still quoted in the neighbourhood, as a memorable instance of female secrecy, that she kept it to herself for a whole week; when she was suddenly absolved from all further restraint, by intelligence brought to the breakfast-table one morning that the young lady was not to be found. Her room was empty—the bed had not been slept in—the window was open, and the bird had flown!

The astonishment and concern with which the intelligence was received, can only be imagined by those who have witnessed the agitation which the mishaps of a great man cause among his friends. Even the poor relations paused for a moment from the indefatigable labours of the trencher; when the aunt, who had at first been struck speechless, wrung her hands, and shrieked out, "The goblin! the goblin! she's carried away by the goblin!"

In a few words she related the fearful scene of the garden, and concluded that the spectre must have carried off his bride. Two of the domestics corroborated the opinion, for they had heard the clattering of a horse's hoofs down the mountain about midnight, and had no doubt that it was the spectre on his black charger, bearing her away to the tomb. All present were struck with the direful probability; for events of the kind are extremely common in Germany, as many well-authenticated histories bear witness.

What a lamentable situation was that of the poor baron! What a heart-rending dilemma for a fond father, and a member of the great family of Katzenellenbogen! His only daughter had either been rapt away to the grave, or he was to have some wood-demon for a son-in-law, and perchance, a troop of goblin grandchildren. As usual, he was completely bewildered, and all the castle in an uproar. The men were ordered to take horse, and scour every road and path and glen of the Odenwald. The baron himself had just drawn on his jack-boots, girded on his sword, and was about to mount his steed to sally forth on the doubtful quest, when he was brought to a pause by a new apparition. A lady was seen approaching the castle, mounted on a palfrey, attended by a cavalier on horseback. She galloped up to the gate, sprang from her horse, and falling at the baron's feet, embraced his knees. It was his lost daughter, and her companion—the Spectre Bridegroom! The baron was astounded. He looked at his daughter, then at the spectre, and almost doubted the evidence of his senses. The latter, too, was wonderfully improved in his appearance since his visit to the world of spirits. His dress was splendid, and set off a noble figure of manly symmetry. He was no longer pale and melancholy. His fine countenance was flushed with the glow of youth, and joy rioted in his large dark eye.

The mystery was soon cleared up. The cavalier (for, in truth, as you must have known all the while, he was no goblin) announced himself as Sir Herman Von Starkenfaust. He related his adventure with the young count. He told how he had hastened to the castle to deliver the unwelcome tidings, but that the eloquence of the baron had interrupted him in every attempt to tell his tale. How the sight of the bride had completely captivated him, and that to pass a few hours near her, he had tacitly suffered the mistake to continue. How he had been sorely perplexed in what way to make a decent retreat, until the baron's goblin stories had suggested his eccentric exit. How, fearing the feudal hostility of the family, he had repeated his visits by stealth—had haunted the garden beneath the young lady's window—had wooed—had won—had borne away in triumph—and, in a word, had wedded the fair.

Under any other circumstances the baron would have been inflexible, for he was tenacious of paternal authority, and devoutly obstinate in all family feuds; but he loved his daughter; he had lamented her as lost; he rejoiced to find her still alive; and, though her husband was of a hostile house, yet, thank heaven, he was not a goblin. There was something, it must be acknowledged, that did not exactly accord with his notions of strict veracity, in the joke the knight had passed upon him of his being a dead man; but several old friends present, who had served in the wars, assured him that every stratagem was excusable in love, and that the cavalier was entitled to especial privilege, having lately served as a trooper.

Matters, therefore, were happily arranged. The baron pardoned the young couple on the spot. The revels at the castle were resumed. The poor relations overwhelmed this new member of the family with loving-kindness; he was so gallant, so generous—and so rich. The aunts, it is true, were somewhat scandalised that their system of strict seculsion and passive obedience should be so badly exemplified, but attributed it all to their negligence in not having the windows grated. One of them was particularly mortified at having her marvellous story marred, and that the only spectre she had ever seen should turn out a counterfeit; but the niece seemed perfectly happy at having found him substantial flesh and blood—and so the story ends.

WESTMINSTER ABBEY

When I behold with deep astonishment,
To famous Westminster how there resorte,
Living in brasse or stoney monument,
The princes and the worthies of all sorte;
Doe not I see reformde nobilitie,
Without contempt, or pride, or ostentation,
And looke upon offenselesse majesty,
Naked of pomp or earthly domination?
And how a play-game of a painted stone
Contents the quiet now and silent sprites,
Whome all the world which late they stood upon
Could not content nor quench their appetites.
    Life is a frost of cold felicite,
    And death the thaw of all our vanitie.
            "CHRISTOLERO'S EPIGRAMS," by T. B., 1598.

ON ONE of those sober and rather melancholy days, in the latter part of autumn, when the shadows of morning and evening almost mingle together, and throw a gloom over the decline of the year, I passed several hours in rambling about Westminster Abbey. There was something congenial to the season in the mournful magnificence of the old pile; and as I passed its threshold, seemed like stepping back into the regions of antiquity, and losing myself among the shades of former ages.

I entered from the inner court of Westminster School, through a long, low, vaulted passage, that had an almost subterranean look, being dimly lighted in one part by circular perforations in the massive walls. Through this dark avenue I had a distant view of the cloisters, with the figure of an old verger, in his black gown, moving along their shadowy vaults, and seeming like a spectre from one of the neighbouring tombs. The approach to the abbey through these gloomy monastic remains prepares the mind for its solemn contemplation. The cloisters still retain something of the quiet and seclusion of former days. The grey walls are discoloured by damps, and crumbling with age; a coat of hoary moss has gathered over the inscriptions of the mural monuments, and obscured the death's heads and other funereal emblems. The sharp touches of the chisel are gone from the rich tracery of the arches; the roses which adorned the keystones have lost their leafy beauty; everything bears marks of the gradual dilapidations of time, which yet has something touching and pleasing in its very decay.

The sun was pouring down a yellow autumnal ray into the square of the cloisters; beaming upon a scanty plot of grass in the centre, and lighting up an angle of the vaulted passage with a kind of dusky splendour. From between the arcades the eye glanced up to a bit of blue sky or a passing cloud, and beheld the sun-gilt pinnacles of the abbey towering into the azure heaven.

As I paced the cloisters, sometimes contemplating this mingled picture of glory and decay, and sometimes endeavouring to decipher the inscriptions on the tombstones, which formed the pavement beneath my feet, my eye was attracted to three figures, rudely carved in relief, but nearly worn away by the footsteps of many generations. They were the effigies of three of the early abbots; the epitaphs were entirely effaced; the names alone remained, having no doubt been renewed in later times. (Vitalis. Abbas. 1082, and Gislebertus Crispinus. Abbas. 1114, and Laurentius. Abbas. 1176). I remained some little while, musing over these casual relics of antiquity, thus left like wrecks upon this distant shore of time, telling no tale but that such beings had been and had perished; teaching no moral but the futility of that pride which hopes still to exact homage in its ashes, and to live in an inscription. A little longer, and even these faint records will be obliterated, and the monument will cease to be a memorial. Whilst I was yet looking down upon these gravestones, I was roused by the sound of the abbey clock, reverberating from buttress to buttress, and echoing among the cloisters. It is almost startling to hear this warning of departed time sounding among the tombs, and telling the lapse of the hour, which, like a billow, has rolled us onward towards the grave. I pursued my walk to an arched door opening to the interior of the abbey. On entering here, the magnitude of the building breaks fully upon the mind, contrasted with the vaults of the cloister. The eyes gaze with wonder at clustered columns of gigantic dimensions, with arches springing from them to such an amazing height; and man wandering about their bases, shrunk into insignificance in comparison with his own handiwork. The spaciousness and gloom of this vast edifice produce a profound and mysterious awe. We step cautiously and softly about, as if fearful of disturbing the hallowed silence of the tomb; while every footfall whispers along the walls, and chatters among the sepulchres, making us more sensible of the quiet we have interrupted.

It seems as if the awful nature of the place presses down upon the soul, and hushes the beholder into noiseless reverence. We feel that we are surrounded by the congregated bones of the great men of past times, who have filled history with their deeds, and the earth with their renown.

And yet it almost provokes a smile at the vanity of human ambition, to see how they are crowded together and jostled in the dust; what parsimony is observed in doling out a scanty nook, a gloomy corner, a little portion of earth, to those whom, when alive, kingdoms could not satisfy; and how many shapes, and forms, and artifices are devised to catch the casual notice of the passenger, and save from forgetfulness, for a few short years, a name which once aspired to occupy ages of the world's thought and admiration.

I passed some time in Poets' Corner, which occupies an end of one of the transepts or cross aisles of the abbey. The monuments are generally simple; for the lives of literary men afford no striking themes for the sculptor. Shakspeare and Addison have statues erected to their memories; but the greater part have busts, medallions, and sometimes mere inscriptions. Notwithstanding the simplicity of these memorials, I have always observed that the visitors to the abbey remained longest about them. A kinder and fonder feeling takes the place of that cold curiosity or vague admiration with which they gaze on the splendid monuments of the great and the heroic. They linger about these as about the tombs of friends and companions; for indeed there is something of companionship between the author and the reader. Other men are known to posterity only through the medium of history, which is continually growing faint and obscure; but the intercourse between the author and his fellow-men is ever new, active, and immediate. He has lived for them more than for himself; he has sacrificed surrounding enjoyments, and shut himself up from the delights of social life, that he might the more intimately commune with distant minds and distant ages. Well may the world cherish his renown; for it has been purchased, not by deeds of violence and blood, but by the diligent dispensation of pleasure. Well may posterity be grateful to his memory; for he has left it an inheritance, not of empty names and sounding actions, but whole treasures of wisdom, bright gems of thought, and golden veins of language.

From Poets' Corner, I continued my stroll towards that part of the abbey which contains the sepulchres of the kings. I wandered among what once were chapels, but which are now occupied by the tombs and monuments of the great. At every turn I met with some illustrious name; or the cognisance of some powerful house renowned in history. As the eye darts into these dusky chambers of death, it catches glimpses of quaint effigies; some kneeling in niches, as if in devotion; others stretched upon the tombs, with hands piously pressed together; warriors in armour, as if reposing after battle; prelates with crosiers and mitres; and nobles in robes and coronets, lying as it were in state. In glancing over this scene, so strangely populous, yet where every form is so still and silent, it seems almost as if we were treading a mansion of that fabled city, where every being had been suddenly transmuted into stone.

I paused to contemplate a tomb on which lay the effigy of a knight in complete armour. A large buckler was on one arm; the hands were pressed together in supplication upon the breast: the face was almost covered by the morion;

the legs were crossed, in token of the warrior's having been engaged in the holy war. It was the tomb of a crusader; of one of those military enthusiasts, who so strangely mingled religion and romance, and whose exploits form the connecting link between fact and fiction; between the history and the fairy tale. There is something extremely picturesque in the tombs of these adventurers, decorated as they are with rude armorial bearings and Gothic sculpture. They comport with the antiquated chapels in which they are generally found; and in considering them, the imagination is apt to kindle with the legendary associations, the romantic fiction, the chivalrous pomp and pageantry, which poetry has spread over the wars for the sepulchre of Christ. They are the relics of times utterly gone by; of beings passed from recollection; of customs and manners with which ours have no affinity. They are like objects from some strange and distant land, of which we have no certain knowledge, and about which all our conceptions are vague and visionary. There is something extremely solemn and awful in those effigies on Gothic tombs, extended as if in the sleep of death, or in the supplication of the dying hour. They have an effect infinitely more impressive on my feelings than the fanciful attitudes, the over-wrought conceits, and allegorical groups, which abound on modern monuments. I have been struck, also, with the superiority of many of the old sepulchral inscriptions. There was a noble way, in former times, of saying things simply, and yet saying them proudly; and I do not know an epitaph that breathes a loftier consciousness of family worth and honourable lineage, than one which affirms of a noble house, that "all the brothers were brave, and all the sisters virtuous."

In the opposite transept to Poets' Corner stands a monument which is among the most renowned achievements of modern art; but which to me appears horrible rather than sublime. It is the tomb of Mrs Nightingale, by Roubilliac. The bottom of the monument is represented as throwing open its marble doors, and a sheeted skeleton is starting forth. The shroud is falling from his fleshless frame as he launches his dart at his victim. She is sinking into her affrighted husband's arms, who strives, with vain and frantic effort, to avert the blow. The whole is executed with terrible truth and spirit; we almost fancy we hear the gibbering yell of triumph bursting from the distended jaws of the spectre. But why should we thus seek to clothe death with unnecessary terrors, and to spread horrors round the tomb of those we love? The grave should be surrounded by everything that might inspire tenderness and veneration for the dead; or that might win the living to virtue. It is the place, not of disgust and dismay, but of sorrow and meditation.

While wandering about these gloomy vaults and silent aisles, studying the records of the dead, the sound of busy existence from without occasionally reaches the ear;—the rumbling of the passing equipage; the murmur of the multitude; or perhaps the light laugh of pleasure. The contrast is striking with the death-like repose around; and it has a strange effect upon the feelings, thus to hear the surges of active life hurrying along, and beating against the very walls of the sepulchre.

I continued in this way to move from tomb to tomb, and from chapel to chapel. The day was gradually wearing away; the distant tread of loiterers about the abbey grew less and less frequent; the sweet-tongued bell was summoning to evening prayers, and I saw at a distance the choristers, in their white surplices, crossing the aisle and entering the choir. I stood before the entrance to Henry the Seventh's chapel. A flight of steps lead up to it, through a deep and gloomy, but magnificent arch. Great gates of brass, richly and delicately wrought, turn heavily upon their hinges, as if proudly reluctant to admit the feet of common mortals into this most gorgeous of sepulchres.

On entering, the eye is astonished by the pomp of architecture, and the elaborate beauty of sculptured detail. The very walls are wrought into universal ornament, incrusted with tracery, and scooped into niches, crowded with the statues of saints and martyrs. Stone seems, by the cunning labour of the chisel, to have been robbed of its weight and density, suspended aloft, as if by magic, and the fretted roof achieved with the wonderful minuteness and airy security of a cobweb.

Along the sides of the chapel are the lofty stalls of the Knights of the Bath, richly carved of oak, though with the grotesque decorations of Gothic architecture. On the pinnacles of the stalls are affixed the helmets and crests of knights, with their scarfs and swords; and above them are suspended their banners, emblazoned with armorial bearings, and contrasting the splendour of gold and purple and crimson, with the cold gray fretwork of the roof. In the midst of this grand mausoleum stands the sepulchre of its founder,—his effigy, with that of his queen, extended on a sumptuous tomb, and the whole surrounded by a superbly-wrought brazen railing.

There is a sad dreariness in this magnificence; this strange mixture of tombs and trophies; these emblems of living and aspiring ambition, close beside mementoes which show the dust and oblivion in which all must, sooner or later, terminate. Nothing impresses the mind with a deeper feeling of loneliness, than to tread the silent and deserted scene of former throng and pageant. On looking round on the vacant stalls of the knights and their esquires, and on the rows of dusty but gorgeous banners that were once borne before them, my imagination conjured up the scene when this hall was bright with the valour and beauty of the land; glittering with the splendour of jewelled rank and military array; alive with the tread of many feet and the hum of an admiring multitude. All had passed away; the silence of death had settled again upon the place, interrupted only by the casual chirping of birds, which had found their way into the chapel, and built their nests among its friezes and pendants—sure signs of solitariness and desertion.

When I read the names inscribed on the banners, they were those of men scattered far and wide about the world; some tossing upon distant seas; some under arms in distant lands; some mingling in the busy intrigues of courts and cabinets; all seeking to deserve one more distinction in this mansion of shadowy honours: the melancholy reward of a monument.

Two small aisles on each side of this chapel present a touching instance of the equality of the grave, which brings down the oppressor to a level with the oppressed, and mingles the dust of the bitterest enemies together. In one is the sepulchre of the haughty Elizabeth; in the other is that of her victim, the lovely and unfortunate Mary. Not an hour in the day but some ejaculation of pity is uttered over the fate of the latter, mingled with indignation at her oppressor. The walls of Elizabeth's sepulchre continually echo with the sighs of sympathy heaved at the grave of her rival.

A peculiar melancholy reigns over the aisle where Mary lies buried. The light struggles dimly through windows darkened by dust. The greater part of the place is in deep shadow, and the walls are stained and tinted by time and weather. A marble figure of Mary is stretched upon the tomb, round which is an iron railing, much corroded, bearing her national emblem—the thistle. I was weary with wandering, and sat down to rest myself by the monument, revolving in my mind the chequered and disastrous story of poor Mary.

The sound of casual footsteps had ceased from the abbey. I could only hear, now and then, the distant voice of the priest repeating the evening service, and the faint responses of the choir; these paused for a time, and all was hushed. The stillness, the desertion, and obscurity that were gradually prevailing around, gave a deeper and more solemn interest to the place:—

> For in the silent grave no conversation,
> No joyful tread of friends, no voice of lovers,
> No careful father's counsel—nothing's heard,
> For nothing is, but all oblivion,
> Dust, and an endless darkness.

Suddenly the notes of the deep-labouring organ burst upon the ear, falling with doubled and redoubled intensity, and rolling, as it were, huge billows of sound. How well do their volume and grandeur accord with this mighty building! With what pomp do they swell through its vast vaults, and breathe their awful harmony through these caves of death, and make the silent sepulchre vocal! And now they rise in triumphant acclamation, heaving higher and higher their accordant notes, and piling sound on sound. And now they pause, and the soft voices of the choir break out into sweet gushes of melody; they soar aloft, and warble along the roof, and seem to play about these lofty vaults like the pure airs of heaven. Again the pealing organ heaves its thrilling thunders, compressing air into music, and rolling it forth upon the soul. What long-drawn cadences! What solemn sweeping concords! It grows more and more dense and powerful—it fills the vast pile, and seems to jar the very walls —the ear is stunned—the senses are overwhelmed. And now it is winding up in full jubilee—it is rising from the earth to heaven—the very soul seems rapt away and floated upwards on this swelling tide of harmony!

I sat for some time lost in that kind of reverie which a strain of music is apt sometimes to inspire: the shadows of evening were gradually thickening round me; the monuments began to cast deeper and deeper gloom; and the distant clock again gave token of the slowly waning day.

I rose and prepared to leave the abbey. As I descended the flight of steps which led into the body of the building, my eye was caught by the shrine of

Edward the Confessor, and I ascended the small staircase that conducts to it, to take from thence a general survey of this wilderness of tombs. The shrine is elevated upon a kind of platform, and close around it are the sepulchres of various kings and queens. From this eminence the eye looks down between pillars and funereal trophies to the chapels and chambers below, crowded with tombs; where warriors, prelates, courtiers, and statesmen, lie mouldering in their "beds of darkness." Close by me stood the great chair of coronation, rudely carved of oak, in the barbarous taste of a remote and Gothic age. The scene seemed almost as if contrived, with theatrical artifice, to produce an effect upon the beholder. Here was a type of the beginning and the end of human pomp and power; here it was literally but a step from the throne to the sepulchre. Would not one think that these incongruous mementoes had been gathered together as a lesson to living greatness?—to show it, even in the moment of its proudest exaltation, the neglect and dishonour to which it must soon arrive; how soon that crown which encircles its brow must pass away, and it must lie down in the dust and disgraces of the tomb, and be trampled upon by the feet of the meanest of the multitude. For, strange to tell, even the grave is here no longer a sanctuary. There is a shocking levity in some natures, which leads them to sport with awful and hallowed things; and there are base minds, which delight to revenge on the illustrious dead the abject homage and grovelling servility which they pay to the living. The coffin of Edward the Confessor has been broken open, and his remains despoiled of their funereal ornaments; the sceptre has been stolen from the hand of the imperious Elizabeth, and the effigy of Henry the Fifth lies headless. Not a royal monument but bears some proof how false and fugitive is the homage of mankind. Some are plundered, some mutilated; some covered with ribaldry and insult—all more or less outraged and dishonoured!

The last beams of day were now faintly streaming through the painted windows in the high vaults above me; the lower parts of the abbey were already wrapped in the obscurity of twilight. The chapel and aisles grew darker and darker. The effigies of the kings faded into shadows; the marble figures of the monuments assumed strange shapes in the uncertain light; the evening breeze crept through the aisles like the cold breath of the grave; and even the distant footfall of a verger, traversing the Poets' Corner, had something strange and dreary in its sound. I slowly retraced my morning's walk, and as I passed out at the portal of the cloisters, the door, closing with a jarring noise behind me, filled the whole building with echoes.

I endeavoured to form some arrangement in my mind of the objects I had been contemplating, but found they were already fallen into indistinctness and confusion. Names, inscriptions, trophies, had all become confounded in my recollection, though I had scarcely taken my foot from off the threshold. What, thought I, is this vast assemblage of sepulchres but a treasury of humiliation; a huge pile of reiterated homilies on the emptiness of renown, and the certainty of oblivion! It is, indeed, the empire of Death; his great shadowy palace, where he sits in state, mocking at the relics of human glory, and spreading dust and forgetfulness on the monuments of princes. How idle a boast, after all, is the immortality of a name! Time is ever silently turning over his pages; we are too much engrossed by the story of the present, to think of the characters and anecdotes that gave interest to the past; and each age is a volume thrown aside to be speedily forgotten. The idol of to-day pushes the hero of yesterday out of our recollection; and will, in turn, be supplanted by his successor of to-morrow. "Our fathers," says Sir Thomas Brown, "find their graves in our short memories, and sadly tell us how we may be buried in our survivors." History fades into fable; fact becomes clouded with doubt and controversy; the inscription moulders from the tablet; the statue falls from the pedestal. Columns, arches, pyramids, what are they but heaps of sand; and their epitaphs, but characters written in the dust? What is the security of a tomb, or the perpetuity of an embalmment? The remains of Alexander the Great have been scattered to the wind, and his empty sarcophagus is now the mere curiosity of a museum. "The Egyptian mummies, which Cambyses or time hath spared, avarice now consumeth; Mizraim cures wounds, and Pharaoh is sold for balsams."[1]

What, then, is to insure this pile which now towers above me from sharing the fate of mightier mausoleums? The time must come when its gilded vaults, which now spring so loftily, shall lie in rubbish beneath the feet; when, instead of the sound of melody and praise, the wind shall whistle through the broken arches, and the owl hoot from the shattered tower—when the garish sunbeam shall break into these gloomy mansions of death, and the ivy twine round the fallen column; and the foxglove hang its blossoms about the nameless urn, as if in mockery of the dead. Thus man passes away; his name perishes from record and recollection; his history is as a tale that is told, and his very monument becomes a ruin.

NOTES CONCERNING WESTMINSTER ABBEY.

Toward the end of the sixth century, when Britain, under the dominion of the Saxons, was in a state of barbarism and idolatry, Pope Gregory the Great, struck with the beauty of some Anglo-Saxon youths exposed for sale in the market-place at Rome, conceived a fancy for the race, and determined to send missionaries to preach the gospel among these comely but benighted islanders. He was encouraged to this by learning that Ethelbert, king of Kent, and the most potent of the Anglo-Saxon princes, had married Bertha, a Christian princess, only daughter of the king of Paris, and that she was allowed by stipulation the full exercise of her religion.

The shrewd pontiff knew the influence of the sex in matters of religious faith. He forthwith despatched Augustine, a Roman monk, with forty associates, to the Court of Ethelbert at Canterbury, to effect the conversion of the king, and to obtain through him a foothold in the island.

Ethelbert received them warily, and held a conference in the open air; being distrustful of foreign priestcraft, and fearful of spells and magic. They ultimately succeeded in making him as good a Christian as his wife: the conversion of the king of course produced the conversion of his loyal subjects. The zeal and success of Augustine were rewarded by his being made archbishop of Canterbury, and being endowed with authority over all the British churches.

[1]Sir T. Brown.

One of the most prominent converts was Segebert or Sebert, king of the East Saxons, a nephew of Ethelbert. He reigned at London, of which Mellitus, one of the Roman monks who had come over with Augustine, was made bishop.

Sebert, in 605, in his religious zeal, founded a monastery by the river side to the west on the city, on the ruins of a temple of Apollo, being in fact the origin of the present pile of Westminster Abbey. Great preparations were made for the consecration of the church, which was to be dedicated to St. Peter. On the morning of the appointed day, Mellitus, the bishop, proceeded with great pomp and solemnity to perform the ceremony. On approaching the edifice, he was met by a fisherman, who informed him that it was needless to proceed, as the ceremony was over. The bishop stared with surprise when the fisherman went on to relate, that the night before, as he was in his boat on the Thames, St Peter appeared to him, and told him that he intended to consecrate the church himself, that very night. The apostle accordingly went into the church, which suddenly became illuminated. The ceremony was performed in sumptuous style, accompanied by strains of heavenly music and clouds of fragrant incense. After this, the apostle came into the boat and ordered the fisherman to cast his net. He did so, and had a miraculous draught of fishes; one of which he was commanded to present to the bishop, and to signify to him that the apostle had relieved him from the necessity of consecrating the church.

Mellitus was a wary man, slow of belief, and required confirmation of the fisherman's tale. He opened the church doors, and beheld wax candles, crosses, holy water; oil sprinkled in various places, and various other traces of a grand ceremonial. If he had still any lingering doubts, they were completely removed on the fisherman's producing the identical fish which he had been ordered by the apostle to present to him. To resist this would have been to resist ocular demonstration. The good bishop accordingly was convinced that the church had actually been consecrated by St Peter in person; so he reverently abstained from proceeding further in the business.

The foregoing tradition is said to be the reason why King Edward the Confessor chose this place as the site of a religious house which he meant to endow. He pulled down the old church and built another in its place in 1045. In this his remains were deposited in a magnificent shrine.

The sacred edifice again underwent modifications, if not a reconstruction, by Henry III. in 1220, and began to assume its present appearance.

Under Henry VIII. it lost its conventual character, that monarch turning the monks away, and seizing upon the revenues.

RELICS OF EDWARD THE CONFESSOR.

A curious narrative was printed in 1688 by one of the choristers of the cathedral, who appears to have been the Paul Pry of the sacred edifice, giving an account of his rummaging among the bones of Edward the Confessor after they had quietly reposed in their sepulchre upwards of six hundred years, and of his drawing forth the crucifix and golden chain of the deceased monarch. During eighteen years that he had officiated in the choir, it had been a common tradition, he says, among his brother choristers and the gray-headed servants of the abbey, that the body of King Edward was deposited in a kind of chest or coffin, which was indistinctly seen in the upper part of the shrine erected to his memory. None of the abbey gossips, however, had ventured upon a nearer inspection, until the worthy narrator, to gratify his curiosity, mounted to the coffin by the aid of a ladder, and found it to be made of wood, apparently very strong and firm, being secured by bands of iron.

Subsequently, in 1685, on taking down the scaffolding used in the coronation of James II., the coffin was found to be broken, a hole appearing in the lid, probably made through accident by the workmen. No one ventured, however, to meddle with the sacred depository of royal dust—until, several weeks afterwards, the circumstance came to the knowledge of the aforesaid chorister. He forthwith repaired to the abbey in company with two friends, of congenial tastes, who were desirous of inspecting the tombs. Procuring a ladder, he again mounted to the coffin, and found, as had been represented, a hole in the lid about six inches long and four inches broad, just in front of the left breast. Thrusting in his hand, and groping among the bones, he drew from underneath the shoulder a crucifix, richly adorned and enamelled, affixed to a gold chain twenty-four inches long. These he showed to his inquisitive friends, who were equally surprised with himself.

"At the time," says he, "when I took the cross and chain out of the coffin, *I drew the head to the hole and viewed it*, being very sound and firm, with the upper and nether jaws whole and full of teeth, and a list of gold above an inch broad, in the nature of a coronet, surrounding the temples. There was also in the coffin white linen and gold-coloured flowered silk, that looked indifferent fresh; but the least stress put thereto showed it was well-nigh perished. There were all his bones, and much dust likewise, which I left as I found."

It is difficult to conceive a more grotesque lesson to human pride than the skull of Edward the Confessor thus irreverently pulled about in its coffin by a prying chorister and brought to grin face to face with him through a hole in the lid!

Having satisfied his curiosity, the chorister put the crucifix and chain back again into the coffin, and sought the dean, to apprise him of his discovery. The dean not being accessible at the time, and fearing that the "holy treasure" might be taken away by other hands, he got a brother chorister to accompany him to the shrine about two or three hours afterwards, and in his presence again drew forth the relics. These he afterwards delivered on his knees to King James. The king subsequently had the old coffin enclosed in a new one of great strength, "each plank being two inches thick, and clamped together with large iron wedges, where it now remains (1688) as a testimony of his pious care, that no abuse might be offered to the sacred ashes therein reposited."

As the history of this shrine is full of moral, I subjoin a description of it in modern times. "The solitary and forlorn shrine," says a British writer, "now stands a mere skeleton of what it was. A few faint traces of its sparkling decorations inlaid on solid mortar catch the rays of the sun, for ever set on its splendour. . . . . Only two of the spiral pillars remain. The wooden Ionic top is much broken, and covered with dust. The mosaic is picked away in every part within reach; only the lozenges of about a foot square and five circular pieces of the rich marble remain."—MALCOLM, LOND. REDIV.

INSCRIPTION ON A MONUMENT ALLUDED TO IN THE SKETCH

Here lyes the Loyal Duke of Newcastle, and his Dutchess his second wife, by whom he had no issue. Her name was Margaret Lucas, youngest sister to the Lord Lucas of Colchester, a noble family; for all the brothers were valiant and all the sisters virtuous. This Dutchess was a wise, witty, and learned lady, which her many Bookes do well testify: she was a most virtuous, and loving and careful wife, and was with her lord all the time of his banishment and miseries, and when he came home never parted from him in his solitary retirements.

In the winter time when the days are short, the service in the afternoon is performed by the light of tapers. The effect is fine of the choir partially lighted up, while the main body of the cathedral and the transepts are in profound and cavernous darkness. The white dresses of the choristers gleam amidst the deep brown of the oaken slats and canopies; the partial illumination makes enormous shadows from columns and screens, and darting into the surrounding gloom, catches here and there upon a sepulchral decoration, or monumental effigy. The swelling notes of the organ accord well with the scene.

When the service is over, the dean is lighted to his dwelling, in the old conventual part of the pile, by the boys of the choir, in their white dresses, bearing tapers, and the procession passes through the abbey and along the shadowy cloisters, lighting up angles and arches and grim sepulchral monuments, and leaving all behind in darkness.

On entering the cloisters at night from what is called the Dean's yard, the eye ranging through a dark vaulted passage catches a distant view of a white marble figure reclining on a tomb, on which a strong glare thrown by a gas-light has quite a spectral effect. It is a mural monument of one of the Pultneys.

The cloisters are well worth visiting by moonlight, when the moon is in the full.

CHRISTMAS

But is old, old, good old Christmas gone? Nothing but the hair of his good, gray, old head and beard left? Well, I will have that, seeing I cannot have more of him.—"HUE AND CRY AFTER CHRISTMAS."

> *A man might then behold*
>   *At Christmas, in each hall*
> *Good fires to curb the cold,*
>   *And meat for great and small.*
> *The neighbours were friendly bidden,*
>   *And all had welcome true,*
> *The poor from the gates were not chidden,*
>   *When this old cap was new.*—OLD SONG.

NOTHING in England exercises a more delightful spell over my imagination, than the lingerings of the holiday customs and rural games of former times. They recall the pictures my fancy used to draw in the May morning of life, when as yet I only knew the world through books, and believed it to be all that poets had painted it; and they bring with them the flavour of those honest days of yore, in which, perhaps, with equal fallacy, I am apt to think the world was more homebred, social, and joyous than at present. I regret to say that they are daily growing more and more faint, being gradually worn away by time, but still more obliterated by modern fashion. They resemble those picturesque morsels of Gothic architecture, which we see crumbling in various parts of the country, partly dilapidated by the waste of ages, and partly lost in the additions and alterations of latter days. Poetry, however, clings with cherishing fondness about the rural game and holiday revel, from which it has derived so many of its themes—as the ivy winds its rich foliage about the Gothic arch and mouldering tower, gratefully repaying their support, by clasping together their tottering remains, and, as it were, embalming them in verdure.

Of all the old festivals, however, that of Christmas awakens the strongest and most heartfelt associations. There is a tone of solemn and sacred feeling that blends with our conviviality, and lifts the spirit to a state of hallowed and elevated enjoyment. The services of the church about this season are extremely tender and inspiring. They dwell on the beautiful story of the origin of our faith, and the pastoral scenes that accompanied its announcement. They gradually increase in fervour and pathos during the season of Advent, until they break forth in full jubilee on the morning that brought peace and good-will to men. I do not know a grander effect of music on the moral feelings, than to hear the full choir and the pealing organ performing a Christmas anthem in a cathedral, and filling every part of the vast pile with triumphant harmony.

It is a beautiful arrangement, also, derived from days of yore, that this festival, which commemorates the announcement of the religion of peace and love, has been made the season for gathering together of family connections, and drawing closer again those bands of kindred hearts, which the cares and pleasures and sorrows of the world are continually operating to cast loose: of calling back the children of a family, who have launched forth in life, and wandered widely asunder, once more to assemble about the paternal hearth, that rallying-place of the affections, there to grow young and loving again among the endearing mementoes of childhood.

There is something in the very season of the year that gives a charm to the festivity of Christmas. At other times we derive a great portion of our pleasures from the mere beauties of nature. Our feelings sally forth and dissipate themselves over the sunny landscape, and we "live abroad and everywhere." The song of the bird, the murmur of the stream, the breathing fragrance of spring, the soft voluptuousness of summer, the golden pomp of autumn; earth with its mantle of refreshing green, and heaven with its deep delicious blue and its cloudy magnificence, all fill us with mute but exquisite delight, and we revel in the luxury of mere sensation. But in the depth of winter, when nature lies despoiled of every charm, and wrapped in her shroud of sheeted snow, we turn for our gratifications to moral sources. The dreariness and desolation of the landscape, the short gloomy days and darksome nights, while they circumscribe our wanderings, shut in our feelings also from rambling abroad, and make us more keenly disposed for the pleasure of the social circle. Our thoughts are more concentrated: our friendly sympathies more aroused. We feel more sensibly the charm of each other's society, and are brought more closely together by dependence on each other for enjoyment. Heart calleth unto heart; and we draw our pleasures from the deep wells of loving-kindness, which lie in the quiet recesses of our bosoms; and which, when resorted to, furnish forth the pure element of domestic felicity.

The pitchy gloom without makes the heart dilate on entering the room filled with the glow and warmth of the evening fire. The ruddy blaze diffuses an artificial summer and sunshine through the room, and lights up each countenance in a kindlier welcome. Where does the honest face of hospitality expand into a broader and more cordial smile—where is the shy glance of love more sweetly eloquent—than by the winter fireside? and as the hollow blast of wintry wind rushes through the hall, claps the distant door, whistles about the casement, and rumbles down the chimney, what can be more grateful than that feeling of sober and sheltered security, with which we look round upon the comfortable chamber and the scene of domestic hilarity?

The English, from the great prevalence of rural habit throughout every class of society, have always been fond of those festivals and holidays which agreeably interrupt the stillness of country life; and they were, in former days, particularly observant of the religious and social rites of Christmas. It is inspiring to read even the dry details which some antiquaries have given of the quaint humours, the burlesque pageants, the complete abandonment to mirth and good-fellowship, with which this festival was celebrated. It seemed to throw open every door, and unlock every heart. It brought the peasant and the peer together, and blended all ranks in one warm generous flow of joy and kindness. The old halls of castles and manor-houses resounded with the harp and the Christmas carol, and their ample boards groaned under the weight of hospitality. Even the poorest cottage welcomed the festive season with green decorations of bay and holly—the cheerful fire glanced its rays through the lattice, inviting the passengers to raise the latch, and join the gossip knot huddled round the hearth, beguiling the long evening with legendary jokes and oft-told Christmas tales.

One of the least pleasing effects of modern refinement is the havoc it has made among the hearty old holiday customs. It has completely taken off the sharp touchings and spirited reliefs of these embellishments of life, and has worn down society into a more smooth and polished, but certainly a less characteristic surface. Many of the games and ceremonials of Christmas have entirely disappeared, and, like the sherris sack of old Falstaff, are become matters of speculation and dispute among commentators. They flourished in times full of spirit and lustihood, when men enjoyed life roughly, but heartily and vigorously; times wild and picturesque, which have furnished poetry with its richest materials, and the drama with its most attractive variety of characters and manners. The world has become more worldly. There is more of dissipation, and less of enjoyment. Pleasure has expanded into a broader, but a shallower stream; and has forsaken many of those deep and quiet channels where it flowed sweetly throught the calm bosom of domestic life. Society has acquired a more enlightened and elegant tone; but it has lost many of its strong local peculiarities, its home-bred feelings, its honest fireside delights. The traditionary customs of golden-hearted antiquity, its feudal hospitalities, and lordly wassailings, have passed away with the baronial castles and stately manor-houses in which they were celebrated. They comported with the shadowy hall, the great oaken gallery, and the tapestried parlour, but are unfitted to the light showy saloons and gay drawing-rooms of the modern villa.

Shorn, however, as it is, of its ancient and festive honours, Christmas is still a period of delightful excitement in England. It is gratifying to see that home feeling completely aroused which holds so powerful a place in every English bosom. The preparations making on every side for the social board that is again to unite friends and kindred; the presents of good cheer passing and repassing, those tokens of regard, and quickeners of kind feelings; the evergreens distributed about houses and churches, emblems of peace and gladness; all these have the most pleasing effect in producing fond associations, and kindling benevolent sympathies. Even the sound of the Waits, rude as may be their minstrelsy, breaks upon the mid-watches of a winter night with the effect of perfect harmony. As I have been awakened by them in that still and solemn hour, "when deep sleep falleth upon man," I have listened with a hushed delight, and, connecting them with the sacred and joyous occasion, have almost fancied them into another celestial choir, announcing peace and good-will to mankind.

How delightfully the imagination, when wrought upon by these moral influences, turns everything to melody and beauty! The very crowing of the cock, heard sometimes in the profound repose of the country, "telling the night watches to his feathery dames," was thought by the common people to announce the approach of this sacred festival:—

"Some say that ever 'gainst the season comes
Wherein our Saviour's birth is celebrated,
This bird of dawning singeth all night long;
And then, they say, no spirit dares stir abroad;
The nights are wholesome—then no planets strike,
No fairy takes, no witch hath power to charm,
So hallowed and so gracious is the time."

Amidst the general call to happiness, the bustle of the spirits, and stir of the affections, which prevail at this period, what bosom can remain insensible? It is, indeed, the season of regenerated feeling—the season for kindling, not merely the fire of hospitality in the hall, but the genial flame of charity in the heart.

The scene of early love again rises green to memory beyond the sterile waste of years; and the idea of home, fraught with the fragrance of home-dwelling joys, reanimates the drooping spirit; as the Arabian breeze will sometimes waft the freshness of the distant fields to the weary pilgrim of the desert.

Stranger and sojourner as I am in the land—though for me no social hearth may blaze, no hospitable roof throw open its doors, nor the warm grasp of friendship welcome me at the threshold—yet I feel the influence of the season beaming into my soul from the happy looks of those around me. Surely happiness is reflective, like the light of heaven; and every countenance, bright with smiles, and glowing with innocent enjoyment, is a mirror transmitting to others the rays of a supreme and ever-shining benevolence. He who can turn churlishly away from contemplating the felicity of his fellow-beings, and can sit down darkling and repining in his loneliness when all around is joyful, may have his moments of strong excitement and selfish gratification, but he wants the genial and social sympathies which constitute the charm of a merry Christmas.

THE STAGE COACH

Omne bene
Sine pœnâ
Tempus est ludendi,
Venit hora
Absque morâ
Libros deponendi.

OLD HOLIDAY SCHOOL SONG.

IN THE preceding paper I have made some general observations on the Christmas festivities of England, and am tempted to illustrate them by some anecdotes of a Christmas passed in the country; in perusing which I would most courteously invite my reader to lay aside the austerity of wisdom, and to put on that genuine holiday spirit which is tolerant of folly, and anxious only for amusement.

In the course of a December tour in Yorkshire, I rode for a long distance in one of the public coaches, on the day preceding Christmas. The coach was crowded, both inside and out, with passengers, who, by their talk, seemed principally bound to the mansions of relations or friends, to eat the Christmas dinner. It was loaded also with hampers of game, and baskets and boxes of delicacies; and hares hung dangling their long ears about the coachman's box, presents from distant friends for the impending feast. I had three fine rosy-cheeked school-boys for my fellow-passengers inside, full of the buxom health and manly spirit which I have observed in the children of this country. They were returning home for the holidays in high glee, and promising themselves a world of enjoyment. It was delightful to hear the gigantic plans of the little rogues, and the impracticable feats they were to perform during their six weeks' emancipation from the abhorred thraldom of book, birch, and pedagogue. They were full of anticipations of the meeting with the family and household, down to the very cat and dog; and of the joy they were to give their little sisters by the presents with which their pockets were crammed; but the meeting to which they seemed to look forward with the greatest impatience was with Bantam, which I found to be a pony, and according to their talk, possessed of more virtues than any steed since the days of Bucephalus. How he could trot! how he could run! and then such leaps as he would take—there was not a hedge in the whole country that he could not clear.

They were under the particular guardianship of the coachman, to whom, whenever an opportunity presented, they addressed a host of questions, and pronounced him one of the best fellows in the world. Indeed, I could not but notice the more than ordinary air of bustle and importance of the coach·man, who wore his hat a little on one side, and had a large bunch of Christmas greens stuck in the buttonhole of his coat. He is always a personage full of mighty care and business, but he is particularly so during this season, having so many commissions to execute in consequence of the great inter-change of presents. And here, perhaps, it may not be unacceptable to my untravelled readers, to have a sketch that may serve as a general representation of this very numerous and important class of functionaries, who have a dress, a manner, a language, and air, peculiar to themselves, and prevalent throughout the fraternity; so that, wherever an English stage-coachman may be seen, he cannot be mistaken for one of any other craft or mystery.

He has commonly a broad, full face, curiously mottled with red, as if the blood had been forced by hard feeding into every vessel of the skin; he is swelled into jolly dimensions by frequent potations of malt liquors, and his bulk is still further increased by a multiplicity of coats, in which he is buried like a cauliflower, the upper one reaching to his heels. He wears a broad-rimmed, low-crowned hat; a huge roll of coloured handkerchief about his neck, knowingly knotted and tucked in at the bosom; and has in summer time a large bouquet of flowers in his buttonhole; the present, most probably, of some enamoured country lass. His waistcoat is commonly of some bright colour, striped, and his small-clothes extend far below the knees, to meet a pair of jockey-boots which reach about half-way up his legs.

All this costume is maintained with much precision; he has a pride in having his clothes of excellent materials; and, notwithstanding the seeming grossness of his appearance, there is still discernible that neatness and propriety of person which is almost inherent in an Englishman. He enjoys great con-sequence and consideration along the road; has frequent conferences with the village housewives, who look upon him as a man of great trust and dependence; and he seems to have a good understanding with every bright-eyed country lass. The moment he arrives where the horses are to be changed, he throws down the reins with something of an air, and abandons the cattle to the care of the ostler; his duty being merely to drive from one stage to another. When off the box, his hands are thrust into the pockets of his great coat, and he rolls about the inn yard with an air of the most absolute lordliness. Here he is generally surrounded by an admiring throng of ostlers, stable-boys, shoeblacks, and those nameless hangers-on that infest inns and taverns, and run errands, and do all kinds of odd jobs, for the privilege of battening on the drippings of the kitchen and the leakage of the taproom. These all look up to him as to an oracle; treasure up his cant phrases; echo his opinions about horses and other topics of jockey lore; and above all, endeavour to imitate his air and carriage. Every ragamuffin that has a coat to his back thrusts his hands in the pockets, rolls in his gait, talks slang, and is an embryo Coachey.

Perhaps it might be owing to the pleasing serenity that reigned in my own mind, that I fancied I saw cheerfulness in every countenance throughout the journey. A stage coach, however, carries animation always with it, and puts the world in motion as it whirls along. The horn, sounded at the entrance of a village, produces a general bustle. Some hasten forth to meet friends, some with bundles and bandboxes to secure places, and in the hurry of the moment can hardly take leave of the group that accompanies them. In the meantime the coachman has a world of small commissions to execute Sometimes he delivers a hare or pheasant; sometimes jerks a small parcel or newspaper to the door of a public-house; and sometimes, with knowing leer and words of sly import, hands to some half-blushing, half-laughing housemaid an odd-shaped billet-doux from some rustic admirer. As the coach rattles through the village, everyone runs to the window, and you have glances on every side of fresh country faces and blooming giggling girls. At the corners are assembled juntos of village idlers and wise men, who take their stations there for the important purpose of seeing company pass; but the sagest knot is generally at the blacksmith's, to whom the passing of the coach is an event fruitful of much speculation. The smith, with the horse's heel in his lap, pauses as the vehicle whirls by; the cyclops round the anvil suspend their ringing hammers, and suffer the iron to grow cool; and the sooty spectre in brown paper cap, labouring at the bellows, leans on the handle for a moment, and permits the asthmatic engine to heave a long-drawn sigh, while he glares through the murky smoke and sulphureous gleams of the smithy.

Perhaps the impending holiday might have given a more than usual anima-tion to the country, for it seemed to me as if everybody was in good looks and good spirits. Game, poultry, and other luxuries of the table, were in brisk circulation in the villages; the grocers', butchers', and fruiterers' shops were thronged with customers. The housewives were stirring briskly about, putting their dwellings in order; and the glossy branches of holly, with their bright red berries, began to appear at the windows. The scene brought to mind an old writer's account of Christmas preparations:—"Now capons and hens, besides turkeys, geese, and ducks, with beef and mutton—must all die— for in twelve days a multitude of people will not be fed with a little. Now plums and spice, sugar and honey, square it among pies and broth. Now or never must music be in tune, for the youth must dance and sing to get them a heat, while the aged sit by the fire. The country maid leaves half her market, and must be sent again, if she forgets a pack of cards on Christmas eve. Great is the contention of holly and ivy, whether master or dame wears the breeches. Dice and cards benefit the butler; and if the cook do not lack wit, he will sweetly lick his fingers."

I was roused from this fit of luxurious meditation, by a shout from my little travelling companions. They had been looking out of the coach windows for the last few miles, recognising every tree and cottage as they approached home, and now there was a general burst of joy—"There's John! and there's old Carlo! and there's Bantam!" cried the happy little rogues, clapping their hands.

At the end of the lane there was an old sober-looking servant in livery, waiting for them; he was accompanied by a superannuated pointer, and by the redoubtable Bantam, a little old rat of a pony, with a shaggy mane and long rusty tail, who stood dozing quietly by the roadside, little dreaming of the bustling times that awaited him.

I was pleased to see the fondness with which the little fellows leaped about the steady old footman, and hugged the pointer; who wriggled his whole body for joy. But Bantam was the great object of interest; all wanted to mount at once, and it was with some difficulty that John arranged that they should ride by turns, and the eldest should ride first.

Off they set at last; one on the pony, with the dog bounding and barking before him, and the others holding John's hands; both talking at once, and overpowering him with questions about home, and with school anecdotes. I looked after them with a feeling in which I do not know whether pleasure or melancholy predominated; for I was reminded of those days when, like them, I had neither known care nor sorrow, and a holiday was the summit of earthly felicity. We stopped a few moments afterwards to water the horses, and on resuming our route, a turn of the road brought us in sight of a neat country seat. I could just distinguish the forms of a lady and two young girls in the portico, and I saw my little comrades, with Bantam, Carlo, and old John, trooping along the carriage road. I leaned out of the coach window, in hopes of witnessing the happy meeting, but a grove of trees shut it from my sight.

In the evening we reached a village where I had determined to pass the night. As we drove into the great gateway of the inn, I saw on one side the light of a rousing kitchen fire beaming through a window. I entered, and admired, for the hundredth time, that picture of convenience, neatness, and broad, honest enjoyment, the kitchen of an English inn. It was of spacious dimensions, hung round with copper and tin vessels highly polished, and decorated here and there with a Christmas green. Hams, tongues, and flitches of bacon, were suspended from the ceiling; a smoke-jack made its ceaseless clanking beside the fireplace, and a clock ticked in one corner. A well-scoured deal table extended along one side of the kitchen, with a cold round of beef and other hearty viands upon it, over which two foaming tankards of ale seemed mounting guard. Travellers of inferior order were preparing to attack this stout repast, while others sat smoking and gossiping over their ale on two high-backed oaken settles beside the fire. Trim housemaids were hurrying backwards and forwards under the directions of a fresh bustling landlady; but still seizing an occasional moment to exchange a flippant word, and have a rallying laugh with the group round the fire. The scene completely realised Poor Robin's humble idea of the comforts of mid-winter,—

> *Now trees their leafy hats do bare*
> *To reverence Winter's silver hair;*
> *A handsome hostess, merry host,*
> *A pot of ale now and a toast,*
> *Tobacco and a good coal fire,*
> *Are things this season doth require.*[1]

I had not been long at the inn when a post-chaise drove up to the door. A young gentleman stepped out, and by the light of the lamps I caught a glimpse of a countenance which I thought I knew. I moved forward to get

[1] Poor Robin's *Almanac*, 1684.

a nearer view, when his eye caught mine. I was not mistaken; it was Frank Bracebridge, a sprightly good-humoured young fellow, with whom I had once travelled on the continent. Our meeting was extremely cordial, for the countenance of an old fellow-traveller always brings up the recollection of a thousand pleasant scenes, odd adventures, and excellent jokes. To discuss all these in a transient interview at an inn was impossible; and finding that I was not pressed for time, and was merely making a tour of observation, he insisted that I should give him a day or two at his father's country seat, to which he was going to pass the holidays, and which lay at a few miles' distance. "It is better than eating a solitary Christmas dinner at an inn," said he, "and I can assure you of a hearty welcome in something of the old-fashioned style." His reasoning was cogent, and I must confess the preparation I had seen for universal festivity and social enjoyment had made me feel a little impatient of my loneliness. I closed, therefore, at once, with his invitation; the chaise drove up to the door, and in a few moments I was on my way to the family mansion of the Bracebridges.

CHRISTMAS EVE

Saint Francis and Saint Benedight
Blesse this house from wicked wight;
From the night-mare and the goblin,
That is hight good fellow Robin:
Keep it from all evil spirits,
Fairies, weezels, rats, and ferrets:
*   From curfew time*
*   To the next prime.*—CARTWRIGHT.

IT WAS a brilliant moonlight night, but extremely cold; our chaise whirled rapidly over the frozen ground; the postboy smacked his whip incessantly, and a part of the time his horses were on a gallop. "He knows where he is going," said my companion, laughing, "and is eager to arrive in time for some of the merriment and good cheer of the servants' hall. My father, you must know, is a bigoted devotee of the old school, and prides himself upon keeping up something of old English hospitality. He is a tolerable specimen of what you will rarely meet with nowadays in its purity, the old English country gentleman; for our men of fortune spend so much of their time in town, and fashion is carried so much into the country, that the strong rich peculiarities of ancient rural life are almost polished away. My father, however, from early years, took honest Peacham[1] for his text-book, instead of Chesterfield; he determined, in his own mind, that there was no condition more truly honourable and enviable than that of a country gentleman on his paternal lands, and therefore passes the whole of his time on his estate. He is a strenuous advocate for the revival of the old rural games and holiday observances, and is deeply read in the writers, ancient and

[1] Peacham's *Complete Gentleman*, 1622.

modern, who have treated on the subject. Indeed, his favourite range of reading is among the authors who flourished at least two centuries since; who, he insists, wrote and thought more like true Englishmen than any of their successors. He even regrets sometimes that he had not been born a few centuries earlier, when England was itself, and had its peculiar manners and customs. As he lives at some distance from the main road, in rather a lonely part of the country, without any rival gentry near him, he has that most enviable of all blessings to an Englishman, an opportunity of indulging the bent of his own humour without molestation. Being representative of the oldest family in the neighbourhood, and a great part of the peasantry being his tenants, he is much looked up to, and, in general, is known simply by the appellation of 'The Squire'; a title which has been accorded to the head of the family since time immemorial. I think it best to give you these hints about my worthy old father, to prepare you for any eccentricities that might otherwise appear absurd."

We had passed for some time along the wall of a park, and at length the chaise stopped at the gate. It was in a heavy magnificent old style, of iron bars, fancifully wrought at top into flourishes and flowers. The huge square columns that supported the gate were surmounted by the family crest. Close adjoining was the porter's lodge, sheltered under dark fir-trees, and almost buried in shrubbery.

The postboy rang a large porter's bell, which resounded through the still frosty air, and was answered by the distant barking of dogs, with which the mansion-house seemed garrisoned. An old woman immediately appeared at the gate. As the moonlight fell strongly upon her, I had a full view of a little primitive dame, dressed very much in the antique taste, with a neat kerchief and stomacher, and her silver hair peeping from under a cap of snowy whiteness. She came curtseying forth, with many expressions of simple joy at seeing her young master. Her husband, it seemed, was up at the house keeping Christmas eve in the servants' hall; they could not do without him, as he was the best hand at a song and story in the household.

My friend proposed that we should alight and walk through the park to the hall, which was at no great distance, while the chaise should follow on. Our road wound through a noble avenue of trees, among the naked branches of which the moon glittered as she rolled through the deep vault of a cloudless sky. The lawn beyond was sheeted with a slight covering of snow, which here and there sparkled as the moonbeams caught a frosty crystal; and at a distance might be seen a thin transparent vapour, stealing up from the low grounds and threatening gradually to shroud the landscape.

My companion looked around him with transport:—"How often," said he, "have I scampered up this avenue, on returning home on school vacations! How often have I played under these trees when a boy! I feel a degree of filial reverence for them, as we look up to those who have cherished us in childhood. My father was always scrupulous in exacting our holidays, and having us around him on family festivals. He used to direct and superintend our games with the strictness that some parents do the studies of their children. He was very particular that we should play the old English games according to their original form; and consulted old books for precedent and authority for every 'merrie disport'; yet I assure you there never was pedantry so delightful. It was the policy of the good old gentleman to make his children feel that home was the happiest place in the world; and I value this delicious home feeling as one of the choicest gifts a parent could bestow."

We were interrupted by the clamour of a troop of dogs of all sorts and sizes, "mongrel, puppy, whelp and hound, and curs of low degree," that, disturbed by the ring of the porter's bell, and the rattling of the chaise, came bounding, open-mouthed, across the lawn.

> "——The little dogs and all,
> Tray, Blanch, and Sweetheart—see, they bark at me!"

cried Bracebridge, laughing. At the sound of his voice, the bark was changed into a yelp of delight, and in a moment he was surrounded and almost overpowered by the caresses of the faithful animals.

We had now come in full view of the old family mansion, partly thrown in deep shadow, and partly lit up by the cold moonshine. It was an irregular building, of some magnitude, and seemed to be of the architecture of different periods. One wing was evidently very ancient, with heavy stone-shafted bow windows jutting out and overrun with ivy, from among the foliage of which the small diamond-shaped panes of glass glittered with the moon-beams. The rest of the house was in the French taste of Charles the Second's time, having been repaired and altered, as my friend told me, by one of his ancestors, who returned with that monarch at the Restoration. The grounds about the house were laid out in the old formal manner of artificial flower-beds, clipped shrubberies, raised terraces, and heavy stone balustrades, orna-mented with urns, a leaden statue or two, and a jet of water. The old gentle-man, I was told, was extremely careful to preserve this obsolete finery in all its original state. He admired this fashion in gardening; it had an air of magnificence, was courtly and noble, and befitting good old family style. The boasted imitation of nature in modern gardening, had sprung up with modern republican notions, but did not suit a monarchical government; it smacked of the levelling system.—I could not help smiling at this introduction of politics into gardening, though I expressed some apprehension that I should find the old gentleman rather intolerant in his creed.—Frank assured me, however, that it was almost the only instance in which he had ever heard his father meddle with politics; and he believed that he had got this notion from a member of parliament who once passed a few weeks with him. The squire was glad of any argument to defend his clipped yew-trees and formal terraces, which had been occasionally attacked by modern landscape-gardeners.

As we approached the house, we heard the sound of music, and now and then a burst of laughter, from one end of the building. This, Bracebridge said, must proceed from the servants' hall, where a great deal of revelry was permitted, and even encouraged, by the squire, throughout the twelve days of Christmas, provided everything was done conformably to ancient usage.

Here were kept up the old games of hoodman blind, shoe the wild mare, hot cockles, steal the white loaf, bob apple, and snap dragon: the Yule clog and Christmas candle were regularly burnt, and the mistletoe, with its white berries, hung up, to the imminent peril of all the pretty housemaids.[2]

So intent were the servants upon their sports, that we had to ring repeatedly before we could make ourselves heard. On our arrival being announced, the squire came out to receive us, accompanied by his two other sons; one a young officer in the army, home on leave of absence; the other an Oxonian, just from the University. The squire was a fine healthy-looking old gentleman, with silver hair curling lightly round an open florid countenance; in which the physiognomist, with the advantage, like myself, of a previous hint or two, might discover a singular mixture of whim and benevolence.

The family meeting was warm and affectionate: as the evening was far advanced, the squire would not permit us to change our travelling dresses, but ushered us at once to the company, which was assembled in a large old-fashioned hall. It was composed of different branches of a numerous family connection, where there were the usual proportion of old uncles and aunts, comfortable married dames, superannuated spinsters, blooming country cousins, half-fledged striplings, and bright-eyed boarding-school hoydens. They were variously occupied; some at a round game of cards; others conversing around the fireplace; at one end of the hall was a group of the young folks, some nearly grown up, others of a more tender and budding age, fully engrossed by a merry game; and a profusion of wooden horses, penny trumpets, and tattered dolls, about the floor, showed traces of a troop of little fairy beings, who, having frolicked through a happy day, had been carried off to slumber through a peaceful night.

While the mutual greetings were going on between young Bracebridge and his relatives, I had time to scan the apartment. I have called it a hall, for so it had certainly been in old times, and the squire had evidently endeavoured to restore it to something of its primitive state. Over the heavy projecting fireplace was suspended a picture of a warrior in armour, standing by a white horse, and on the opposite wall hung a helmet, buckler and lance. At one end an enormous pair of antlers were inserted in the wall, the branches serving as hooks on which to suspend hats, whips, and spurs; and in the corners of the apartment were fowling-pieces, fishing-rods, and other sporting implements. The furniture was of the cumbrous workmanship of former days, though some articles of modern convenience had been added, and the oaken floor had been carpeted; so that the whole presented an odd mixture of parlour and hall.

The grate had been removed from the wide overwhelming fireplace, to make way for a fire of wood, in the midst of which was an enormous log glowing and blazing, and sending forth a vast volume of light and heat; this I understood was the Yule clog, which the squire was particular in having

[2]The mistletoe is still hung up in farmhouses and kitchens at Christmas, and the young men have the privilege of kissing the girls under it, plucking each time a berry from the bush. When the berries are all plucked, the privilege ceases.

brought in and illumined on a Christmas eve, according to ancient custom.[3]

It was really delightful to see the old squire seated in his hereditary elbow chair, by the hospitable fireplace of his ancestors, and looking around him like the sun of a system, beaming warmth and gladness to every heart. Even the very dog that lay stretched at his feet, as he lazily shifted his position and yawned, would look fondly up in his master's face, wag his tail against the floor, and stretch himself again to sleep, confident of kindness and protection. There is an emanation from the heart in genuine hospitality which cannot be described, but is immediately felt, and puts the stranger at once at his ease. I had not been seated many minutes by the comfortable hearth of the worthy old cavalier, before I found myself as much at home as if I had been one of the family.

Supper was announced shortly after our arrival. It was served up in a spacious oaken chamber, the panels of which shone with wax, and around which were several family portraits decorated with holly and ivy. Besides the accustomed lights, two great wax tapers, called Christmas candles, wreathed with greens, were placed on a highly-polished beaufet among the family plate. The table was abundantly spread with substantial fare; but the squire made his supper of frumenty, a dish made of wheat cakes boiled in milk, with rich spices, being a standing dish in old times for Christmas eve. I was happy to find my old friend, minced pie, in the retinue of the feast; and finding him to be perfectly orthodox, and that I need not be ashamed of my predilection, I greeted him with all the warmth wherewith we usually greet an old and very genteel acquaintance.

The mirth of the company was greatly promoted by the humours of an eccentric personage whom Mr. Bracebridge always addressed with the quaint appellation of Master Simon. He was a tight brisk little man, with the air of an arrant old bachelor. His nose was shaped like the bill of a parrot; his face slightly pitted with the small-pox, with a dry perpetual bloom on it, like a frostbitten leaf in autumn. He had an eye of great quickness and vivacity,

[3]The *Yule clog* is a great log of wood, sometimes the root of a tree, brought into the house with great ceremony, on Christmas eve, laid in the fireplace, and lighted with the brand of last year's clog. While it lasted, there was great drinking, singing, and telling of tales. Sometimes it was accompanied by Christmas candles; but in the cottages the only light was from the ruddy blaze of the great wood fire. The Yule clog was to burn all night; if it went out, it was considered a sign of ill-luck. Herrick mentions it in one of his songs—

> Come, bring with a noise
> My merrie, merrie boyes,
> The Christmas log to the firing;
> While my good dame, she
> Bids ye all be free,
> And drink to your hearts' desiring.

The Yule clog is still burnt in many farmhouses and kitchens in England, particularly in the north, and there are several superstitions connected with it among the peasantry. If a squinting person come to the house while it is burning, or a person barefooted, it is considered an ill omen. The brand remaining from the Yule clog is carefully put away to light the next year's Christmas fire.

with a drollery and lurking waggery of expression that was irresistible. He
was evidently the wit of the family, dealing very much in sly jokes and
innuendoes with the ladies, and making infinite merriment by harpings upon
old themes; which, unfortunately, my ignorance of the family chronicles
did not permit me to enjoy. It seemed to be his great delight during supper
to keep a young girl next to him in a continual agony of stifled laughter,
in spite of her awe of the reproving looks of her mother, who sat opposite.
Indeed, he was the idol of the younger part of the company, who laughed
at everything he said or did, and at every turn of his countenance. I could
not wonder at it; for he must have been a miracle of accomplishments in
their eyes. He could imitate Punch and Judy; make an old woman of his
hand, with the assistance of a burnt cork and pocket-handkerchief; and cut
an orange into such a ludicrous caricature, that the young folks were ready
to die with laughing.

I was let briefly into his history by Frank Bracebridge. He was an old
bachelor, of a small independent income, which, by careful management, was
sufficient for all his wants. He revolved through the family system like a
vagrant comet in its orbit; sometimes visiting one branch and sometimes
another quite remote; as is often the case with gentlemen of extensive connections and small fortunes in England. He had a chirping buoyant disposition,
always enjoying the present moment; and his frequent change of scene and
company prevented his acquiring those rusty unaccommodating habits with
which old bachelors are so uncharitably charged. He was a complete family
chronicle, being versed in the genealogy, history, and intermarriages of
the whole house of Bracebridge, which made him a great favourite with
the old folks; he was the beau of all the elder ladies and superannuated spinsters,
among whom he was habitually considered rather a young fellow, and he
was master of the revels among the children; so that there was not a more
popular being in the sphere in which he moved than Mr. Simon Bracebridge.
Of late years he had resided almost entirely with the squire, to whom he had
become a factotum, and whom he particularly delighted by jumping with
his humour in respect to old times, and by having a scrap of an old song
to suit every occasion. We had presently a specimen of his last-mentioned
talent, for no sooner was supper removed, and spiced wines and other beverages peculiar to the season introduced, than Master Simon was called on
for a good old Christmas song. He bethought himself for a moment, and
then, with a sparkle of the eye, and a voice that was by no means bad,
excepting that it ran occasionally into a falsetto, like the notes of a split reed,
he quavered forth a quaint old ditty.

> *Now Christmas is come,*
> *Let us beat up the drum,*
> *And call all our neighbours together,*
> *And when they appear,*
> *Let us make them such cheer,*
> *As will keep out the wind and the weather, etc.*

The supper had disposed everyone to gaiety, and an old harper was summoned from the servants' hall, where he had been strumming all the evening, and to all appearance comforting himself with some of the squire's home-brewed. He was a kind of hanger-on, I was told, of the establishment, and, though ostensibly a resident of the village, was oftener to be found in the squire's kitchen than his own home, the old gentleman being fond of the sound of "harp in hall."

The dance, like most dances after supper, was a merry one; some of the older folks joined in it, and the squire himself figured down several couple with a partner, with whom he affirmed he had danced at every Christmas for nearly half a century. Master Simon, who seemed to be a kind of connecting link between the old times and the new, and to be withal a little antiquated in the taste of his accomplishments, evidently piqued himself on his dancing, and was endeavouring to gain credit by the heel and toe, rigadoon, and other graces of the ancient school; but he had unluckily assorted himself with a little romping girl from boarding-school, who, by her wild vivacity, kept him continually on the stretch, and defeated all his sober attempts at elegance:—such are the ill-assorted matches to which antique gentlemen are unfortunately prone!

The young Oxonian, on the contrary, had led out one of his maiden aunts, on whom the rogue played a thousand little knaveries with impunity; he was full of practical jokes, and his delight was to tease his aunts and cousins; yet, like all madcap youngsters, he was a universal favourite among the women. The most interesting couple in the dance was the young officer and a ward of the squire's, a beautiful blushing girl of seventeen. From several shy glances which I had noticed in the course of the evening, I suspected there was a little kindness growing up between them; and, indeed, the young soldier was just the hero to captivate a romantic girl. He was tall, slender, and handsome, and like most young British officers of late years, had picked up various small accomplishments on the Continent—he could talk French and Italian—draw landscapes, sing very tolerably—dance divinely; but, above all, he had been wounded at Waterloo:—what girl of seventeen, well read in poetry and romance, could resist such a mirror of chivalry and perfection!

The moment the dance was over, he caught up a guitar, and lolling against the old marble fireplace, in an attitude which I am half inclined to suspect was studied, began the little French air of the Troubadour. The squire, however, exclaimed against having anything on Christmas eve but good old English; upon which the young minstrel, casting up his eye for a moment, as if in an effort of memory, struck into another strain, and, with a charming air of gallantry, gave Herrick's "Night-Piece to Julia."

> Her eyes the glow-worm lend thee,
> The shooting stars attend thee,
> And the elves also,
> Whose little eyes glow
> Like the sparks of fire befriend thee.

No Will-o'-the-Wisp mislight thee;
Nor snake nor slow-worm bite thee;
  But on, on thy way,
  Not making a stay,
Since ghost there is none to affright thee.

Then let not the dark thee cumber,
What tho' the moon does slumber,
  The stars of the night
  Will lend thee their light,
Like tapers clear without number.

Then, Julia, let me woo thee,
Thus, thus, to come unto me
  And when I shall meet
  Thy silvery feet,
My soul I'll pour into thee.

The song might or might not have been intended in compliment to the fair Julia, for so I found his partner was called; she, however, was certainly unconscious of any such application, for she never looked at the singer, but kept her eyes cast upon the floor. Her face was suffused, it is true, with a beautiful blush, and there was a gentle heaving of the bosom, but all that was doubtless caused by the exercise of the dance; indeed, so great was her indifference, that she amused herself with plucking to pieces a choice bouquet of hot-house flowers, and by the time the song was concluded the nosegay lay in ruins on the floor.

The party now broke up for the night with the kind-hearted old custom of shaking hands. As I passed through the hall, on my way to my chamber, the dying embers of the Yule clog still sent forth a dusky glow, and had it not been the season when "no spirit dares stir abroad," I should have been half tempted to steal from my room at midnight, and peep whether the fairies might not be at their revels about the hearth.

My chamber was in the old part of the mansion, the ponderous furniture of which might have been fabricated in the days of the giants. The room was panelled, with cornices of heavy carved work, in which flowers and grotesque faces were strangely intermingled; and a row of black-looking portraits stared mournfully at me from the walls. The bed was of rich though faded damask, with a lofty tester, and stood in a niche opposite a bow window. I had scarcely got into bed when a strain of music seemed to break forth in the air just below the window. I listened, and found it proceeded from a band, which I concluded to be the Waits from some neighbouring village. They went round the house, playing under the windows. I drew aside the curtains to hear them more distinctly. The moonbeams fell through the upper part of the casement, partially lighting up the antiquated apartment. The sounds, as they receded, became more soft and aerial, and seemed to accord with the quiet and moonlight. I listened and listened—they became more and more tender and remote, and, as they gradually died away, my head sunk upon the pillow, and I fell asleep.

CHRISTMAS DAY

Dark and dull night, flie hence away,
And give the honour to this day
That sees December turn'd to May.

*   *   *   *

Why does the chilling winter's morne
Smile like a field beset with corn?
Or smell like to a meade new-shorne,
Thus on the sudden?—Come and see
The cause why things thus fragrant be.—HERRICK.

WHEN I WOKE the next morning, it seemed as if all the events of the preceding evening had been a dream, and nothing but the identity of the ancient chamber convinced me of their reality. While I lay musing on my pillow, I heard the sound of little feet pattering outside of the door, and a whispering consultation. Presently a choir of small voices chanted forth an old Christmas carol, the burden of which was—

Rejoice, our Saviour he was born
On Christmas day in the morning.

I rose softly, slipped on my clothes, opened the door suddenly, and beheld one of the most beautiful little fairy groups that a painter could imagine. It consisted of a boy and two girls, the eldest not more than six, and lovely as seraphs. They were going the rounds of the house, and singing at every chamber door; but my sudden appearance frightened them into mute bashfulness. They remained for a moment playing on their lips with their fingers, and now and then stealing a shy glance, from under their eyebrows, until, as if by one impulse, they scampered away, and as they turned an angle of the gallery, I heard them laughing in triumph at their escape.

Everything conspired to produce kind and happy feelings in this stronghold of old-fashioned hospitality. The window of my chamber looked out upon what in summer would have been a beautiful landscape. There was a sloping lawn, a fine stream winding at the foot of it, and a tract of park beyond, with noble clumps of trees, and herds of deer. At a distance was a neat hamlet, with the smoke from the cottage chimneys hanging over it; and a church with its dark spire in strong relief against the clear cold sky. The house was surrounded with evergreens, according to the English custom, which would have given almost an appearance of summer; but the morning was extremely frosty; the light vapour of the preceding evening had been precipitated by the cold, and covered all the trees and every blade of grass with its fine crystallisations. The rays of a bright morning sun had a dazzling effect among the glittering foliage. A robin, perched upon the top of a mountain ash that hung its clusters of red berries just before my window, was basking himself in the sunshine, and piping a few querulous notes; and a peacock was displaying all the glories of his train, and strutting with the pride and gravity of a Spanish grandee, on the terrace walk below.

I had scarcely dressed myself, when a servant appeared to invite me to family prayers. He showed me the way to a small chapel in the old wing of the house, where I found the principal part of the family already assembled in a kind of gallery, furnished with cushions, hassocks, and large prayer-books; the servants were seated on benches below. The old gentleman read prayers from a desk in front of the gallery, and Master Simon acted as clerk, and made the responses; and I must do him the justice to say that he acquitted himself with great gravity and decorum.

The service was followed by a Christmas carol, which Mr. Bracebridge himself had constructed from a poem of his favourite author, Herrick; and it had been adapted to an old church melody by Master Simon. As there were several good voices among the household, the effect was extremely pleasing; but I was particularly gratified by the exaltation of heart, and sudden sally of grateful feeling, with which the worthy squire delivered one stanza: his eye glistening, and his voice rambling out of all the bounds of time and tune.

> 'Tis thou that crown'st my glittering hearth
>   With guiltlesse mirth,
> And givest me Wassaile bowles to drink
>   Spiced to the brink:
> Lord, 'tis thy plenty-dropping hand
>   That soiles my land:
> And giv'st me for my bushell sowne,
>   Twice ten for one.

I afterwards understood that early morning service was read on every Sunday and saint's day throughout the year, either by Mr. Bracebridge or by some member of the family. It was once almost universally the case at the seats of the nobility and gentry of England, and it is much to be regretted that the custom is falling into neglect; for the dullest observer must be sensible of the order and serenity prevalent in those households, where the occasional exercise of a beautiful form of worship in the morning gives, as it were, the key-note to every temper for the day, and attunes every spirit to harmony.

Our breakfast consisted of what the squire denominated true old English fare. He indulged in some bitter lamentations over modern breakfasts of tea and toast, which he censured as among the causes of modern effeminacy and weak nerves, and the decline of old English heartiness; and though he admitted them to his table to suit the palates of his guests, yet there was a brave display of cold meats, wine, and ale on the sideboard.

After breakfast I walked about the grounds with Frank Bracebridge and

Master Simon, or Mr. Simon, as he was called by everybody but the squire. We were escorted by a number of gentlemanlike dogs, that seemed loungers about the establishment; from the frisking spaniel to the steady old stag-hound; the last of which was of a race that had been in the family time out of mind; they were all obedient to a dog-whistle which hung to Master Simon's buttonhole, and in the midst of their gambols would glance an eye occasionally upon a small switch he carried in his hand.

The old mansion had a still more venerable look in the yellow sunshine than by pale moonlight; and I could not but feel the force of the squire's idea, that the formal terraces, heavily-moulded balustrades, and clipped yew-trees, carried with them an air of proud aristocracy. There appeared to be an unusual number of peacocks about the place, and I was making some remarks upon what I termed a flock of them, that were basking under a sunny wall, when I was gently corrected in my phraseology by Master Simon, who told me that, according to the most ancient and approved treatise on hunting, I must say a *muster* of peacocks. "In the same way," added he, with' a slight air of pedantry, "we say a flight of doves or swallows, a bevy of quails, a herd of deer, of wrens or cranes, a skulk of foxes, or a building of rooks." He went on to inform me that, according to Sir Anthony Fitzherbert, we ought to ascribe to this bird "both understanding and glory; for, being praised, he will presently set up his tail, chiefly against the sun, to the intent you may the better behold the beauty thereof. But at the fall of the leaf, when his tail falleth, he will mourn and hide himself in corners, till his tail come again as it was."

I could not help smiling at this display of small erudition on so whimsical a subject; but I found that the peacocks were birds of some consequence at the hall; for Frank Bracebridge informed me that they were great favourites with his father, who was extremely careful to keep up the breed; partly because they belonged to chivalry, and were in great request at the stately banquets of the olden time; and partly because they had a pomp and magnificence about them, highly becoming an old family mansion. Nothing, he was accustomed to say, had an air of greater state and dignity than a peacock perched upon an antique stone balustrade.

Master Simon had now to hurry off, having an appointment at the parish church with the village choristers, who were to perform some music of his selection. There was something extremely agreeable in the cheerful flow of animal spirits of the little man; and I confess I had been somewhat surprised at his apt quotations from authors who certainly were not in the range of everyday reading. I mentioned this last circumstance to Frank Bracebridge, who told me with a smile that Master Simon's whole stock of erudition was confined to some half a dozen old authors, which the squire had put into his hands, and which he read over and over whenever he had a studious fit, as he sometimes had on a rainy day, or a long winter evening. Sir Anthony Fitzherbert's *Book of Husbandry;* Markham's *Country Contentments;* the *Tretyse of Hunting,* by Sir Thomas Cockayne, Knight; Isaac Walton's *Angler,* and two or three more such ancient worthies of the pen, were his standard authorities; and, like all men who know but a few books, he looked up to them with a kind of idolatry, and quoted them on all occasions. As to his songs, they were chiefly picked out of old books in the squire's library, and adapted to tunes that were popular among the choice spirits of the last century. His practical application of scraps of literature, however, had caused him to be looked upon as a prodigy of book knowledge by all the grooms, huntsmen, and small sportsmen of the neighbourhood.

While we were talking, we heard the distant toll of the village bell, and I was told that the squire was a little particular in having his household at church on a Christmas morning; considering it a day of pouring out of thanks and rejoicing; for, as old Tusser observed,

> At Christmas be merry, and thankful withal,
> And feast thy poor neighbours, the great with the small.

"If you are disposed to go to church," said Frank Bracebridge, "I can promise you a specimen of my cousin Simon's musical achievements. As the church is destitute of an organ, he has formed a band from the village amateurs, and established a musical club for their improvement; he has also sorted a choir, as he sorted my father's pack of hounds, according to the directions of Jervaise Markham, in his *Country Contentments;* for the bass he has sought out all the 'deep, solemn mouths,' and for the tenor the 'loud-ringing mouths,' among the country bumpkins, and for 'sweet mouths,' he has culled with curious taste among the prettiest lasses in the neighbourhood; though these last, he affirms, are the most difficult to keep in tune; your pretty female singer being exceedingly wayward and capricious, and very liable to accident."

As the morning, though frosty, was remarkably fine and clear, the most of the family walked to the church, which was a very old building of gray stone, and stood near a village, about half a mile from the park gate. Adjoining it was a low snug parsonage, which seemed coeval with the church. The front of it was perfectly matted with a yew-tree that had been trained against its walls, through the dense foliage of which, apertures had been formed to admit light into the small antique lattices. As we passed this sheltered nest, the parson issued forth and preceded us.

I had expected to see a sleek well-conditioned pastor, such as is often found in a snug living in the vicinity of a rich patron's table, but I was disappointed. The parson was a little, meagre, black-looking man, with a grizzled wig that was too wide, and stood off from each ear, so that his head seemed to have shrunk away within it, like a dried filbert in its shell. He wore a rusty coat, with great skirts, and pockets that would have held the church bible and prayer-book; and his small legs seemed still smaller, from being planted in large shoes, decorated with enormous buckles.

I was informed by Frank Braceridge, that the parson had been a chum of his father's at Oxford, and had received this living shortly after the latter had come to his estate. He was a complete black-letter hunter, and would scarcely read a work printed in the Roman character. The editions of Caxton and Wynkin de Worde were his delight; and he was indefatigable in his researches after such old English writers as have fallen into oblivion from their worthlessness. In deference, perhaps to the notions of Mr. Bracebridge, he had made diligent investigations into the festive rites and holiday customs of former times, and had been as zealous in the inquiry as if he had been a boon companion, but it was merely with that plodding spirit with which men of adust temperament follow up any track of study merely because it is denominated learning, indifferent to its intrinsic nature, whether it be the illustration of the wisdom or of the ribaldry and obscenity of antiquity. He had pored over these old volumes so intensely, that they seemed to have been reflected into his countenance, which, if the face be indeed an index of the mind, might be compared to a title-page of black-letter.

On reaching the church porch, we found the parson rebuking the gray-headed sexton for having used mistletoe among the greens with which the church was decorated. It was, he observed, an unholy plant, profaned by having been used by the Druids in their mystic ceremonies; and though it might be innocently employed in the festive ornamenting of halls and kitchens, yet it had been deemed by the Fathers of the Church as unhallowed, and totally unfit for sacred purposes. So tenacious was he on this point, that the poor sexton was obliged to strip down a great part of the humble trophies of his taste, before the parson would consent to enter upon the service of the day.

The interior of the church was venerable but simple; on the walls were several mural monuments of the Bracebridges, and just beside the altar was a tomb of ancient workmanship, on which lay the effigy of a warrior in armour, with his legs crossed, a sign of his having been a crusader. I was told it was one of the family who had signalised himself in the Holy Land, and the same whose picture hung over the fireplace in the hall.

During service, Master Simon stood up in the pew, and repeated the responses very audibly; evincing that kind of ceremonious devotion punctually observed by a gentleman of the old school, and a man of old family connections. I observed, too, that he turned over the leaves of a folio prayer-book with something of a flourish; possibly to show off an enormous seal-ring which enriched one of his fingers, and which had the look of a family relic. But he was evidently most solicitous about the musical part of the service, keeping his eye fixed intently on the choir, and beating time with much gesticulation and emphasis.

The orchestra was in a small gallery, and presented a most whimsical grouping of heads, piled one above the other, among which I particularly noticed that of the village tailor, a pale fellow with a retreating forehead and chin, who played on the clarionet, and seemed to have blown his face to a point; and there was another, a short pursy man, stooping and labouring at a bass-viol, so as to show nothing but the top of a round bald head, like the egg of an ostrich. There were two or three pretty faces among the female singers, to which the keen air of a frosty morning had given a bright rosy tint; but the gentlemen choristers had evidently been chosen, like old Cremona fiddles, more for tone than looks; and as several had to sing from the same book, there were clusterings of odd physiognomies, not unlike those groups of cherubs we sometimes see on country tombstones.

The usual services of the choir were managed tolerably well, the vocal parts generally lagging a little behind the instrumental, and some loitering fiddler now and then making up for lost time by travelling over a passage with prodigious celerity, and clearing more bars than the keenest fox-hunter to be in at the death. But the great trial was an anthem that had been prepared and arranged by Master Simon, and on which he had founded great expectation. Unluckily there was a blunder at the very onset; the musicians became flurried; Master Simon was in a fever, everything went on lamely and irregularly until they came to a chorus beginning "Now let us sing with one accord," which seemed to be a signal for parting company: all became discord and confusion; each shifted for himself, and got to the end as well, or rather, as soon as he could, excepting one old chorister in a pair of horn spectacles, bestriding and pinching a long sonorous nose, who happened to stand a little apart, and, being wrapped up in his own melody, kept on a quavering course, wriggling his head, ogling his book, and winding all up by a nasal solo of at least three bars' duration.

The parson gave us a most erudite sermon on the rites and ceremonies of Christmas, and the propriety of observing it not merely as a day of thanksgiving, but of rejoicing; supporting the correctness of his opinions by the earliest usages of the church, and enforcing them by the authorities of Theophilus of Cesarea, St Cyprian, St Chrysostom, St Augustine, and a cloud more of saints and fathers, from whom he made copious quotations. I was a little at a loss to perceive the necessity of such a mighty array of forces to maintain a point which no one present seemed inclined to dispute; but I soon found that the good man had a legion of ideal adversaries to contend with; having, in the course of his researches on the subject of Christmas, got completely embroiled in the sectarian controversies of the Revolution, when the Puritans made such a fierce assault upon the ceremonies of the church, and poor old Christmas was driven out of the land by proclamation of Parliament.[1] The worthy parson lived but with times past, and knew but little of the present.

Shut up among worm-eaten tomes in the retirement of his antiquated little study, the pages of old times were to him as the gazettes of the day; while the era of the Revolution was mere modern history. He forgot that nearly two centuries had elapsed since the fiery persecution of poor mince-pie throughout the land; when plum porridge was denounced as mere "popery," and roast-beef as anti-christian; and that Christmas had been brought in again triumphantly

[1]From the *Flying Eagle*, a small gazette, published December 24th 1652—"The House spent much time this day about the business of the Navy, for settling the affairs at sea, and before they rose, were presented with a terrible remonstrance against Christmas day, grounded upon divine Scriptures, 2 Cor. v. 16; 1 Cor. xv. 14, 17; and in honour of the Lord's day, grounded upon these Scriptures: John xx. 1; Rev. i. 10; Psalms cxviii. 24; Lev. xxiii. 7, 11; Mark xv. 8; Psalms lxxxiv. 10; in which Christmas is called Anti-Christ's masse, and those Masse-mongers and Papists who observe it, &c. In consequence of which Parliament spent some time in consultation about the abolition of Christmas day, passed orders to that effect, and resolved to sit on the following day, which was commonly called Christmas day."

with the merry court of King Charles at the Restoration. He kindled into warmth with the ardour of his contest, and the host of imaginary foes with whom he had to combat; he had a stubborn conflict with old Prynne and two or three other forgotten champions of the Roundheads, on the subject of Christmas festivity; and concluded by urging his hearers, in the most solemn and affecting manner, to stand to the traditional customs of their fathers, and feast and make merry on this joyful anniversary of the church.

I have seldom known a sermon attended apparently with more immediate effects; for on leaving the church the congregation seemed one and all possessed with the gaiety of spirit so earnestly enjoined by their pastor. The elder folks gathered in knots in the churchyard, greeting and shaking hands; and the children ran about crying "Ule! Ule!" and repeating some uncouth rhymes[2] which the parson, who had joined us, informed me had been handed down from days of yore. The villagers doffed their hats to the squire as he passed, giving him the good wishes of the season with every appearance of heartfelt sincerity, and were invited by him to the hall, to take something to keep out the cold of the weather; and I heard blessings uttered by several of the poor, which convinced me that, in the midst of his enjoyments, the worthy old cavalier had not forgotten the true Christmas virtue of charity.

On our way homeward his heart seemed overflowed with generous and happy feelings. As we passed over a rising ground which commanded something of a prospect, the sounds of rustic merriment now and then reached our ears: the squire paused for a few moments, and looked around with an air of inexpressible benignity. The beauty of the day was of itself sufficient to inspire philanthropy. Notwithstanding the frostiness of the morning, the sun in his cloudless journey had acquired sufficient power to melt away the thin covering of snow from every southern declivity, and to bring out the living green which adorns an English landscape even in mid-winter. Large tracts of smiling verdure contrasted with the dazzling whiteness of the shaded slopes and hollows. Every sheltered bank, on which the broad rays rested, yielded its silver rill of cold and limpid water, glittering through the dripping grass; and sent up slight exhalations to contribute to the thin haze that hung just above the surface of the earth. There was something truly cheering in this triumph of warmth and verdure over the frosty thraldom of winter; it was, as the squire observed, an emblem of Christmas hospitality, breaking through the chills of ceremony and selfishness, and thawing every heart into a flow. He pointed with pleasure to the indications of good cheer reeking from the chimneys of the comfortable farm-houses, and low thatched cottages. "I love," said he, "to see this day well kept by rich and poor; it is a great thing to have one day in the year, at least, when you are sure of being welcome wherever you go, and of having, as it were, the world all thrown open to you; and I am almost disposed to join with Poor Robin, in his malediction on every churlish enemy to this honest festival:—

[2]Ule! Ule!
Three puddings in a pule
Crack nuts and cry Ule!

Those who at Christmas do repine,
And would fain hence despatch him,
May they with old Duke Humphry dine,
Or else may Squire Ketch catch 'em.

The squire went on to lament the deplorable decay of the games and amusements which were once prevalent at this season among the lower orders, and countenanced by the higher; when the old halls of castles and manor-houses were thrown open at daylight; when the tables were covered with brawn and beef, and humming ale; when the harp and the carol resounded all day long, and when rich and poor were alike welcome to enter and make merry.[3] "Our old games and local customs," said he, "had a great effect in making the peasant fond of his home, and the promotion of them by the gentry made him fond of his lord. They made the times merrier, and kinder, and better; and I can truly say with one of our old poets:—

"I like them well—the curious preciseness
And all-pretended gravity of those
That seek to banish hence these harmless sports,
Have thrust away much ancient honesty.

"The nation," continued he, "is altered; we have almost lost our simple true-hearted peasantry. They have broken asunder from the higher classes, and seem to think their interests are separate. They have become too knowing, and begin to read newspapers, listen to ale-house politicians, and talk of reform. I think one mode to keep them in good humour in these hard times would be for the nobility and gentry to pass more time on their estates, mingle more among the country people, and set the merry old English games going again."

Such was the good squire's project for mitigating public discontent; and, indeed, he had once attempted to put his doctrine in practice, and a few years before had kept open house during the holidays in the old style. The country people, however, did not understand how to play their parts in the scene of hospitality; many uncouth circumstances occurred; the manor was overrun by all the vagrants of the country, and more beggars drawn into the neighbourhood in one week than the parish officers could get rid of in a year. Since then he had contented himself with inviting the decent part of the neighbouring peasantry to call at the hall on Christmas day, and with distributing beef, and bread, and ale, among the poor, that they might make merry in their own dwellings.

[3]An English gentleman, at the opening of the great day (*i.e.* on Christmas day in the morning), had all his tenants and neighbours enter his hall by daybreak. The strong beer was broached, and the black-jacks went plentifully about with toast, sugar and nutmeg, and good Cheshire cheese. The Hackin (the great sausage) must be boiled by daybreak, or else two young men must take the maiden (*i.e.* the cook) by the arms, and run her round the market-place till she is shamed of her laziness."— "ROUND ABOUT OUR SEA COAL FIRE."

We had not been long home when the sound of music was heard from a distance. A band of country lads, without coats, their shirt sleeves fancifully tied with ribands, their hats decorated with greens, and clubs in their hands, were seen advancing up the avenue, followed by a large number of villagers and peasantry. They stopped before the hall door, where the music struck up a peculiar air, and the lads performed a curious and intricate dance, advancing, retreating, and striking their clubs together, keeping exact time to the music; while one, whimsically crowned with the fox's skin, the tail of which flaunted down his back, kept capering round the skirts of the dance, and rattling a Christmas box, with many antic gesticulations.

The squire eyed this fanciful exhibition with great interest and delight, and gave me a full account of its origin, which he traced to the times when the Romans held possession of the island, plainly proving that this was a lineal descendant of the sword dance of the ancients. "It was now," he said, "nearly extinct, but he had accidentally met with traces of it in the neighbourhood, and had encouraged its revival; though, to tell the truth, it was too apt to be followed up by the rough cudgel-play and broken heads in the evening."

After the dance was concluded, the whole party was entertained with brawn and beef, and stout home-brewed. The squire himself mingled among the rustics, and was received with awkward demonstrations of deference and regard. It is true, I perceived two or three of the younger peasants, as they were raising their tankards to their mouths, when the squire's back was turned, making something of a grimace, and giving each other the wink, but the moment they caught my eye, they pulled grave faces, and were exceedingly demure. With Master Simon, however, they all seemed more at their ease. His varied occupations and amusements had made him well known throughout the neighbourhood. He was a visitor at every farm-house and cottage, gossiped with the farmers and their wives, romped with their daughters, and, like that type of a vagrant bachelor, the humble-bee, tolled the sweets from all the rosy lips of the country round.

The bashfulness of the guests soon gave way before good cheer and affability. There is something genuine and affectionate in the gaiety of the lower orders, when it is excited by the bounty and familiarity of those above them; the warm glow of gratitude enters into their mirth, and a kind word or a small pleasantry frankly uttered by a patron, gladdens the heart of the dependant more than oil and wine. When the squire had retired, the merriment increased, and there was much joking and laughter, particularly between Master Simon and a hale, ruddy-faced, white-headed farmer, who appeared to be the wit of the village; for I observed all his companions to wait with open mouths for his retorts, and burst into a gratuitous laugh before they could well understand them.

The whole house, indeed, seemed abandoned to merriment; as I passed to my room to dress for dinner, I heard the sound of music in a small court, and looking through a window that commanded it, I perceived a band of wandering musicians, with pandean pipes and tambourine; a pretty, coquettish housemaid was dancing a jig with a smart country lad, while several of the other servants were looking on. In the midst of her sport, the girl caught a glimpse of my face at the window, and, colouring up, ran off with an air of roguish affected confusion.

THE CHRISTMAS DINNER

> *Lo! now is come our joyful'st feast!*
> *Let every man be jolly;*
> *Eache roome with yvie leaves is drest,*
> *And every post with holly.*
> *Now all our neighbours' chimneys smoke,*
> *And Christmas blocks are burning;*
> *Their ovens they with bak't meats choke,*
> *And all their spits are turning.*
> *Without the door let sorrow lie,*
> *And if, for cold, it hap to die,*
> *We'll bury 't in a Christmas pye,*
> *And evermore be merry.*—WITHERS' "JUVENILLA."

I HAD FINISHED my toilet, and was loitering with Frank Bracebridge in the library, when we heard a distinct thwacking sound, which he informed me was a signal for the serving up of the dinner. The squire kept up old customs in kitchen as well as hall; and the rolling-pin, struck upon the dresser by the cook, summoned the servants to carry in the meats.

> *Just in this nick the cook knock'd thrice,*
> *And all the waiters in a trice*
> *His summons did obey;*
> *Each serving man, with dish in hand,*
> *March'd boldly up, like our train band,*
> *Presented and away.*[1]

The dinner was served up in the great hall, where the squire always held his Christmas banquet. A blazing crackling fire of logs had been heaped on to warm the spacious apartment, and the flame went sparkling and wreathing up the wide-mouthed chimney. The great picture of the crusader and his white horse had been profusely decorated with greens for the occasion; and holly and ivy had likewise been wreathed round the helmet and weapons on the opposite wall, which I understood were the arms of the same warrior. I must own, by-the-bye, I had strong doubts about the authenticity of the painting and armour as having belonged to the crusader, they certainly having the stamp of more recent days; but I was told that the painting had been so considered time out of mind; and that, as to the armour, it had been found in a lumber-room, and elevated to its present situation by the squire, who at once determined it to be the armour of the family hero; and as he was absolute authority on all such subjects in his own household, the matter had passed into current accepta- tion. A sideboard was set out just under this chivalric trophy, on which was

[1] Sir John Suckling.

a display of plate that might have vied (at least in variety) with Belshazzar's parade of the vessels of the temple; "flagons, cans, cups, beakers, goblets, basins, and ewers"; the gorgeous utensils of good companionship that had gradually accumulated through many generations of jovial housekeepers. Before these stood the two Yule candles, beaming like two stars of the first magnitude; other lights were distributed in branches, and the whole array glittered like a firmament of silver.

We were ushered into this banqueting scene with the sound of minstrelsy, the old harper being seated on a stool beside the fireplace, and twanging his instrument with a vast deal more power than melody. Never did Christmas board display a more goodly and gracious assemblage of countenances; those who were not handsome were, at least, happy; and happiness is a rare improver of your hard-favoured visage. I always consider an old English family as well worth studying as a collection of Holbein's portraits or Albert Dürer's prints. There is much antiquarian lore to be acquired; much knowledge of the physiognomies of former times. Perhaps it may be from having continually before their eyes those rows of old family portraits with which the mansions of this country are stocked; certain it is, that the quaint features of antiquity are often most faithfully perpetuated in these ancient lines; and I have traced an old family nose through a whole picture-gallery, legitimately handed down from generation to generation, almost from the time of the Conquest. Something of the kind was to be observed in the worthy company around me. Many of their faces had evidently originated in a Gothic age, and been merely copied by succeeding generations; and there was one little girl in particular, of staid demeanour, with a high Roman nose, and an antique vinegar aspect, who was a great favourite of the squire's, being, as he said, a Bracebridge all over, and the very counterpart of one of his ancestors who figured in the court of Henry VIII.

The parson said grace, which was not a short familiar one, such as is commonly addressed to the Deity in these unceremonious days; but a long, courtly, well-worded one of the ancient school. There was now a pause, as if something was expected; when suddenly the butler entered the hall with some degree of bustle: he was attended by a servant on each side with a large waxlight, and bore a silver dish, on which was an enormous pig's head, decorated with rosemary, with a lemon in its mouth, which was placed with great formality at the head of the table. The moment this pageant made its appearance, the harper struck up a flourish; at the conclusion of which the young Oxonian, on receiving a hint from the squire, gave, with an air of the most comic gravity, an old carol, the first verse of which was as follows:

> *Caput apri defero,*
> *Reddens laudes Domino.*
> *The boar's head in hand bring I,*
> *With garlands gay and rosemary.*
> *I pray you all synge merrily*
> *Qui estis in convivio.*

Though prepared to witness many of these little eccentricities, from being apprised of the peculiar hobby of mine host; yet, I confess, the parade with which so odd a dish was introduced somewhat perplexed me, until I gathered from the conversation of the squire and the parson, that it was meant to represent the bringing in of the boar's head; a dish formerly served up with much ceremony and the sound of minstrelsy and song, at great tables, on Christmas day. "I like the old custom," said the squire, "not merely because it is stately and pleasing in itself, but because it was observed at the college at Oxford at which I was educated. When I hear the old song chanted, it brings to mind the time when I was young and gamesome—and the noble old college hall— and my fellow-students loitering about in their black gowns; many of whom, poor lads, are now in their graves!"

The parson, however, whose mind was not haunted by such associations, and who was always more taken up with the text than the sentiment, objected to the Oxonian's version of the carol, which, he affirmed, was different from that sung at college. He went on, with the dry perseverance of a commentator, to give the college reading, accompanied by sundry annotations; addressing himself at first to the company at large; but finding their attention gradually diverted to other talk and other objects, he lowered his tone as his number of auditors diminished, until he concluded his remarks in an under voice to a fat-headed old gentleman next him, who was silently engaged in the discussion of a huge plateful of turkey.[2]

The table was literally loaded with good cheer, and presented an epitome of country abundance, in this season of overflowing larders. A distinguished post was allotted to "ancient sirloin," as mine host termed it; being, as he

[2]The old ceremony of serving up the boar's head on Christmas day is still observed in the hall of Queen's College, Oxford. I was favoured by the parson with a copy of the carol as now sung; and as it may be acceptable to such of my readers as are curious in these grave and learned matters, I give it entire:—

> The boar's head in hand bear I,
> Bedeck'd with bays and rosemary;
> And I pray you, my masters, be merry,
>   Quot estis in convivio,
>   Caput apri defero,
>   Reddens laudes Domino.
>
> The boar's head, as I understand,
> Is the rarest dish in all this land,
> Which thus bedeck'd with a gay garland
>   Let us servire cantico.
>   Caput apri defero, etc.
>
> Our steward hath provided this
> In honour of the King of Bliss,
> Which on this day to be served is
>   In Reginensi Atrio.
>   Caput apri defero, etc., etc., etc.

added, "the standard of old English hospitality, and a joint of goodly presence, and full of expectation." There were several dishes quaintly decorated, and which had evidently something traditional in their embellishments; but about which, as I did not like to appear over-curious, I asked no questions.

I could not, however, but notice a pie, magnificently decorated with peacock's feathers, in imitation of the tail of that bird, which overshadowed a considerable tract of the table. This, the squire confessed, with some little hesitation, was a pheasant pie, though a peacock pie was certainly the most authentical; but there had been such a mortality among the peacocks this season, that he could not prevail upon himself to have one killed.[3]

It would be tedious, perhaps, to my wiser readers, who may not have that foolish fondness for odd and obsolete things, to which I am a little given, were I to mention the other makeshifts of this worthy old humorist, by which he was endeavouring to follow up, though at humble distance, the quaint customs of antiquity. I was pleased, however, to see the respect shown to his whims by his children and relatives; who, indeed, entered readily into the full spirit of them, and seemed all well versed in their parts; having doubtless been present at many a rehearsal. I was amused, too, at the air of profound gravity, with which the butler and other servants executed the duties assigned them, however eccentric. They had an old-fashioned look; having, for the most part, been brought up in the household, and grown into keeping with the antiquated mansion, and the humours of its lord; and most probably looked upon all his whimsical regulations as the established laws of honourable housekeeping.

When the cloth was removed, the butler brought in a huge silver vessel of rare and curious workmanship, which he placed before the squire. Its appearance was hailed with acclamation; being the Wassail Bowl, so renowned in Christmas festivity. The contents had been prepared by the squire himself; for it was a beverage in the skilful mixture of which he particularly prided himself; alleging that it was too abstruse and complex for the comprehension of an ordinary servant. It was a potation, indeed, that might well make the heart of a toper leap within him; being composed of the richest and raciest wines,

[3]The peacock was anciently in great demand for stately entertainments. Sometimes it was made into a pie, at one end of which the head appeared above the crust, in all its plumage, with the beak richly gilt; at the other end the tail was displayed. Such pies were served up at the solemn banquets of chivalry, when knights-errant pledged themselves to undertake any perilous enterprise; whence came the ancient oath, used by Justice Shallow, "by cock and pie."

The peacock was also an important dish for the Christmas feast; and Massinger, in his "City Madam," gives some idea of the extravagance with which this, as well as other dishes, was prepared for the gorgeous revels of the olden times:—

"Men may talk of country Christmases:
  Their thirty pound butter'd eggs—their pies of carps' tongues:
  Their pheasants drench'd with ambergris; *the carcases of three fat wethers bruised*
    for gravy to make sauce for a single peacock!"

highly spiced and sweetened, with roasted apples bobbing about the surface.[4]

The old gentleman's whole countenance beamed with a serene look of indwelling delight, as he stirred this mighty bowl. Having raised it to his lips, with a hearty wish of a merry Christmas to all present, he sent it brimming round the board, for every one to follow his example, according to the primitive style; pronouncing it "the ancient fountain of good-feeling, where all hearts met together."[5]

There was much laughing and rallying as the honest emblem of Christmas joviality circulated, and was kissed rather coyly by the ladies. When it reached Master Simon, he raised it in both hands, and with the air of a boon companion struck up an old Wassail chanson:

> *The brown bowle,*
> *The merry brown bowle,*
> *As it goes round-about-a,*
>   *Fill*
>   *Still,*
> *Let the world say what it will,*
> *And drink your fill all out-a.*
>
> *The deep canne,*
> *The merry deep canne,*
> *As thou dost freely quaff-a,*
>   *Sing*
>   *Fling,*
> *Be as merry as a king,*
> *And sound a lusty laugh-a.*[6]

Much of the conversation during dinner turned upon family topics, to which I was a stranger. There was, however, a great deal of rallying of Master Simon about some gay widow, with whom he was accused of having a flirtation. This

[4]The Wassail Bowl was sometimes composed of ale instead of wine; with nutmeg, sugar, toast, ginger, and roasted crabs; in this way the nut-brown beverage is still prepared in some old families, and round the hearths of substantial farmers at Christmas. It is also called Lamb's Wool, and is celebrated by Herrick in his "Twelfth Night"—

> *Next crowne the bowle full*
>   *With gentle Lamb's Wool;*
> *Add sugar, nutmeg, and ginger,*
>   *With store of ale too;*
>   *And thus ye must doe*
> *To make the Wassaile a swinger.*

[5]The custom of drinking out of the same cup gave place to each having his cup. When the steward came to the doore with the Wassel, he was to cry three times, *Wassel, Wassel, Wassel,* and then the chappell (chaplein) was to answer with a song.—"ARCHÆOLOGIA."

[6]From Poor Robin's *Almanac.*

attack was commenced by the ladies; but it was continued throughout the dinner by the fat-headed old gentleman next the parson, with the persevering assiduity of a slow hound; being one of those long-winded jokers, who, though rather dull at starting game, are unrivalled for their talent in hunting it down. At every pause in the general conversation, he renewed his bantering in pretty much the same terms; winking hard at me with both eyes, whenever he gave Master Simon what he considered a home thrust. The latter, indeed, seemed fond of being teased on the subject, as old bachelors are apt to be; and he took occasion to inform me, in an under tone, that the lady in question was a prodigiously fine woman, and drove her own curricle.

The dinner-time passed away in this flow of innocent hilarity; and, though the old hall may have resounded in its time with many a scene of broader rout and revel, yet I doubt whether it ever witnessed more honest and genuine enjoyment. How easy it is for one benevolent being to diffuse pleasure around him; and how truly is a kind heart a fountain of gladness, making everything in its vicinity to freshen into smiles! the joyous disposition of the worthy squire was perfectly contagious; he was happy himself, and disposed to make all the world happy; and the little eccentricities of his humour did but season, in a manner, the sweetness of his philanthropy.

When the ladies had retired, the conversation, as usual, became still more animated; many good things were broached which had been thought of during dinner, but which would not exactly do for a lady's ear; and though I cannot positively affirm that there was much wit uttered, yet I have certainly heard many contests of rare wit produce much less laughter. Wit, after all, is a mighty, tart, pungent, ingredient, and much too acid for some stomachs; but honest good humour is the oil and wine of a merry meeting, and there is no jovial companionship equal to that where the jokes are rather small, and the laughter abundant.

The squire told several long stories of early college pranks and adventures, in some of which the parson had been a sharer; though in looking at the latter, it required some effort of imagination to figure such a little dark anatomy of a man into the perpetrator of a madcap gambol. Indeed, the two college chums presented pictures of what men may be made by their different lots in life. The squire had left the university to live lustily on his paternal domains, in the vigorous enjoyment of prosperity and sunshine, and had flourished on to a hearty and florid old age; whilst the poor parson, on the contrary, had dried and withered away, among dusty tomes, in the silence and shadows of his study. Still there seemed to be a spark of almost extinguished fire, feebly glimmering in the bottom of his soul; and as the squire hinted at a sly story of the parson and a pretty milk-maid, whom they once met on the banks of the Isis, the old gentleman made an "alphabet of faces," which, as far as I could decipher his physiognomy, I verily believe was indicative of laughter; indeed, I have rarely met with an old gentleman that took absolute offence at the imputed gallantries of his youth.

I found the tide of wine and wassail fast gaining on the dry land of sober judgment. The company grew merrier and louder as their jokes grew duller.

Master Simon was in as chirping a humour as a grasshopper filled with dew; his old songs grew of a warmer complexion, and he began to talk maudlin about the widow. He even gave a long song about the wooing of a widow, which he informed me he had gathered from an excellent black-letter work, entitled *Cupid's Solicitor for Love* containing store of good advice for bachelors, and which he promised to lend me; the first verse was to this effect:—

> He that will woo a widow must not dally,
> He must make hay while the sun doth shine;
> He must not stand with her—shall I, shall I?
> But boldly say, Widow, thou must be mine.

This song inspired the fat-headed old gentleman, who made several attempts to tell a rather broad story out of Joe Miller, that was pat to the purpose; but he always stuck in the middle, everybody recollecting the latter part excepting himself. The parson, too, began to show the effects of good cheer, having gradually settled down into a doze, and his wig sitting most suspiciously on one side. Just at this juncture we were summoned to the drawing-room, and I suspect, at the private instigation of mine host, whose joviality seemed always tempered with a proper love of decorum.

After the dinner-table was removed, the hall was given up to the younger members of the family who, prompted to all kind of noisy mirth by the Oxonian and Master Simon, made its old walls ring with their merriment, as they played at romping games. I delight in witnessing the gambols of children, and particularly at this happy holiday season, and could not help stealing out of the drawing-room on hearing one of their peals of laughter. I found them at the game of blind-man's-buff. Master Simon, who was the leader of their revels, and seemed on all occasions to fulfil the office of that ancient potentate, the Lord of Misrule,[7] was blinded in the midst of the hall. The little beings were as busy about him as the mock fairies about Falstaff; pinching him, plucking at the skirts of his coat, and tickling him with straws. One fine blue-eyed girl of about thirteen, with her flaxen hair all in beautiful confusion, her frolic face in a glow, her frock half torn off her shoulders, a complete picture of a romp, was the chief tormentor; and, from the slyness with which Master Simon avoided the smaller game, and hemmed this wild little nymph in corners, and obliged her to jump shrieking over chairs, I suspected the rogue of being not a whit more blinded than was convenient.

When I returned to the drawing-room, I found the company seated round the fire listening to the parson, who was deeply ensconced in a high-backed oaken chair, the work of some cunning artificer of yore, which had been brought from the library for his particular accommodation. From this venerable piece of furniture, with which his shadowy figure and dark weazen face so admirably accorded, he was dealing out strange accounts of the popular

[7]At Christmasse there was in the Kinge's house, wheresoever hee was lodged, a lorde of misrule, or mayster of merie disportes, and the like had ye in the house of every nobleman of honour, or good worshippe, were he spirituall or temporall.—STOWE.

superstitions and legends of the surrounding country, with which he had become acquainted in the course of his antiquarian researches. I am half inclined to think that the old gentleman was himself somewhat tinctured with superstition, as men are very apt to be who live a recluse and studious life in a sequestered part of the country, and pore over black-letter tracts, so often filled with the marvellous and supernatural. He gave us several anecdotes of the fancies of the neighbouring peasantry, concerning the effigy of the crusader, which lay on the tomb by the church altar. As it was the only monument of the kind in that part of the country it had always been regarded with feelings of superstition by the good wives of the village. It was said to get up from the tomb and walk the rounds of the churchyard in stormy nights, particularly when it thundered; and one old woman, whose cottage bordered on the churchyard, had seen it through the windows of the church, when the moon shone, slowly pacing up and down the aisles. It was the belief that some wrong had been left unredressed by the deceased, or some treasure hidden, which kept the spirit in a state of trouble and restlessness. Some talked of gold and jewels buried in the tomb, over which the spectre kept watch; and there was a story current of a sexton in old times who endeavoured to break his way to the coffin at night, but, just as he reached it, received a violent blow from the marble hand of the effigy, which stretched him senseless on the pavement. These tales were often laughed at by some of the sturdier among the rustics, yet when night came on, there were many of the stoutest unbelievers that were shy of venturing alone in the footpath that led across the churchyard.

From these and other anecdotes that followed, the crusader appeared to be the favourite hero of ghost stories throughout the vicinity. His picture which hung up in the hall, was thought by the servants to have something supernatural about it; for they remarked that, in whatever part of the hall you went, the eyes of the warrior were still fixed on you. The old porter's wife too, at the lodge, who had been born and brought up in the family, and was a great gossip among the maidservants, affirmed, that in her young days she had often heard say, that on Midsummer eve, when it was well known all kinds of ghosts, goblins, and fairies become visible and walk abroad, the crusader used to mount his horse, come down from his picture, ride about the house, down the avenue, and so to the church to visit the tomb; on which occasion the church door most civilly swung open of itself; not that he needed it; for he rode through closed gates and even stone walls, and had been seen by one of the dairymaids to pass between two bars of the great park gate, making himself as thin as a sheet of paper.

All these superstitions I found had been very much countenanced by the squire, who, though not superstitious himself, was very fond of seeing others so. He listened to every goblin tale of the neighbouring gossips with infinite gravity, and held the porter's wife in high favour on account of her talent for the marvellous. He was himself a great reader of old legends and romances, and often lamented that he could not believe in them; for a superstitious person, he thought, must live in a kind of fairy land.

Whilst we were all attention to the parson's stories, our ears were suddenly assailed by a burst of heterogeneous sounds from the hall, in which were mingled something like the clang of rude minstrelsy, with the uproar of many small voices and girlish laughter. The door suddenly flew open, and a train came trooping into the room, that might almost have been mistaken for the breaking-up of the court of Fairy. That indefatigable spirit, Master Simon, in the faithful discharge of his duties as Lord of Misrule, had conceived the idea of a Christmas mummery or masking; and having called in to his assistance the Oxonian and the young officer, who were equally ripe for anything that should occasion romping and merriment, they had carried it into instant effect. The old housekeeper had been consulted; the antique clothes-presses and wardrobes rummaged, and made to yield up the relics of finery that had not seen the light for several generations; the younger part of the company had been privately convened from the parlour and hall, and the whole had been bedizened out, into a burlesque imitation of an antique mask.[8]

Master Simon led the van, as "Ancient Christmas," quaintly apparelled in a ruff, a short cloak, which had very much the aspect of one of the old housekeeper's petticoats, and a hat that might have served for a village steeple, and must indubitably have figured in the days of the Covenanters. From under this his nose curved boldly forth, flushed with a frost-bitten bloom, that seemed the very trophy of a December blast. He was accompanied by the blue-eyed romp, dished up as "Dame Mince Pie," in the venerable magnificence of a faded brocade, long stomacher, peaked hat, and high-heeled shoes. The young officer appeared as Robin Hood, in a sporting dress of Kendal green, and a foraging cap with a gold tassel.

The costume, to be sure, did not bear testimony to deep research, and there was an evident eye to the picturesque, natural to a young gallant in the presence of his mistress. The fair Julia hung on his arm in a pretty rustic dress, as "Maid Marian." The rest of the train had been metamorphosed in various ways; the girls trussed up in the finery of the ancient belles of the Bracebridge line, and the striplings bewhiskered with burnt cork, and gravely clad in broad skirts, hanging sleeves, and full-bottomed wigs, to represent the character of Roast Beef, Plum Pudding, and other worthies celebrated in ancient maskings. The whole was under the control of the Oxonian, in the appropriate character of Misrule; and I observed that he exercised rather a mischievous sway with his wand over the smaller personages of the pageant.

The irruption of this motley crew, with beat of drum, according to ancient custom, was the consummation of uproar and merriment. Master Simon covered himself with glory by the stateliness with which, as Ancient Christmas, he walked a minuet with the peerless, though giggling, Dame Mince Pie. It was followed by a dance of all the characters, which, from its medley of costumes, seemed as though the old family portraits had skipped down from their frames to join in the sport. Different centuries were figuring at cross hands

[8]Maskings or mummeries were favourite sports at Christmas in old times; and the wardrobes at halls and manor-houses were often laid under contribution to furnish dresses and fantastic disguisings. I strongly suspect Master Simon to have taken the idea of his from Ben Jonson's "Masque of Christmas."

and right and left; the dark ages were cutting pirouettes and rigadoons; and the days of Queen Bess jiggling merrily down the middle, through a line of succeeding generations.

The worthy squire contemplated these fantastic sports, and this resurrection of his old wardrobe, with the simple relish of childish delight. He stood chuckling and rubbing his hands, and scarcely hearing a word the parson said, notwithstanding that the latter was discoursing most authentically on the ancient and stately dance at the Pavan, or peacock, from which he conceived the minuet to be derived.[9] For my part I was in a continual excitement, from the varied scenes of whim and innocent gaiety passing before me. It was inspiring to me to see wild-eyed frolic and warm-hearted hospitality breaking out from among the chills and glooms of winter, and old age throwing off his apathy, and catching once more the freshness of youthful enjoyment. I felt also an interest in the scene, from the consideration that these fleeting customs were posting fast into oblivion, and that this was, perhaps, the only family in England in which the whole of them were still punctiliously observed. There was a quaintness, too, mingled with all this revelry, that gave it a peculiar zest: it was suited to the time and place; and as the old manor-house almost reeled with mirth and wassail, it seemed echoing back the joviality of long-departed years.[10]

But enough of Christmas and its gambols; it is time for me to pause in this garrulity. Methinks I hear the questions asked by my grave readers, "To what purpose is all this—how is the world to be made wiser by this talk?" Alas! is there not wisdom enough extant for the instruction of the world? And if not, are there not thousands of abler pens labouring for its improvement!—It is so much pleasanter to please than to instruct—to play the companion rather than the preceptor.

What, after all, is the mite of wisdom that I could throw into the mass of knowledge; or how am I sure that my sagest deductions may be safe guides for the opinion of others? But in writing to amuse, if I fail, the only evil is in my own disappointment. If, however, I can by any lucky chance, in these days of evil, rub out one wrinkle from the brow of care, or beguile the heavy heart of one moment of sorrow; if I can now and then penetrate through the gathering film of misanthropy, prompt a benevolent view of human nature, and make my reader more in good humour with his fellow-beings and himself, surely, surely, I shall not then have written entirely in vain.

[9]Sir John Hawkins, speaking of the dance called the Pavan, from pavo, a peacock, says, "It is a grave and majestic dance; the method of dancing it anciently was by gentlemen dressed with caps and swords, by those of the long robe in their gowns, by the peers in their mantles, and by the ladies in gowns with long trains, the motion whereof, in dancing, resembled that of a peacock."—"HISTORY OF MUSIC."

[10]At the time of the first publication of this paper, the picture of an old-fashioned Christmas in the country was pronounced by some as out of date. The author had afterwards an opportunity of witnessing almost all the customs above described, existing in unexpected vigour in the skirts of Derbyshire and Yorkshire, where he passed the Christmas holidays. The reader will find some notice of them in the author's account of his sojourn at Newstead Abbey.

LONDON ANTIQUES

——I do walk,
Methinks, like Guido Vaux, with my dark lanthorn,
Stealing to set the town o' fire; i' th' country
I should be taken for William o' the Wisp,
Or Robin Goodfellow.—FLETCHER.

I AM somewhat of an antiquity hunter, and am fond of exploring London in quest of the relics of old times. These are principally to be found in the depths of the city, swallowed up and almost lost in a wilderness of brick and mortar; but deriving poetical and romantic interest from the commonplace prosaic world around them. I was struck with an instance of the kind in the course of a recent summer ramble into the city; for the city is only to be explored to advantage in summer-time, when free from the smoke and fog, and rain and mud of winter. I had been buffeting for some time against the current of population setting through Fleet Street. The warm weather had unstrung my nerves, and made me sensitive to every jar and jostle and discordant sound. The flesh was weary, the spirit faint, and I was getting out of humour with the bustling busy throng through which I had to struggle, when in a fit of desperation I tore my way through the crowd, plunged into a by-lane, and after passing through several obscure nooks and angles, emerged into a quaint and quiet court with a grass-plot in the centre, overhung by elms, and kept perpetually fresh and green by a fountain with its sparkling jet of water. A student with book in hand was seated on a stone bench, partly reading, partly meditating on the movements of two or three trim nursery-maids with their infant charges.

I was like an Arab who had suddenly come upon an oasis amid the panting sterility of the desert. By degrees the quiet and coolness of the place soothed my nerves and refreshed my spirit. I pursued my walk, and came, hard by, to a very ancient chapel, with a low-browed Saxon portal of massive and rich architecture. The interior was circular and lofty, and lighted from above. Around were monumental tombs of ancient date, on which were extended the marble effigies of warriors in armour. Some had the hands devoutly crossed upon the breast; others grasped the pommel of the sword, menacing hostility even in the tomb!—while the crossed legs of several indicated soldiers of the Faith who had been on crusades to the Holy Land.

I was, in fact, in the chapel of the Knights Templars, strangely situated in the very centre of sordid traffic; and I do not know a more impressive lesson for the man of the world than thus suddenly to turn aside from the highway of busy money-seeking life, and sit down among these shadowy sepulchres, where all is twilight, dust, and forgetfulness.

In a subsequent tour of observation, I encountered another of these relics of a "foregone world" locked up in the heart of the city. I had been wandering for some time through dull monotonous streets, destitute of anything to strike the eye or excite the imagination, when I beheld before me a Gothic gateway of mouldering antiquity. It opened into a spacious quadrangle forming the court-yard of a stately Gothic pile, the portal of which stood invitingly open.

It was apparently a public edifice, and, as I was antiquity hunting, I ventured in, though with dubious steps. Meeting no one either to oppose or rebuke my intrusion, I continued on until I found myself in a great hall, with a lofty arched roof and oaken gallery, all of Gothic architecture. At one end of the hall was an enormous fireplace, with wooden settles on each side; at the other end was a raised platform, or dais, the seat of state, above which was the portrait of a man in antique garb, with a long robe, a ruff, and a venerable gray beard.

The whole establishment had an air of monastic quiet and seclusion, and what gave it a mysterious charm was, that I had not met with a human being since I had passed the threshold.

Encouraged by this loneliness, I seated myself in a recess of a large bow window, which admitted a broad flood of yellow sunshine, chequered here and there by tints from panes of coloured glass; while an open casement let in the soft summer air. Here, leaning my head on my hand, and my arm on an old oaken table, I indulged in a sort of reverie about what might have been the ancient uses of this edifice. It had evidently been of monastic origin; perhaps one of those collegiate establishments built of yore for the promotion of learning, where the patient monk, in the ample solitude of the cloister, added page to page, and volume to volume, emulating in the productions of his brain the magnitude of the pile he inhabited.

As I was seated in this musing mood, a small panelled door in an arch at the upper end of the hall was opened, and a number of gray-headed old men, clad in long black cloaks, came forth one by one; proceeding in that manner through the hall, without uttering a word, each turning a pale face on me as he passed, and disappearing through a door at the lower end.

I was singularly struck with their appearance; their black cloaks and antiquated air comported with the style of this most venerable and mysterious pile. It was as if the ghosts of the departed years about which I had been musing were passing in review before me. Pleasing myself with such fancies, I set out, in the spirit of romance, to explore what I pictured to myself a realm of shadows, existing in the very centre of substantial realities.

My ramble led me through a labyrinth of interior courts and corridors and dilapidated cloisters, for the main edifice had many additions and dependencies, built at various times and in various styles; in one open space a number of boys, who evidently belonged to the establishment, were at their sports; but everywhere I observed those mysterious old gray men in black mantles, sometimes sauntering alone, sometimes conversing in groups: they appeared to be the pervading genii of the place. I now called to mind what I had read of certain colleges in old times, where judicial astrology, geomancy, necromancy, and other forbidden and magical sciences were taught. Was this an establishment of the kind, and were these black-cloaked old men really professors of the black art?

These surmises were passing through my mind as my eye glanced into a chamber hung round with all kinds of strange and uncouth objects, implements of savage warfare; strange idols and stuffed alligators; bottled serpents and monsters decorated the mantelpiece; while on the high tester of an old-fashioned bedstead grinned a human skull, flanked on each side by a dried cat.

I approached to regard more narrowly this mystic chamber, which seemed a fitting laboratory for a necromancer, when I was startled at beholding a human countenance staring at me from a dusky corner. It was that of a small, shrivelled old man, with thin cheeks, bright eyes, and gray wiry projecting eyebrows. I at first doubted whether it was not a mummy curiously preserved, but it moved, and I saw that it was alive. It was another of these black-cloaked old men; and, as I regarded his quaint physiognomy, his obsolete garb, and the hideous and sinister objects by which he was surrounded, I began to persuade myself that I had come upon the arch mago, who ruled over this magical fraternity.

Seeing me pausing before the door, he rose and invited me to enter. I obeyed with singular hardihood, for how did I know whether a wave of his wand might not metamorphose me into some strange monster, or conjure me into one of the bottles on his mantelpiece? He proved, however, to be anything but a conjurer, and his simple garrulity soon dispelled all the magic and mystery with which I had enveloped this antiquated pile and its no less antiquated inhabitants.

It appeared that I had made my way into the centre of an ancient asylum for superannuated tradesmen and decayed householders, with which was connected a school for a limited number of boys. It was founded upwards of two centuries since on an old monastic establishment, and retained somewhat of the conventual air and character. The shadowy line of old men in black mantles who had passed before me in the hall, and whom I had elevated into magi, turned out to be the pensioners returning from morning service in the chapel.

John Hallum, the little collector of curiosities whom I had made the arch magician, had been for six years a resident of the place, and had decorated this final nestling-place of his old age with relics and rarities picked up in the course of his life. According to his own account he had been somewhat of a traveller, having been once in France, and very near making a visit to Holland. He regretted not having visited the latter country, "as then he might have said he had been there." He was evidently a traveller of the simple kind.

He was aristocratical, too, in his notions; keeping aloof, as I found, from the ordinary run of pensioners. His chief associates were a blind man who spoke Latin and Greek, of both which languages Hallum was profoundly ignorant; and a broken-down gentleman, who had run through a fortune of forty thousand pounds left him by his father, and ten thousand pounds, the marriage portion of his wife. Little Hallum seemed to consider it an indubitable sign of gentle blood as well as of lofty spirit to be able to squander such enormous sums.

P.S.—The picturesque remnant of old times into which I have thus beguiled the reader is what is called the Charter House, originally the Chartreuse. It was founded in 1611, on the remains of an ancient convent, by Sir Thomas Sutton, being one of those noble charities set on foot by individual munificence, and kept up with the quaintness and sanctity of ancient times amidst the modern changes and innovations of London. Here eighty broken-down men, who have seen better days, are provided, in their old age, with food, clothing, fuel, and a yearly allowance for private expenses. They dine together, as did the monks of old, in the hall, which had been the refectory of the original convent. Attached to the establishment is a school for forty-four boys.

Stowe, whose work I have consulted on the subject, speaking of the obligations of the gray-headed pensioners, says, "They are not to intermeddle with any business touching the affairs of the hospital, but to attend only to the service of God, and take thankfully what is provided for them, without muttering, murmuring, or grudging. None to wear weapon, long hair, coloured boots, spurs, or coloured shoes, feathers in their hats, or any ruffian-like or unseemly apparel, but such as becomes hospital men to wear." "And in truth," adds Stowe, "happy are they that are so taken from the cares and sorrows of the world, and fixed in so good a place as these old men are; having nothing to care for but the good of their souls, to serve God, and to live in brotherly love."

For the amusement of such as have been interested by the preceding sketch, taken down from my own observation, and who may wish to know a little more about the mysteries of London, I subjoin a modicum of local history put into my hands by an odd-looking old gentleman in a small brown wig and a snuff-coloured coat, with whom I became acquainted shortly after my visit to the Charter House. I confess I was a little dubious at first, whether it was not one of those apocryphal tales often passed off upon inquiring travellers like myself, and which have brought our general character for veracity into such unmerited reproach. On making proper inquiries, however, I have received the most satisfactory assurances of the author's probity; and, indeed, have been told that he is actually engaged in a full and particular account of the very interesting region in which he resides; of which the following may be considered merely as a foretaste.

LITTLE BRITAIN

What I write is most true. . . . I have a whole booke of cases lying by me, which if I should sette foorth, some grave auntients (within the hearing of Bow bell) would be out of charity with me.—NASHE.

IN THE CENTRE of the great city of London lies a small neighbourhood, consisting of a cluster of narrow streets and courts, of very venerable and debilitated houses, which goes by the name of LITTLE BRITAIN. Christ Church School and St Bartholomew's Hospital bound it on the west; Smithfield and Longlane on the north; Aldersgate Street, like an arm of the sea, divides it from the eastern part of the city; whilst the yawning gulf of Bull-and-Mouth Street separates it from Butcher Lane, and the regions of Newgate. Over this little territory, thus bounded and designated, the great dome of St Paul's, swelling above the intervening houses of Paternoster Row, Amen Corner, and Ave Maria Lane, looks down with an air of motherly protection.

This quarter derives its appellation from having been, in ancient times, the residence of the Dukes of Brittany. As London increased, however, rank and fashion rolled off to the west, and trade, creeping on at their heels, took possession of their deserted abodes. For some time Little Britain became the great mart of learning, and was peopled by the busy and prolific race of booksellers: these also gradually deserted it, and, emigrating beyond the great strait of Newgate Street, settled down in Paternoster Row and St Paul's Churchyard, where they continue to increase and multiply even at the present day.

But though thus fallen into decline, Little Britain still bears traces of its former splendour. There are several houses ready to tumble down, the fronts of which are magnificently enriched with old oaken carvings of hideous faces, unknown birds, beasts, and fishes; and fruits and flowers which it would perplex a naturalist to classify. There are also, in Aldersgate Street, certain remains of what were once spacious and lordly family mansions, but which have in latter days been subdivided into several tenements. Here may often be found the family of a petty tradesman, with its trumpery furniture, burrowing among the relics of antiquated finery, in great rumbling time-stained apartments, with fretted ceilings, gilded cornices, and enormous marble fireplaces. The lanes and courts also contain many smaller houses, not on so grand a scale, but, like your small ancient gentry, sturdily maintaining their claims to equal antiquity. These have their gable-ends to the street; great bow windows, with diamond panes set in lead, grotesque carvings, and low arched door-ways.[1]

In this most venerable and sheltered little nest have I passed several quiet years of existence, comfortably lodged in the second floor of one of the smallest but oldest edifices. My sitting-room is an old wainscoted chamber, with small panels, and set off with a miscellaneous array of furniture. I have a particular respect for three or four high-backed claw-footed chairs, covered with tarnished brocade, which bear the marks of having seen better days, and have doubtless figured in some of the old palaces of Little Britain. They seem to me to keep together, and to look down with sovereign contempt upon their leathern-bottomed neighbours; as I have seen decayed gentry carry a high head among the plebeian society with which they were reduced to associate. The whole front of my sitting-room is taken up with a bow window; on the panes of which are recorded the names of previous occupants for many generations, mingled with scraps of very indifferent gentleman-like poetry, written in characters which I can scarcely decipher, and which extol the charms of many a beauty of Little Britain, who has long, long since bloomed, faded, and passed away. As I am an idle personage, with no apparent occupation, and

[1]It is evident that the author of this interesting communication has included, in his general title of Little Britain, many of those little lanes and courts that belong immediately to Cloth Fair.

pay my bill regularly every week, I am looked upon as the only independent gentleman of the neighbourhood; and being curious to learn the internal state of a community so apparently shut up within itself, I have managed to work my way into all the concerns and secrets of the place.

Little Britain may truly be called the heart's core of the city; the strong-hold of true John Bullism. It is a fragment of London as it was in its better days, with its antiquated folks and fashions. Here flourish in great preservation many of the holiday games and customs of yore. The inhabitants most religiously eat pancakes on Shrove Tuesday, hot cross buns on Good Friday, and roast goose at Michaelmas; they send love-letters on Valentine's Day, burn the Pope on the fifth of November, and kiss all the girls under the mistletoe at Christmas. Roast beef and plum pudding are also held in superstitious veneration, and port and sherry maintain their grounds as the only true English wines; all others being considered vile outlandish beverages.

Little Britain has its long catalogue of city wonders, which its inhabitants consider the wonders of the world; such as the great bell of St Paul's, which sours all the beer when it tolls; the figures that strike the hours at St Dunstan's clock; the Monument; the lions in the Tower; and the wooden giants in Guildhall. They still believe in dreams and fortune-telling, and an old woman that lives in Bull-and-Mouth Street makes a tolerable subsistence by detecting stolen goods, and promising the girls good husbands. They are apt to be rendered uncomfortable by comets and eclipses; and if a dog howls dolefully at night, it is looked upon as a sure sign of a death in the place. There are even many ghost-stories current, particularly concerning the old mansion-houses; in several of which it is said strange sights are sometimes seen. Lords and ladies, the former in full-bottomed wigs, hanging sleeves and swords, the latter in lappets, stays, hoops, and brocade, have been seen walking up and down the great waste chambers, on moonlight nights; and are supposed to be the shades of the ancient proprietors in their court-dresses.

Little Britain has likewise its sages and great men. One of the most important of the former is a tall, dry old gentleman, of the name of Skryme, who keeps a small apothecary's shop. He has a cadaverous countenance, full of cavities and projections; with a brown circle round each eye, like a pair of horn spectacles. He is much thought of by the old women, who consider him as a kind of conjurer, because he has two or three stuffed alligators hanging up in his shop, and several snakes in bottles. He is a great reader of almanacs and newspapers, and is much given to pore over alarming accounts of plots, conspiracies, fires, earthquakes, and volcanic eruptions; which last phenomena he considers as signs of the times. He has always some dismal tale of the kind to deal out to his customers, with their doses; and thus at the same time puts both soul and body into an uproar. He is a great believer in omens and predictions; and has the prophecies of Robert Nixon and Mother Shipton by heart. No man can make so much out of an eclipse, or even an unusually dark day; and he shook the tail of the last comet over the heads of his customers and disciples until they were nearly frightened out of their wits. He has lately got hold of a popular legend or prophecy, on which he has been unusually eloquent. There has been a saying current among the ancient sybils, who treasure up these things, that when the grasshopper on the top of the Exchange shook hands with the dragon on the top of Bow church steeple, fearful events would take place. This strange conjunction, it seems, has as strangely come to pass. The same architect has been engaged lately on the repairs of the cupola of the Exchange, and the steeple of Bow church; and, fearful to relate, the dragon and the grasshopper actually lie, cheek by jowl, in the yard of his workshop.

"Others," as Mr Skryme is accustomed to say, "may go star-gazing, and look for conjunctions in the heavens, but here is a conjunction on the earth, near at home, and under our own eyes, which surpasses all the signs and calculations of astrologers." Since these portentous weathercocks have thus laid their heads together, wonderful events had already occurred. The good old king, notwithstanding that he had lived eighty-two years, had all at once given up the ghost; another king had mounted the throne; a royal duke had died suddenly—another in France had been murdered; there had been Radical meetings in all parts of the kingdom; the bloody scenes at Manchester; the great plot in Cato Street;—and, above all, the Queen had returned to England! All these sinister events are recounted by Mr Skryme with a mysterious look and a dismal shake of the head; and being taken with his drugs and associated in the minds of his auditors with stuffed sea-monsters, bottled serpents, and his own visage, which is a title-page of tribulation, they have spread great gloom through the minds of the people of Little Britain. They shake their heads whenever they go by Bow church, and observe, that they never expected any good to come of taking down that steeple, which in old times told nothing but glad tidings, as the history of Whittington and his Cat bears witness.

The rival oracle of Little Britain is a substantial cheesemonger, who lives in a fragment of one of the old family mansions, and is as magnificently lodged as a round-bellied mite in the midst of one of his own Cheshires. Indeed, he is a man of no little standing and importance; and his renown extends through Huggin Lane, and Lad Lane, and even unto Aldermanbury. His opinion is very much taken in affairs of state, having read the Sunday papers for the last half century, together with the *Gentleman's Magazine*, Rapin's *History of England*, and the *Naval Chronicle*. His head is stored with invaluable maxims which have borne the test of time and use for centuries. It is his firm opinion that "it is a moral impossible," so long as England is true to herself, that anything can shake her; and he has much to say on the subject of the national debt; which, somehow or other, he proves to be a great national bulwark and blessing. He passed the greater part of his life in the purlieus of Little Britain, until of late years, when, having become rich, and grown into the dignity of a Sunday cane, he begins to take his pleasure and see the world. He has therefore made several excursions to Hampstead, Highgate, and other neighbouring towns, where he has passed whole afternoons in looking back upon the metropolis through a telescope, and endeavouring to descry the steeple of St Bartholomew's. Not a stage-coachman of Bull-and-Mouth Street but touches his hat as he passes; and he is considered quite a patron at the coach-office of the Goose and Gridiron, St Paul's Churchyard. His family have been very urgent for him

to make an expedition to Margate, but he has great doubts of those new gim-
cracks, the steamboats, and, indeed, thinks himself too advanced in life to
undertake sea voyages.

Little Britain has occasionally its factions and divisions, and party spirit ran
very high at one time in consequence of two rival "Burial Societies" being set up
in the place. One held its meeting at the Swan and Horse Shoe, and was patronised by the cheesemonger; the other at the Cock and Crown, under the auspices
of the apothecary; it is needless to say that the latter was the most flourishing.
I have passed an evening or two at each, and have acquired much valuable
information, as to the best mode of being buried, the comparative merits of
churchyards, together with divers hints on the subject of patent-iron coffins.
I have heard the question discussed in all its bearings as to the legality of
prohibiting the latter on account of their durability. The feuds occasioned by
these societies have happily died of late; but they were for a long time prevailing themes of controversy, the people of Little Britain being extremely
solicitous of funereal honours and of lying comfortably in their graves.

Besides these two funeral societies, there is a third of quite a different cast,
which tends to throw the sunshine of good-humour over the whole neighbourhood. It meets once a week at a little old-fashioned house, kept by a jolly
publican of the name of Wagstaff, and bearing for insignia a resplendent half-
moon, with a most seductive bunch of grapes. The whole edifice is covered
with inscriptions to catch the eye of the thirsty wayfarer; such as "Truman,
Hanbury, and Co.'s Entire," "Wine, Rum, and Brandy Vaults," "Old Tom,
Rum, and Compounds," etc. This, indeed, has been a temple of Bacchus and
Momus from time immemorial. It has always been in the family of the Wag-
staffs, so that its history is tolerably preserved by the present landlord. It was
much frequented by the gallants and cavalieros of the reign of Elizabeth, and
was looked into now and then by the wits of Charles the Second's day. But
what Wagstaff principally prides himself upon is, that Henry the Eighth, in
one of his nocturnal rambles, broke the head of one of his ancestors with his
famous walking-staff. This, however, is considered as rather a dubious and
vain-glorious boast of the landlord.

The club which now holds its weekly sessions here goes by the name of "the
Roaring Lads of Little Britain." They abound in old catches, glees, and choice
stories, that are traditional in the place, and not to be met with in any other part
of the metropolis. There is a mad-cap undertaker who is inimitable at a merry
song; but the life of the club, and indeed the prime wit of Little Britain, is
bully Wagstaff himself. His ancestors were all wags before him, and he has
inherited with the inn a large stock of songs and jokes, which go with it from
generation to generation as heir-looms. He is a dapper little fellow, with bandy
legs and pot belly, a red face, with a moist merry eye, and a little shock of gray
hair behind. At the opening of every club-night he is called in to sing his
"Confession of Faith," which is the famous old drinking trowl from Gammer
Gurton's Needle. He sings it, to be sure, with many variations, as he received
it from his father's lips; for it has been a standing favourite at the Half-Moon
and Bunch of Grapes ever since it was written; nay, he affirms that his prede-

cessors have often had the honour of singing it before the nobility and gentry at Christmas mummeries, when Little Britain was in all its glory.[2]

[2]As mine host of the Half-Moon's "Confession of Faith" may not be familiar to the majority of readers, and as it is a specimen of the current songs of Little Britain, I subjoin it in its original orthography. I would observe, that the whole club always join in the chorus with a fearful thumping on the table and clattering of pewter pots:—

> *I cannot eate but lytle meate,*
> *My stomacke is not good,*
> *But sure I thinke that I can drinke*
> *With him that wears a hood.*
> *Though I go bare, take ye no care,*
> *I nothing am a colde,*
> *I stuff my skyn so full within,*
> *Of joly good ale and olde.*
> CHORUS. *Backe and syde go bare, go bare,*
> *Booth foote and hand go colde,*
> *But belly, God send thee good ale ynoughe,*
> *Whether it be new or olde.*

> *I have no rost, but a nut brawne toste,*
> *And a crab laid in the fyre;*
> *A little breade shall do me steade,*
> *Much bread I not desyre.*
> *No frost nor snow, nor winde, I trowe,*
> *Can hurte mee, if I wolde,*
> *I am so wrapt and throwly lapt*
> *Of joly good ale and olde.*
> CHORUS. *Backe and syde go bare, go bare, etc.*

> *And Tyb my wife, that, as her lyfe,*
> *Loveth well good ale to seeke,*
> *Full oft drynkes shee, tyll ye may see*
> *The teares run downe her cheeke.*
> *Then doth shee trowle to me the bowle,*
> *Even as a mault-worme sholde,*
> *And sayth, sweete harte, I took my parte*
> *Of this joly good ale and olde.*
> CHORUS. *Backe and syde go bare, go bare, etc.*

> *Now let them drynke, tyll they nod and winke,*
> *Even as goode fellowes sholde doe,*
> *They shall not mysse to have the blisse*
> *Good ale doth bring men to;*
> *And all poore soules that have scowred bowles,*
> *Or have them lustily trolde,*
> *God save the lyves of them and their wives,*
> *Whether they be yonge or olde.*
> CHORUS. *Backe and syde go bare, go bare, etc.*

It would do one's heart good to hear, on a club night, the shouts of merriment, the snatches of song, and now and then the choral bursts of half a dozen discordant voices, which issue from this jovial mansion. At such times the street is lined with listeners, who enjoy a delight equal to that of gazing into a confectioner's window, or snuffing up the steams of a cook-shop.

There are two annual events which produce great stir and sensation in Little Britain; these are St Bartholomew's fair, and the Lord Mayor's day. During the time of the fair, which is held in the adjoining regions of Smithfield, there is nothing going on but gossiping and gadding about. The late quiet streets of Little Britain are overrun with an irruption of strange figures and faces; every tavern is a scene of rout and revel. The fiddle and the song are heard from the tap-room, morning, noon, and night; and at each window may be seen some group of boon companions, with half-shut eyes, hats on one side, pipe in mouth, and tankard in hand, fondling, and prosing, and singing maudlin songs over their liquor. Even the sober decorum of private families, which I must say is rigidly kept up at other times among my neighbours, is no proof against this Saturnalia. There is no such thing as keeping maid-servants within doors. Their brains are absolutely set maddening with Punch and the Puppet Show; the Flying Horses; Signior Polito; the Fire-Eater; the celebrated Mr Paap; and the Irish Giant. The children, too, lavish all their holiday money in toys and gilt gingerbread, and fill the house with the Lilliputian din of drums, trumpets, and penny whistles.

But the Lord Mayor's day is the great anniversary. The Lord Mayor is looked up to by the inhabitants of Little Britain as the greatest potentate upon earth; his gilt coach with six horses as the summit of human splendour; and his procession, with all the Sheriffs and Aldermen in his train, as the grandest of earthly pageants. How they exult in the idea, that the King himself dare not enter the city, without first knocking at the gate of Temple Bar, and asking permission of the Lord Mayor; for if he did, heaven and earth! there is no knowing what might be the consequence. The man in armour who rides before the Lord Mayor, and is the city champion, has orders to cut down everybody that offends against the dignity of the city; and then there is the little man with a velvet porringer on his head, who sits at the window of the state coach, and holds the city sword, as long as a pike-staff—Odd's blood! If he once draws that sword, Majesty itself is not safe!

Under the protection of this mighty potentate, therefore, the good people of Little Britain sleep in peace. Temple Bar is an effectual barrier against all interior foes; and as to foreign invasion, the Lord Mayor has but to throw himself into the Tower, call in the train bands, and put the standing army of beefeaters under arms, and he may bid defiance to the world!

Thus wrapped up in its own concerns, its own habits, and its own opinions, Little Britain has long flourished as a sound heart to this great fungus metropolis. I have pleased myself with considering it as a chosen spot, where the principles of sturdy John Bullism were garnered up, like seed corn, to renew the national character, when it had run to waste and degeneracy. I have rejoiced also in the general spirit of harmony that prevailed throughout it; for though there might now and then be a few clashes of opinion between the adherents of the cheesemonger and the apothecary, and an occasional feud between the burial societies, yet these were but transient clouds, and soon passed away. The neighbours met with good-will, parted with a shake of the hand, and never abused each other except behind their backs.

I could give rare descriptions of snug junketing parties at which I have been present; where we played at All-Fours, Pope-Joan, Tom-come-tickle-me, and other choice old games; and where we sometimes had a good old English country dance to the tune of Sir Roger de Coverley. Once a year also the neighbours would gather together and go on a gipsy party to Epping Forest. It would have done any man's heart good to see the merriment that took place here as we banqueted on the grass under the trees. How we made the woods ring with bursts of laughter at the songs of little Wagstaff and the merry undertaker! After dinner, too, the young folks would play at blind-man's-buff and hide-and-seek; and it was amusing to see them tangled among the briers, and to hear a fine romping girl now and then squeak from among the bushes. The elder folks would gather round the cheesemonger and the apothecary, to hear them talk politics; for they generally brought out a newspaper in their pockets, to pass away time in the country. They would now and then, to be sure, get a little warm in argument; but their disputes were always adjusted by reference to a worthy old umbrella-maker in a double chin, who, never exactly comprehending the subject, managed somehow or other to decide in favour of both parties.

All empires, however, says some philosopher or historian, are doomed to changes and revolutions. Luxury and innovation creep in; factions arise; and families now and then spring up, whose ambition and intrigues throw the whole system into confusion. Thus, in latter days, has the tranquillity of Little Britain been grievously disturbed, and its golden simplicity of manners threatened with total subversion, by the aspiring family of a retired butcher.

The family of the Lambs had long been among the most thriving and popular in the neighbourhood: the Miss Lambs were the belles of Little Britain, and everybody was pleased when Old Lamb had made money enough to shut up shop, and put his name on a brass plate on his door. In an evil hour, however, one of the Miss Lambs had the honour of being a lady in attendance on the Lady Mayoress, at her grand annual ball, on which occasion she wore three towering ostrich feathers on her head. The family never got over it; they were immediately smitten with a passion for high life; set up a one-horse carriage, put a bit of gold lace round the errand boy's hat, and have been the talk and detestation of the whole neighbourhood ever since. They could no longer be induced to play at Pope-Joan or blind-man's-buff; they could endure no dances but quadrilles, which nobody had ever heard of in Little Britain; and they took to reading novels, talking bad French, and playing upon the piano. Their brother, too, who had been articled to an attorney, set up for a dandy and a critic, characters hitherto unknown in these parts; and he confounded the worthy folks exceedingly by talking about Kean, the opera, and the *Edinburgh Review*.

What was still worse, the Lambs gave a grand ball, to which they neglected to invite any of their old neighbours; but they had a great deal of genteel company from Theobald's Road, Red Lion Square, and other parts towards the west. There were several beaux of their brother's acquaintance from Gray's Inn Lane and Hatton Garden; and not less than three aldermen's ladies, with their daughters. This was not to be forgotten or forgiven. All Little Britain was in an uproar with the smacking of whips, the lashing of miserable horses, and the rattling and jingling of hackney coaches. The gossips of the neighbourhood might be seen popping their night-caps out at every window, watching the crazy vehicles rumble by; and there was a knot of virulent old cronies, that kept a look-out from a house just opposite the retired butcher's, and scanned and criticised every one that knocked at the door.

This dance was a cause of almost open war, and the whole neighbourhood declared they would have nothing more to say to the Lambs. It is true that Mrs Lamb, when she had no engagements with her quality acquaintance, would give little humdrum tea junketings to some of her old cronies, "quite," as she would say, "in a friendly way"; and it is equally true that her invitations were always accepted, in spite of all previous vows to the contrary. Nay, the good ladies would sit and be delighted with the music of the Miss Lambs, who would condescend to strum an Irish melody for them on the piano; and they would listen with wonderful interest to Mrs Lamb's anecdotes of Alderman Plunket's family, of Portsoken Ward, and the Miss Timberlakes, the rich heiresses of Crutched Friars; but then they relieved their consciences, and averted the reproaches of their confederates, by canvassing at the next gossiping convocation everything that had passed, and pulling the Lambs and their rout all to pieces.

The only one of the family that could not be made fashionable was the retired butcher himself. Honest Lamb, in spite of the meekness of his name, was a rough, hearty old fellow, with the voice of a lion, a head of black hair like a shoe-brush, and a broad face mottled like his own beef. It was in vain that the daughters always spoke of him as "the old gentleman," addressed him as "papa," in tones of infinite softness, and endeavoured to coax him into a dressing-gown and slippers, and other gentlemanly habits. Do what they might, there was no keeping down the butcher. His sturdy nature would break through all their glozings. He had a hearty vulgar good humour that was irrepressible. His very jokes made his sensitive daughters shudder; and he persisted in wearing his blue cotton coat of a morning, dining at two o'clock, and having a "bit of sausage with his tea."

He was doomed, however, to share the unpopularity of his family. He found his old comrades gradually growing cold and civil to him; no longer laughing at his jokes; and now and then throwing out a fling at "some people," and a hint about "quality binding." This both nettled and perplexed the honest butcher, and his wife and daughters, with the consummate policy of the shrewder sex, taking advantage of the circumstance, at length prevailed upon him to give up his afternoon's pipe and tankard at Wagstaff's; to sit after dinner by himself, and take his pint of port—a liquor he detested—and to nod in his chair in solitary and dismal gentility.

The Miss Lambs might now be seen flaunting along the streets in French bonnets, with unknown beaux; and talking and laughing so loud that it distressed the nerves of every good lady within hearing. They even went so far as to attempt patronage, and actually induced a French dancing-master to set up in the neighbourhood; but the worthy folks of Little Britain took fire at it, and did so persecute the poor Gaul, that he was fain to pack up fiddle and dancing-pumps, and decamp with such precipitation that he absolutely forgot to pay for his lodgings.

I had flattered myself, at first, with the idea that all this fiery indignation on the part of the community was merely the overflowing of their zeal for good old English manners, and their horror of innovation; and I applauded the silent contempt they were so vociferous in expressing, for upstart pride, French fashions, and the Miss Lambs. But I grieve to say that I soon perceived the infection had taken hold; and that my neighbours, after condemning, were beginning to follow their example. I overheard my landlady importuning her husband to let their daughters have one quarter at French and music, and that they might take a few lessons in quadrille. I even saw, in the course of a few Sundays, no less than five French bonnets, precisely like those of the Miss Lambs, parading about Little Britain.

I still had my hopes that all this folly would gradually die away; that the Lambs might move out of the neighbourhood, might die, or might run away with attorneys' apprentices; and that quiet and simplicity might be again restored to the community. But unluckily a rival power arose. An opulent oilman died, and left a widow with a large jointure and a family of buxom daughters. The young ladies had long been repining in secret at the parsimony of a prudent father, which kept down all their aspirings. Their ambition, being now no longer restrained, broke out into a blaze, and they openly took the field against the family of the butcher. It is true that the Lambs, having had the first start, had naturally an advantage of them in the fashionable career. They could speak a little bad French, play the piano, dance quadrilles, and had formed high acquaintances; but the Trotters were not to be distanced. When the Lambs appeared with two feathers in their hats, the Miss Trotters mounted four, and of twice as fine colours. If the Lambs gave a dance, the Trotters were sure not to be behindhand; and though they might not boast of as good company, yet they had double the number, and were twice as merry.

The whole community has at length divided itself into fashionable factions under the banners of these two families. The old games of Pope-Joan and Tom-come-tickle-me are entirely discarded; there is no such thing as getting up an honest country dance; and on my attempting to kiss a young lady under the mistletoe last Christmas, I was indignantly repulsed; the Miss Lambs having pronounced it "shocking vulgar." Bitter rivalry has also broken out as to the most fashionable part of Little Britain; the Lambs standing up for the dignity of Cross-Keys Square, and the Trotters for the vicinity of St Bartholomew's.

Thus is this little territory torn by factions and internal dissensions, like the great empire whose name it bears; and what will be the result would puzzle the apothecary himself, with all his talent at prognostics, to determine; though I apprehend that it will terminate in the total downfall of genuine John Bullism.

The immediate effects are extremely unpleasant to me. Being a single man, and, as I observed before, rather an idle good-for-nothing personage, I have been considered the only gentleman by profession in the place. I stand therefore in high favour with both parties, and have to hear all their cabinet counsels and mutual backbitings. As I am too civil not to agree with the ladies on all occasions, I have committed myself most horribly with both parties, by abusing their opponents. I might manage to reconcile this to my conscience, which is a truly accommodating one, but I cannot to my apprehension—if the Lambs and Trotters ever come to a reconciliation, and compare notes, I am ruined!

I have determined, therefore, to beat a retreat in time, and am actually looking out for some other nest in this great city, where old English manners are still kept up; where French is neither eaten, drunk, danced, nor spoken; and where there are no fashionable families of retired tradesmen. This found, I will, like a veteran rat, hasten away before I have an old house about my ears; bid a long, though a sorrowful adieu to my present abode, and leave the rival factions of the Lambs and the Trotters to divide the distracted empire of LITTLE BRITAIN.

TRAITS OF INDIAN CHARACTER

I appeal to any white man, if ever he entered Logan's cabin hungry, and he gave him not to eat—if ever he came cold and naked, and he clothed him not.—SPEECH OF AN INDIAN CHIEF.

THERE IS something in the character and habits of the North American savage, taken in connection with the scenery over which he is accustomed to range, its vast lakes, boundless forests, majestic rivers, and trackless plains, that is to my mind wonderfully striking and sublime. He is formed for the wilderness, as the Arab is for the desert. His nature is stern, simple, and enduring; fitted to grapple with difficulties, and to support privations. There seems but little soil in his heart for the support of the kindly virtues; and yet, if we would but take the trouble to penetrate through that proud stoicism and habitual taciturnity, which lock up his character from casual observation, we should find him linked to his fellow-man of civilised life by more of those sympathies and affections than are usually ascribed to him.

It has been the lot of the unfortunate aborigines of America, in the early periods of colonization, to be doubly wronged by the white men. They have been dispossessed of their hereditary possessions by mercenary and frequently wanton warfare; and their characters have been traduced by bigoted and interested writers. The colonist often treated them like beasts of the forest; and the author has endeavoured to justify him in his outrages. The former found it easier to exterminate than to civilise; the latter to vilify than to discriminate.

The appellations of savage and pagan were deemed sufficient to sanction the hostilities of both; and thus the poor wanderers of the forest were persecuted and defamed, not because they were guilty, but because they were ignorant.

The rights of the savage have seldom been properly appreciated or respected by the white man. In peace he has too often been the dupe of artful traffic; in war he has been regarded as a ferocious animal, whose life or death was a question of mere precaution and convenience. Man is cruelly wasteful of life when his own safety is endangered, and he is sheltered by impunity; and little mercy is to be expected from him, when he feels the sting of the reptile and is conscious of the power to destroy.

The same prejudices, which were indulged thus early, exist in common circulation at the present day. Certain learned societies have, it is true, with laudable diligence, endeavoured to investigate and record the real characters and manners of the Indian tribes; the American government, too, has wisely and humanely exerted itself to inculcate a friendly and forbearing spirit towards them, and to protect them from fraud and injustice.[1] The current opinion of the Indian character, however, is too apt to be formed from the miserable hordes which infest the frontiers, and hang on the skirts of the settlements. These are too commonly composed of degenerate beings, corrupted and enfeebled by the vices of society, without being benefited by its civilisation. That proud independence, which formed the main pillar of savage virtue, has been shaken down, and the whole moral fabric lies in ruins. Their spirits are humiliated and debased by a sense of inferiority, and their native courage cowed and daunted by the superior knowledge and power of their enlightened neighbours. Society has advanced upon them like one of those withering airs, that will sometimes breed desolation over a whole region of fertility. It has enervated their strength, multiplied their diseases, and superinduced upon their original barbarity the low vices of artificial life. It has given them a thousand superfluous wants, whilst it has diminished their means of mere existence. It has driven before it the animals of the chase, who fly from the sound of the axe and the smoke of the settlement, and seek refuge in the depths of the remotest forests and yet untrodden wilds. Thus do we too often find the Indians on our frontiers to be the mere wrecks and remnants of once powerful tribes, who have lingered in the vicinity of the settlements, and sunk into precarious and vagabond existence. Poverty, repining and hopeless poverty, a canker of the mind unknown in savage life, corrodes their spirits and blights every free and noble quality of their natures. They become drunken, indolent, feeble, thievish, and pusillanimous. They loiter like vagrants about the settlements, among spacious dwellings replete with elaborate comforts, which only render them sensible of the comparative wretchedness of their own condition.

[1] The American government has been indefatigable in its exertions to ameliorate the situation of the Indians, and to introduce among them the arts of civilization, and civil and religious knowledge. To protect them from the frauds of the white traders, no purchase of land from them by individuals is permitted; nor is any person allowed to receive lands from them as a present, without the express sanction of government. These precautions are strictly enforced.

Luxury spreads its ample board before their eyes; but they are excluded from the banquet. Plenty revels over the fields; but they are starving in the midst of its abundance: the whole wilderness has blossomed into a garden; but they feel as reptiles that infest it.

How different was their state while yet the undisputed lords of the soil! Their wants were few, and the means of gratification within their reach. They saw every one around them sharing the same lot, enduring the same hardships, feeding on the same ailments, arrayed in the same rude garments. No roof then rose, but was open to the homeless stranger; no smoke curled among the trees, but he was welcome to sit down by its fire and join the hunter in his repast. "For," says an old historian of New England, "their life is so void of care, and they are so loving also, that they make use of those things they enjoy as common goods, and are therein so compassionate, that rather than one should starve through want, they would starve all; thus they pass their time merrily, not regarding our pomp, but are better content with their own, which some men esteem so meanly of." Such were the Indians whilst in the pride and energy of their primitive natures: they resembled those wild plants which thrive best in the shades of the forest, but shrink from the hand of cultivation, and perish beneath the influence of the sun.

In discussing the savage character, writers have been too prone to indulge in vulgar prejudice and passionate exaggeration, instead of the candid temper of true philosophy. They have not sufficiently considered the peculiar circumstances in which the Indians have been placed, and the peculiar principles under which they have been educated. No being acts more rigidly from rule than the Indian. His whole conduct is regulated according to some general maxims early implanted in his mind. The moral laws that govern him are, to be sure, but few; but then he conforms to them all;—the white man abounds in laws of religion, morals, and manners, but how many does he violate!

A frequent ground of accusation against the Indians is their disregard of treaties, and the treachery and wantonness with which, in time of apparent peace, they will suddenly fly to hostilities. The intercourse of the white men with the Indians, however, is too apt to be cold, distrustful, oppressive, and insulting. They seldom treat them with that confidence and frankness which are indispensable to real friendship; nor is sufficient caution observed not to offend against those feelings of pride or superstition, which often prompt the Indian to hostility quicker than mere considerations of interest. The solitary savage feels silently, but acutely. His sensibilities are not diffused over so wide a surface as those of the white man; but they run in steadier and deeper channels. His pride, his affections, his superstitions, are all directed towards fewer objects; but the wounds inflicted on them are proportionably severe, and furnish motives of hostility which we cannot sufficiently appreciate. Where a community is also limited in number, and forms one great patriarchal family, as in an Indian tribe, the injury of an individual is the injury of the whole; and the sentiment of vengeance is almost instantaneously diffused. One council-fire is sufficient for the discussion and arrangement of a plant of hostilities. Here all the fighting men and sages assemble. Eloquence and superstition combine to inflame the minds of the warriors. The orator awakens their martial ardour, and they are wrought up to a kind of religious desperation, by the visions of the prophet and the dreamer.

An instance of one of those sudden exasperations, arising from a motive peculiar to the Indian character, is extant in an old record of the early settlement of Massachusetts. The planters of Plymouth had defaced the monuments of the dead at Passonagessit, and had plundered the grave of the Sachem's mother of some skins with which it had been decorated. The Indians are remarkable for the reverence which they entertain for the sepulchres of their kindred. Tribes that have passed generations exiled from the abodes of their ancestors, when by chance they have been travelling in the vicinity, have been known to turn aside from the highway, and, guided by wonderfully accurate tradition, have crossed the country for miles, to some tumulus, buried perhaps in woods, where the bones of their tribe were anciently deposited; and there have passed hours in silent meditation. Influenced by this sublime and holy feeling, the Sachem whose mother's tomb had been violated, gathered his men together, and addressed them in the following beautifully simple and pathetic harangue; a curious specimen of Indian eloquence, and an affecting instance of filial piety in a savage:—

"When last the glorious light of all the sky was underneath this globe, and birds grew silent, I began to settle, as my custom is, to take repose. Before mine eyes were fast closed, methought I saw a vision, at which my spirit was much troubled; and trembling at that doleful sight, a spirit cried aloud, 'Behold, my son, whom I have cherished, see the breasts that gave thee suck, the hands that lapped thee warm, and fed thee oft. Canst thou forget to take revenge of those wild people who have defaced my monument in a despiteful manner, disdaining our antiquities and honourable customs? See, now, the Sachem's grave lies like the common people, defaced by an ignoble race. Thy mother doth complain, and implores thy aid against this thievish people, who have newly intruded on our land. If this be suffered, I shall not rest quiet in my everlasting habitation.' This said, the spirit vanished, and I, all in a sweat, not able scarce to speak, began to get some strength, and recollect my spirits that were fled, and determined to demand your counsel and assistance."

I have adduced this anecdote at some length, as it tends to show how these sudden acts of hostility, which have been attributed to caprice and perfidy, may often arise from deep and generous motives, which our inattention to Indian character and customs prevents our properly appreciating.

Another ground of violent outcry against the Indians is their barbarity to the vanquished. This had its origin partly in policy and partly in superstition. The tribes, though sometimes called nations, were never so formidable in their numbers, but that the loss of several warriors was sensibly felt; this was particularly the case when they had been frequently engaged in warfare; and many an instance occurs in Indian history, where a tribe, that had long been formidable to its neighbours, has been broken up and driven away, by the capture and massacre of its principal fighting men. There was a strong temptation, therefore, to the victor to be merciless; not so much to gratify any cruel revenge, as to provide for future security. The Indians had also the superstitious belief, frequent among barbarous nations, and prevalent also among the ancients, that the manes of their friends who had fallen in battle were soothed by the blood of the captives. The prisoners, however, who are not thus sacrificed, are adopted into their families in the place of the slain, and are treated with the confidence and affection of relatives and friends; nay, so hospitable and tender is their entertainment, that when the alternative is offered them, they will often prefer to remain with their adopted brethren, rather than return to the home and the friends of their youth.

The cruelty of the Indians towards their prisoners has been heightened since the colonization of the whites. What was formerly a compliance with policy and superstition, has been exasperated into a gratification of vengeance. They cannot but be sensible that the white men are the usurpers of their ancient dominion, the cause of their degradation, and the gradual destroyers of their race. They go forth to battle, smarting with injuries and indignities which they have individually suffered, and they are driven to madness and despair by the wide-spreading desolation, and the overwhelming ruin of European warfare. The whites have too frequently set them an example of violence, by burning their villages, and laying waste their slender means of subsistence; and yet they wonder that savages do not show moderation and magnanimity towards those who have left them nothing but mere existence and wretchedness.

We stigmatise the Indians, also, as cowardly and treacherous, because they use stratagem in warfare, in preference to open force; but in this they are fully justified by their rude code of honour. They are early taught that stratagem is praiseworthy; the bravest warrior thinks it no disgrace to lurk in silence, and take every advantage of his foe: he triumphs in the superior craft and sagacity by which he has been enabled to surprise and destroy an enemy. Indeed, man is naturally more prone to subtlety than open valour, owing to his physical weakness in comparison with other animals. They are endowed with natural weapons of defence; with horns, with tusks, with hoofs, and talons; but man has to depend on his superior sagacity. In all his encounters with these, his proper enemies, he resorts to stratagem; and when he perversely turns his hostility against his fellow-man, he at first continues the same subtle mode of warfare.

The natural principle of war is to do the most harm to our enemy with the least harm to ourselves: and this of course is to be effected by stratagem. That chivalrous courage which induces us to despise the suggestions of prudence, and to rush in the face of certain danger, is the offspring of society, and produced by education. It is honourable, because it is, in fact, the triumph of lofty sentiment over an instinctive repugnance to pain, and over those yearnings after personal ease and security, which society has condemned as ignoble. It is kept alive by pride and the fear of shame; and thus the dread of real evil is overcome by the superior dread of an evil which exists but in the imagination. It has been cherished and stimulated also by various means. It has been the theme of spirit-stirring song and chivalrous story. The poet and minstrel have delighted to shed round it the splendours of fiction; and even the historian has forgotten the sober gravity of narration, and broken forth into enthusiasm and rhapsody in its praise. Triumphs and gorgeous pageants have been its reward: monuments, on which art has exhausted its skill, and opulence its treasures, have been erected to perpetuate a nation's gratitude and admiration. Thus artificially excited, courage has risen to an extraordinary and factitious degree of heroism, and, arrayed in all the glorious "pomp and circumstance of war," this turbulent quality has even been able to eclipse many of those quiet, but invaluable virtues, which silently ennoble the human character, and swell the tide of human happiness.

But if courage intrinsically consists in the defiance of danger and pain, the life of the Indian is a continual exhibition of it. He lives in a state of perpetual hostility and risk. Peril and adventure are congenial to his nature; or rather seem necessary to arouse his faculties and to give an interest to his existence. Surrounded by hostile tribes, whose mode of warfare is by ambush and surprisal, he is always prepared for fight, and lives with his weapons in his hands. As the ship careers in fearful singleness through the solitudes of ocean; as the bird mingles among clouds and storms, and wings its way, a mere speck, across the pathless fields of air;—so the Indian holds his course, silent, solitary, but undaunted, through the boundless bosom of the wilderness. His expeditions may vie in distance and danger with the pilgrimage of the devotee, or the crusade of the knight-errant. He traverses vast forests, exposed to the hazards of lonely sickness, of lurking enemies, and pining famine. Stormy lakes—those great inland seas—are no obstacles to his wanderings: in his light canoe of bark he sports, like a feather, on their waves; and darts, with the swiftness of an arrow, down the roaring rapids of the rivers. His very subsistence is snatched from the midst of toil and peril. He gains his food by the hardships and dangers of the chase: he wraps himself in the spoils of the bear, the panther, and the buffalo, and sleeps among the thunders of the cataract.

No hero of ancient or modern days can surpass the Indian in his lofty contempt of death, and the fortitude with which he sustains its cruellest affliction. Indeed, we here behold him rising superior to the white man, in consequence of his peculiar education. The latter rushes to glorious death at the cannon's mouth; the former calmly contemplates its approach, and triumphantly endures it, amidst the varied torments of surrounding foes and the protracted agonies of fire. He even takes a pride in taunting his persecutors, and provoking their ingenuity of torture; and as the devouring flames prey on his very vitals, and the flesh shrinks from the sinews, he raises his last song of triumph, breathing the defiance of an unconquered heart, and invoking the spirits of his fathers to witness that he dies without a groan.

Notwithstanding the obloquy with which the early historians have overshadowed the characters of the unfortunate natives, some bright gleams occasionally break through, which throw a degree of melancholy lustre on their memories. Facts are occasionally to be met with in the rude annals of the eastern provinces, which, though recorded with the colouring of prejudice and bigotry, yet speak for themselves and will be dwelt on with applause and sympathy, when prejudice shall have passed away.

In one of the homely narratives of the Indian wars in New England, there is a touching account of the desolation carried into the tribe of the Pequod Indians. Humanity shrinks from the cold-blooded detail of indiscriminate butchery. In one place we read of the surprisal of an Indian fort in the night, when the wigwams were wrapt in flames, and the miserable inhabitants shot down and slain in attempting to escape, "all being despatched and ended in the course of an hour." After a series of similar transactions, "our soldiers," as the historian piously observes, "being resolved by God's assistance to make a final destruction of them," the unhappy savages being hunted from their homes and fortresses, and pursued with fire and sword, a scanty, but gallant band, the sad remnant of the Pequod warriors, with their wives and children, took refuge in a swamp.

Burning with indignation, and rendered sullen by despair; with hearts bursting with grief at the destruction of their tribe, and spirits galled and sore at the fancied ignominy of their defeat, they refused to ask their lives at the hands of an insulting foe and preferred death to submission.

As the night drew on they were surrounded in their dismal retreat, so as to render escape impracticable. Thus situated, their enemy "plied them with shot all the time, by which means many were killed and buried in the mire." In the darkness and fog that preceded the dawn of day, some few broke through the besiegers and escaped into the woods; "the rest were left to the conquerors, of which many were killed in the swamp, like sullen dogs who would rather, in their self-willedness and madness, sit still and be shot through, or cut to pieces," than implore for mercy. When the day broke upon this handful of forlorn but dauntless spirits, the soldiers, we are told, entering the swamp, "saw several heaps of them sitting close together, upon whom they discharged their pieces laden with ten or twelve pistol bullets at a time, putting the muzzles of the pieces under the boughs, within a few yards of them; so as, besides those that were found dead, many more were killed and sunk into the mire, and never were minded more by friend or foe."

Can any one read this plain unvarnished tale without admiring the stern resolution, the unbending pride, the loftiness of spirit, that seemed to nerve the hearts of these self-taught heroes, and to raise them above the instinctive feelings of human nature? When the Gauls laid waste the city of Rome, they found the senators clothed in their robes, and seated with stern tranquillity in their curule chairs; in this manner they suffered death without resistance or even supplication. Such conduct was, in them, applauded as noble and magnanimous; in the hapless Indian it was reviled as obstinate and sullen. How truly are we the dupes of show and circumstance! How different is virtue, clothed in purple and enthroned in state, from virtue, naked and destitute, and perishing obscurely in a wilderness!

But I forbear to dwell on these gloomy pictures. The eastern tribes have long since disappeared; the forests that sheltered them have been laid low; and scarce any traces remain of them in the thickly-settled states of New England, excepting here and there the Indian name of a village or a stream. And such must, sooner or later, be the fate of those other tribes which skirt the frontiers, and have occasionally been inveigled from their forests to mingle in the wars of white men. In a little while, and they will go the way that their brethren have gone before. The few hordes which still linger about the shores of Huron and Superior, and the tributary streams of the Mississippi, will share the fate of those tribes that once spread over Massachusetts and Connecticut, and lorded it along the proud banks of the Hudson; of that gigantic race said to have existed on the borders of the Susquehanna; and of those various nations that flourished about the Potomac and the Rappahannock, and that people the forests of the vast valley of Shenandoah. They will vanish like a vapour from the face of the earth; their very history will be lost in forgetfulness; and "the places that now know them will know them no more for ever." Or if, per-chance, some dubious memorial of them should survive, it may be in the romantic dreams of the poet, to people in imagination his glades and groves like the fauns and satyrs and sylvan deities of antiquity. But should' he venture upon the dark story of their wrongs and wretchedness; should he tell how they were invaded, corrupted, despoiled, driven from their native abodes and the sepulchres of their fathers, hunted like wild beasts about the earth, and sent down with violence and butchery to the grave, posterity will either turn with horror and incredulity from the tale, or blush with indignation at the inhuman-ity of their forefathers.—"We are driven back," said an old warrior, "until we can retreat no farther—our hatchets are broken, our bows are snapped, our fires are nearly extinguished—a little longer and the white man will cease to persecute us—for we shall cease to exist."

JOHN BULL

An old song, made by an aged old pate,
Of an old worshipful gentleman, who had a great estate,
That kept a brave old house at a bountiful rate,
And an old porter to relieve the poor at his gate.
With an old study fill'd full of learned old books,
With an old reverend chaplain, you might know him by his looks,
With an old buttery-hatch worn quite off the hooks,
And an old kitchen that maintained half-a-dozen old cooks.
                    Like an old courtier, etc.—OLD SONG.

THERE IS no species of humour in which the English more excel, than that which consists in caricaturing and giving ludicrous appellations, or nicknames. In this way they have whimsically designated, not merely individuals, but nations; and, in their fondness for pushing a joke, they have not spared even themselves. One would think that, in personifying itself, a nation would be apt to picture something grand, heroic, and imposing; but it is characteristic of the peculiar humour of the English, and of their love for what is blunt, comic, and familiar, that they have embodied their national oddities in the figure of a sturdy, corpulent old fellow, with a three-cornered hat, red waistcoat, leather breeches, and stout oaken cudgel. Thus they have taken a singular delight in exhibiting their most private foibles in a laughable point of view; and have been so successful in their delineations, that there is scarcely a being in actual existence more absolutely present to the public mind than that eccentric personage, John Bull.

Perhaps the continual contemplation of the character thus drawn of them has contributed to fix it upon the nation, and thus to give reality to what at first may have been painted in a great measure from the imagination. Men are apt to acquire peculiarities that are continually ascribed to them. The common orders of English seem wonderfully captivated with the *beau idéal* which they have formed of John Bull, and endeavour to act up to the broad caricature that is perpetually before their eyes. Unluckily, they sometimes make their boasted Bull-ism an apology for their prejudice or grossness; and this I have especially noticed among those truly homebred and genuine sons of the soil who have never migrated beyond the sound of Bow bells. If one of these should be a little uncouth in speech, and apt to utter impertinent truths, he confesses that he is a real John Bull, and always speaks his mind. If he now and then flies into an unreasonable burst of passion about trifles, he observes, that John Bull is a choleric old blade, but then his passion is over in a moment, and he bears no malice. If he betrays a coarseness of taste, and an insensibility to foreign refinements, he thanks Heaven for his ignorance—he is a plain John Bull, and has no relish for frippery and nicknacks. His very proneness to be gulled by strangers, and to pay extravagantly for absurdities, is excused under the plea of munificence—for John is always more generous than wise.

Thus, under the name of John Bull, he will contrive to argue every fault into a merit, and will frankly convict himself of being the honestest fellow in existence.

However little, therefore, the character may have suited in the first instance, it has gradually adapted itself to the nation, or rather they have adapted themselves to each other; and a stranger who wishes to study English peculiarities, may gather much valuable information from the innumerable portraits of John Bull, as exhibited in the windows of the caricature-shops. Still, however, he is one of those fertile humorists, that are continually throwing out new portraits, and presenting different aspects from different points of view; and, often as he has been described, I cannot resist the temptation to give a slight sketch of him, such as he has met my eye.

John Bull, to all appearance, is a plain, downright, matter-of-fact fellow, with much less of poetry about him than rich prose. There is little of romance in his nature, but a vast deal of strong natural feeling. He excels in humour more than in wit; is jolly rather than gay; melancholy rather than morose; can easily be moved to a sudden tear, or surprised into a broad laugh; but he loathes sentiment, and has no turn for light pleasantry. He is a boon companion, if you allow him to have his humour, and to talk about himself; and he will stand by a friend in a quarrel, with life and purse, however soundly he may be cudgelled.

In this last respect, to tell the truth, he has a propensity to be somewhat too ready. He is a busy-minded personage, who thinks not merely for himself and family, but for all the country round, and is most generously disposed to be everybody's champion. He is continually volunteering his services to settle his neighbour's affairs, and takes it in great dudgeon if they engage in any matter of consequence without asking his advice; though he seldom engages in any friendly office of the kind without finishing by getting into a squabble with all parties, and then railing bitterly at their ingratitude. He unluckily took lessons in his youth in the noble science of defence, and having accomplished himself in the use of his limbs and his weapons, and become a perfect master at boxing and cudgel-play, he has had a troublesome life of it ever since. He cannot hear of a quarrel between the most distant of his neighbours, but he begins incontinently to fumble with the head of his cudgel, and consider whether his interest or honour does not require that he should meddle in the broil. Indeed, he has extended his relations of pride and policy so completely over the whole country, that no event can take place without infringing some of his finely-spun rights and dignities. Couched in his little domain, with these filaments stretching forth in every direction, he is like some choleric, bottle-bellied old spider, who has woven his web over a whole chamber, so that a fly cannot buzz, nor a breeze blow, without startling his repose, and causing him to sally forth wrathfully from his den.

Though really a good-hearted, good-tempered old fellow at bottom, yet he is singularly fond of being in the midst of contention. It is one of his peculiarities, however, that he only relishes the beginning of an affray; he always goes into a fight with alacrity, but comes out of it grumbling even when victorious; and though no one fights with more obstinacy to carry a contested point, yet, when the battle is over, and he comes to the reconciliation, he is so much taken up with the mere shaking of hands, that he is apt to let his antagonist pocket all that they have been quarrelling about. It is not, therefore, fighting that he ought so much to be on his guard against, as making friends. It is difficult to cudgel him out of a farthing; but put him in a good humour, and you may bargain him out of all the money in his pocket. He is like a stout ship, which will weather the roughest storm uninjured, but roll its masts overboard in the succeeding calm.

He is a little fond of playing the magnifico abroad; of pulling out a long purse; flinging his money bravely about at boxing-matches, horse-races, cock-fights, and carrying a high head among "gentlemen of the fancy": but immediately after one of these fits of extravagance, he will be taken with violent qualms of economy; stop short at the most trivial expenditure; talk desperately of being ruined and brought upon the parish; and in such moods will not pay the smallest tradesman's bill without violent altercation. He is, in fact, the most punctual and discontented paymaster in the world; drawing his coin out of his breeches pocket with infinite reluctance; paying to the uttermost farthing, but accompanying every guinea with a growl.

With all his talk of economy, however, he is a bountiful provider, and a hospitable housekeeper. His economy is of a whimsical kind, its chief object being to devise how he may afford to be extravagant; for he will begrudge himself a beefsteak and pint of port one day, that he may roast an ox whole, broach a hogshead of ale, and treat all his neighbours on the next.

His domestic establishment is enormously expensive: not so much from any great outward parade, as from the great consumption of solid beef and pudding; the vast number of followers he feeds and clothes; and his singular disposition to pay hugely for small services. He is a most kind and indulgent master, and, provided his servants humour his peculiarities, flatter his vanity a little now and then, and do not peculate grossly on him before his face, they may manage him to perfection. Everything that lives on him seems to thrive and grow fat. His house-servants are well paid and pampered, and have little to do. His horses are sleek and lazy, and prance slowly before his state carriage; and his house-dogs sleep quietly about the door, and will hardly bark at a house-breaker.

His family mansion is an old castellated manor-house, gray with age, and of a most venerable, though weather-beaten appearance. It has been built upon no regular plan, but is a vast accumulation of parts, erected in various tastes and ages. The centre bears evident traces of Saxon architecture, and is as solid as ponderous stone and old English oak can make it. Like all the relics of that style, it is full of obscure passages, intricate mazes, and dusky chambers; and though these have been partially lighted up in modern days, yet there are many places where you must still grope in the dark. Additions have been made to the original edifice from time to time, and great altera-tions have taken place; towers and battlements have been erected during wars and tumults; wings built in time of peace; and outhouses, lodges, and offices, run up according to the whim or convenience of different generations, until it has become one of the most spacious, rambling tenements imaginable. An entire wing is taken up with the family chapel, a reverend pile, that must have been exceedingly sumptuous, and, indeed, in spite of having been altered and simplified at various periods, has still a look of solemn religious pomp. Its walls within are storied with the monuments of John's ancestors; and it is snugly fitted up with soft cushions and well-lined chairs, where such of his family as are inclined to church services, may doze comfortably in the discharge of their duties.

To keep up this chapel has cost John much money; but he is staunch in his religion, and piqued in his zeal, from the circumstance that many dissenting chapels have been erected in his vicinity, and several of his neighbours, with whom he has had quarrels, are strong papists.

To do the duties of the chapel, he maintains, at a large expense, a pious and portly family chaplain. He is a most learned and decorous personage, and a truly well-bred Christian, who always backs the old gentleman in his opinions, winks discreetly at his little peccadilloes, rebukes the children when refractory, and is of great use in exhorting the tenants to read their bibles, say their prayers, and, above all, to pay their rents punctually, and without grumbling.

The family apartments are in a very antiquated taste, somewhat heavy, and often inconvenient, but full of the solemn magnificence of former times; fitted up with rich though faded tapestry, unwieldy furniture, and loads of massy gorgeous old plate. The vast fireplaces, ample kitchens, extensive cellars, and sumptuous banqueting-halls, all speak of the roaring hospitality of days of yore, of which the modern festivity at the manor-house is but a shadow. There are, however, complete suites of rooms apparently deserted and time-worn; and towers and turrets that are tottering to decay; so that in high winds there is danger of their tumbling about the ears of the household.

John has frequently been advised to have the old edifice thoroughly over-hauled; and to have some of the useless parts pulled down, and the others strengthened with their materials; but the old gentleman always grows testy on this subject. He swears the house is an excellent house—that it is tight and weather-proof, and not to be shaken by tempests—that it has stood for several hundred years, and therefore is not likely to tumble down now—that as to its being inconvenient, his family is accustomed to the inconveniences, and would not be comfortable without them—that as to its unwieldy size and irregular construction, these result from its being the growth of centuries, and being improved by the wisdom of every generation—that an old family, like his, requires a large house to dwell in; new, upstart families may live in modern cottages and snug boxes; but an old English family should inhabit an old English manor-house. If you point out any part of the building as superfluous, he insists that it is material to the strength or decoration of the rest, and the harmony of the whole; and swears that the parts are so built into each other, that if you pull down one, you run the risk of having the whole about your ears.

The secret of the matter is, that John has a great disposition to protect and patronise. He thinks it indispensable to the dignity of an ancient and honourable family, to be bounteous in its appointments, and to be eaten up by dependants; and so, partly from pride and partly from kind-heartedness, he makes it a rule always to give shelter and maintenance to his superannuated servants.

The consequence is, that, like many other venerable family establishments, his manor is encumbered by old retainers whom he cannot turn off, and an old style which he cannot lay down. His mansion is like a great hospital of invalids, and, with all its magnitude, is not a whit too large for its inhabitants. Not a nook or corner but is of use in housing some useless personage. Groups of veteran beef-eaters, gouty pensioners, and retired heroes of the buttery and the larder, are seen lolling about its walls, crawling over its lawns, dozing under its trees, or sunning themselves upon the benches at its doors. Every office and outhouse is garrisoned by these supernumeraries and their families; for they are amazingly prolific, and when they die off, are sure to leave John a legacy of hungry mouths to be provided for. A mattock cannot be struck against the most mouldering tumbledown tower, but out pops, from some cranny or loop-hole, the gray pate of some superannuated hanger-on, who has lived at John's expense all his life, and makes the most grievous outcry at their pulling down the roof from over the head of a worn-out servant of the family. This is an appeal that John's honest heart never can withstand; so that a man, who has faithfully eaten his beef and pudding all his life, is sure to be rewarded with a pipe and tankard in his old days.

A great part of his park, also, is turned into paddocks, where his broken-down chargers are turned loose to graze undisturbed for the remainder of their existence—a worthy example of grateful recollection, which, if some of his neighbours were to imitate, would not be to their discredit. Indeed, it is one of his great pleasures to point out these old steeds to his visitors, to dwell on their good qualities, extol their past services, and boast, with some little vainglory, of the perilous adventures and hardy exploits through which they have carried him.

He is given, however, to indulge his veneration for family usages, and family incumbrances, to a whimsical extent. His manor is infested by gangs of gipsies; yet he will not suffer them to be driven off, because they have infested the place time out of mind, and been regular poachers upon every generation of the family. He will scarcely permit a dry branch to be lopped from the great trees that surround the house, lest it should molest the rooks, that have bred there for centuries. Owls have taken possession of the dovecot; but they are hereditary owls, and must not be disturbed. Swallows have nearly choked up every chimney with their nests; martins build in every frieze and cornice; crows flutter about the towers, and perch on every weathercock; and old gray-headed rats may be seen in every quarter of the house, running in and out of their holes undauntedly in broad daylight. In short, John has such a reverence for everything that has been long in the family, that he will not hear even of abuses being reformed, because they are good old family abuses.

All these whims and habits have concurred woefully to drain the old gentleman's purse; and as he prides himself on punctuality on money matters, and wishes to maintain his credit in the neighbourhood, they have caused him great perplexity in meeting his engagements. This, too, has been increased by the altercations and heart-burnings which are continually taking place in his family. His children have been brought up to different callings, and are of different ways of thinking; and as they have always been allowed to speak their minds freely, they do not fail to exercise the privilege most clamorously in the present posture of his affairs. Some stand up for the honour of the race, and are clear that the old establishment should be kept up in all its state, whatever may be the cost; others, who are more prudent and considerate, entreat the old gentleman to retrench his expenses, and to put his whole system of housekeeping on a more moderate footing. He has, indeed, at times, seemed inclined to listen to their opinions, but their wholesome advice has been completely defeated by the obstreperous conduct of one of his sons. This is a noisy, rattle-pated fellow, of rather low habits, who neglects his business to frequent ale-houses—is the orator of village clubs, and a complete oracle among the poorest of his father's tenants. No sooner does he hear any of his brothers mention reform or retrenchment, than up he jumps, takes the words out of their mouths, and roars out for an overturn. When his tongue is once going, nothing can stop it. He rants about the room; hectors the old man about his spendthrift practices; ridicules his tastes and pursuits; insists that he shall turn the old servants out of doors; give the broken-down horses to the hounds; send the fat chaplain packing, and take a field preacher in his place—nay, that the whole family mansion shall be levelled with the ground, and a plain one of brick and mortar built in its place. He rails at every social entertainment and family festivity, and skulks away growling to the ale-house whenever an equipage drives up to the door. Though constantly complaining of the emptiness of his purse, yet he scruples not to spend all his pocket-money in these tavern convocations, and even runs up scores for the liquor, over which he preaches about his father's extravagance.

It may be readily imagined how little such thwarting agrees with the old cavalier's fiery temperament. He has become so irritable, from repeated crossings, that the mere mention of retrenchment or reform is a signal for a brawl between him and the tavern oracle. As the latter is too sturdy and refractory for paternal discipline, having grown out of all fear of the cudgel, they have frequent scenes of wordy warfare, which at times run so high that John is fain to call in the aid of his son Tom, an officer who has served abroad, but is at present living at home, on half-pay. This last is sure to stand by the old gentleman, right or wrong; likes nothing so much as a racketing, roistering life; and is ready at a wink or nod, to out sabre, and flourish it over the orator's head, if he dares to array himself against paternal authority.

These family dissensions, as usual, have got abroad, and are rare food for scandal in John's neighbourhood. People begin to look wise, and shake their heads, whenever his affairs are mentioned. They all "hope that matters are not so bad with him as represented; but when a man's own children begin to rail at his extravagance, things must be badly managed. They understand he is mortgaged over head and ears, and is continually dabbling with money-lenders. He is certainly an open-handed old gentleman, but they fear he has lived too fast; indeed, they never knew any good come of this fondness for hunting, racing, revelling, and prize-fighting. In short, Mr. Bull's estate is a very fine one, and has been in the family a long while; but, for all that, they have known many finer estates come to the hammer."

What is worst of all, is the effect which these pecuniary embarrassments and domestic feuds have had on the poor man himself. Instead of that jolly round corporation, and snug rosy face, which he used to present, he has of late become as shrivelled and shrunk as a frost-bitten apple. His scarlet gold-laced waistcoat, which bellied out so bravely in those prosperous days when he sailed before the wind, now hangs loosely about him like a mainsail in a calm. His leather breeches are all in folds and wrinkles, and apparently have much ado to hold up the boots that yawn on both sides of his once sturdy legs.

Instead of strutting about as formerly, with his three-cornered hat on one side; flourishing his cudgel, and bringing it down every moment with a hearty thump upon the ground; looking every one sturdily in the face, and trolling out a stave of a catch or a drinking song; he now goes about whistling thoughtfully to himself, with his head drooping down, his cudgel tucked under his arm, and his hands thrust to the bottom of his breeches pockets, which are evidently empty.

Such is the plight of honest John Bull at present; yet for all this the old fellow's spirit is as tall and as gallant as ever. If you drop the least expression of sympathy or concern, he takes fire in an instant; swears that he is the richest and stoutest fellow in the country; talks of laying out large sums to adorn his house or buy another estate; and with a valiant swagger and grasping of his cudgel, longs exceedingly to have another bout at quarter-staff.

Though there may be something rather whimsical in all this, yet I confess I cannot look upon John's situation without strong feelings of interest. With all his odd humours and obstinate prejudices, he is a sterling-hearted old blade. He may not be so wonderfully fine a fellow as he thinks himself, but he is at least twice as good as his neighbours represent him. His virtues are all his own; all plain, homebred, and unaffected. His very faults smack of the raciness of his good qualities. His extravagance savours of his generosity; his quarrelsomeness, of his courage; his credulity, of his open faith; his vanity, of his pride; and his bluntness, of his sincerity. They are all the redundancies of a rich and liberal character. He is like his old oak, rough without, but sound and solid within; whose bark abounds with excrescences in proportion to the growth and grandeur of the timber; and whose branches make a fearful groaning and murmuring in the least storm, from their very magnitude and luxuriance. There is something, too, in the appearance of his old family mansion that is extremely poetical and picturesque; and, as long as it can be rendered comfortably habitable, I should almost tremble to see it meddled with, during the present conflict of tastes and opinions. Some of his advisers are no doubt good architects, that might be of service; but many, I fear, are mere levellers, who, when they had once got to work with their mattocks on this venerable edifice, would never stop until they had brought it to the ground, and perhaps buried themselves among the ruins. All that I wish is, that John's present troubles may teach him more prudence in future. That he may cease to distress his mind about other people's affairs; that he may give up the fruitless attempt to promote the good of his neighbours, and the peace and happiness of the world, by dint of the cudgel; that he may remain quietly at home; gradually get his house into repair; cultivate his rich estate according to his fancy; husband his income—if he thinks proper; bring his unruly children into order—if he can; renew the jovial scenes of ancient prosperity; and long enjoy, on his paternal lands, a green, an honourable, and a merry old age.

THE LEGEND OF SLEEPY HOLLOW

FOUND AMONG THE PAPERS OF THE LATE DIEDRICH KNICKERBOCKER

A pleasing land of drowsy head it was,
Of dreams that wave before the half-shut eye;
And of gay castles in the clouds that pass,
For ever flushing round a summer sky.

"CASTLE OF INDOLENCE."

IN THE BOSOM of one of those spacious coves which indent the eastern shore of the Hudson, at that broad expansion of the river denominated by the ancient Dutch navigators the Tappan Zee, and where they always prudently shortened sail, and implored the protection of St. Nicholas when they crossed, there lies a small market-town or rural port, which by some is called Greensburgh, but which is more generally and properly known by the name of Tarry Town. This name was given, we are told, in former days, by the good housewives of the adjacent country, from the inveterate propensity of their husbands to linger about the village tavern on market days. Be that as it may, I do not vouch for the fact, but merely advert to it, for the sake of being precise and authentic. Not far from this village, perhaps about two miles, there is a little valley, or rather lap of land, among high hills, which is one of the quietest places in the whole world. A small brook glides through it, with just murmur enough to lull one to repose; and the occasional whistle of a quail or tapping of a woodpecker, is almost the only sound that ever breaks in upon the uniform tranquillity.

I recollect that, when a stripling, my first exploit in squirrel-shooting was in a grove of tall walnut-trees that shades one side of the valley. I had wandered into it at noon time, when all nature is peculiarly quiet, and was startled by the roar of my own gun, as it broke the Sabbath stillness around, and was prolonged and reverberated by the angry echoes. If ever I should wish for a retreat, whither I might steal from the world and its distractions, and dream quietly away the remnant of a troubled life, I know of none more promising than this little valley.

From the listless repose of the place, and the peculiar character of its inhabitants, who are descendants from the original Dutch settlers, this sequestered glen has long been known by the name of SLEEPY HOLLOW, and its rustic lads are called the Sleepy Hollow Boys throughout all the neighbouring country. A drowsy dreamy influence seems to hang over the land, and to pervade the very atmosphere. Some say that the place was bewitched by a high German doctor, during the early days of the settlement; others, that an old Indian chief, the prophet or wizard of his tribe, held his powwows there before the country was discovered by Master Hendrick Hudson. Certain it is, the place still continues under the sway of some witching power, that holds a spell over the minds of the good people, causing them to walk in a continual reverie. They are given to all kinds of marvellous beliefs; are subject to trances and visions; and frequently see strange sights, and hear music and voices in the air. The whole neighbourhood abounds with local tales, haunted spots, and twilight superstitions; stars shoot and meteors glare oftener across the valley than in any other part of the country, and the nightmare, with her whole nine fold, seems to make it the favourite scene of her gambols.

The dominant spirit, however, that haunts this enchanted region, and seems to be commander-in-chief of all the powers of the air, is the apparition of a figure on horseback without a head. It is said by some to be the ghost of a Hessian trooper, whose head had been carried away by a cannon-ball, in some nameless battle during the revolutionary war; and who is ever and anon seen by the country folk, hurrying along in the gloom of night, as if on the wings of the wind. His haunts are not confined to the valley, but extend at times to the adjacent roads, and especially to the vicinity of a church at no great distance. Indeed, certain of the most authentic historians of those parts, who have been careful in collecting and collating the floating facts concerning this spectre, allege that the body of the trooper, having been buried in the churchyard, the ghost rides forth to the scene of battle in nightly quest of his head; and that the rushing speed with which he some-times passes along the Hollow, like a midnight blast, is owing to his being belated, and in a hurry to get back to the churchyard before daybreak.

Such is the general purport of this legendary superstition, which has fur-nished materials for many a wild story in that region of shadows; and the spectre is known at all the country firesides by the name of the Headless Horseman of Sleepy Hollow.

It is remarkable that the visionary propensity I have mentioned is not confined to the native inhabitants of the valley, but is unconsciously imbibed by every one who resides there for a time. However wide awake they may have been before they entered that sleepy region, they are sure, in a little time, to inhale the witching influence of the air, and begin to grow imaginative—to dream dreams, and see apparitions.

I mention this peaceful spot with all possible laud; for it is in such little retired Dutch valleys, found here and there embosomed in the great state of New York, that population, manners, and customs, remain fixed; while the great torrent of migration and improvement, which is making such incessant changes in other parts of this restless country, sweeps by them unobserved. They are like those little nooks of still water which border a rapid stream; where we may see the straw and bubble riding quietly at anchor, or slowly revolving in their mimic harbour, undisturbed by the rush of the passing current. Though many years have elapsed since I trod the drowsy shades of Sleepy Hollow, yet I question whether I should not still find the same trees and the same families vegetating in its sheltered bosom.

In this by-place of nature there abode, in a remote period of American history, that is to say, some thirty years since, a worthy wight of the name of Ichabod Crane; who sojourned, or, as he expressed it, "tarried," in Sleepy Hollow, for the purpose of instructing the children of the vicinity. He was a native of Connecticut; a state which supplies the Union with pioneers for the mind as well as for the forest, and sends forth yearly its legions of frontier woodmen and country schoolmasters. The cognomen of Crane was not inapplicable to his person. He was tall, but exceedingly lank, with narrow shoulders, long arms and legs, hands that dangled a mile out of his sleeves, feet that might have served for shovels, and his whole frame most loosely hung together. His head was small, and flat at top, with huge ears, large green glassy eyes, and a long snipe nose, so that it looked like a weather-cock, perched upon his spindle neck, to tell which way the wind blew. To see him striding along the profile of a hill on a windy day, with his clothes bagging and fluttering about him, one might have mistaken him for the genius of famine descending upon the earth, or some scarecrow eloped from a corn-field.

His school-house was a low building of one large room, rudely constructed of logs; the windows partly glazed, and partly patched with leaves of old copy-books. It was most ingeniously secured at vacant hours, by a withe twisted in the handle of the door, and stakes set against the window-shutters; so that, though a thief might get in with perfect ease, he would find some embarrassment in getting out; an idea most probably borrowed by the architect, Yost Van Houten, from the mystery of an eel-pot. The school-house stood in a rather lonely but pleasant situation, just at the foot of a woody hill, with a brook running close by, and a formidable birch-tree growing at one end of it. From hence the low murmur of his pupils' voices, conning over their lessons, might be heard in a drowsy summer's day, like the hum of a bee-hive; interrupted now and then by the authoritative voice of the master, in the tone of menace or command; or, peradventure, by the appalling sound of the birch, as he urged some tardy loiterer along the flowery path of knowledge. Truth to say, he was a conscientious man, and ever bore in mind the golden maxim, "Spare the rod and spoil the child." Ichabod Crane's scholars certainly were not spoiled.

I would not have it imagined, however, that he was one of those cruel potentates of the school, who joy in the smart of their subjects; on the contrary, he administered justice with discrimination rather than severity; taking the burthen off the backs of the weak, and laying it on those of the strong. Your mere puny stripling, that winced at the least flourish of the rod, was passed by with indulgence; but the claims of justice were satisfied by inflicting a double portion on some little tough, wrong-headed, broad-skirted Dutch urchin, who sulked and swelled and grew dogged and sullen beneath the birch. All this he called "doing his duty by their parents"; and he never inflicted a chastisement without following it by the assurance, so consolatory to the smarting urchin, that "he would remember it and thank him for it the longest day he had to live."

When school-hours were over, he was even the companion and playmate of the larger boys; and on holiday afternoons would convoy some of the smaller ones home, who happened to have pretty sisters, or good housewives for mothers, noted for the comforts of the cupboard. Indeed, it behoved him to keep on good terms with his pupils. The revenue arising from his school was small, and would have been scarcely sufficient to furnish him with daily bread, for he was a huge feeder, and though lank, had the dilating powers of an anaconda; but to help out his maintenance, he was, according to country custom in those parts, boarded and lodged at the houses of the farmers, whose children he instructed. With these he lived successively a week at a time; thus going the rounds of the neighbourhood, with all his worldly effects tied up in a cotton handkerchief.

That all this might not be too onerous on the purses of his rustic patrons, who are apt to consider the costs of schooling a grievous burden, and school-masters as mere drones, he had various ways of rendering himself both useful and agreeable. He assisted the farmers occasionally in the lighter labours of their farms; helped to make hay; mended the fences; took the horses to water; drove the cows from pasture; and cut wood for the winter fire. He laid aside, too, all the dominant dignity and absolute sway with which he lorded it in his little empire, the school, and became wonderfully gentle and ingratiating. He found favour in the eyes of the mothers by petting the children, particularly the youngest; and like the lion bold, which whilom so magnanimously the lamb did hold, he would sit with a child on one knee, and rock a cradle with his foot for whole hours together.

In addition to his other vocations, he was the singing-master of the neighbourhood, and picked up many bright shillings by instructing the young folks in psalmody. It was a matter of no little vanity to him, on Sundays, to take his station in front of the church gallery, with a band of chosen singers; where, in his own mind, he completely carried away the palm from the parson. Certain it is, his voice resounded far above all the rest of the congregation; and there are peculiar quavers still to be heard in that church, and which may even be heard half a mile off, quite to the opposite side of the mill-pond, on a still Sunday morning, which are said to be legitimately descended from the nose of Ichabod Crane. Thus, by divers little make-shifts, in that ingenious way which is commonly denominated "by hook and by crook," the worthy pedagogue got on tolerably enough, and was thought, by all who understand nothing of the labour of head-work, to have a wonderfully easy life of it.

The schoolmaster is generally a man of some importance in the female circle of a rural neighbourhood; being considered a kind of idle gentleman-like personage, of vastly superior taste and accomplishments to the rough country swains, and, indeed, inferior in learning only to the parson. His appearance, therefore, is apt to occasion some little stir at the tea-table of a farm-house and the addition of a supernumerary dish of cakes or sweet-meats, or peradventure the parade of a silver tea-pot. Our man of letters, therefore, was peculiarly happy in the smiles of all the country damsels. How he would figure among them in the churchyard between services on Sundays! gathering grapes for them from the wild vines that overran the surrounding trees; reciting for their amusement all the epitaphs on the tombstones; or sauntering with a whole bevy of them along the banks of the adjacent mill-pond; while the more bashful country bumpkins hung sheepishly back, envying his superior elegance and address.

From his half itinerant life, also, he was a kind of travelling gazette, carrying the whole budget of local gossip from house to house; so that his appearance was always greeted with satisfaction. He was, moreover, esteemed by the women as a man of great erudition, for he had read several books quite through, and was a perfect master of Cotton Mather's *History of New England Witchcraft*, in which, by the way, he most firmly and potently believed.

He was, in fact, an odd mixture of small shrewdness and simple credulity. His appetite for the marvellous, and his powers of digesting it, were equally extraordinary; and both had been increased by his residence in this spell-bound region. No tale was too gross or monstrous for his capacious swallow. It was often his delight, after his school was dismissed in the afternoon, to stretch himself on the rich bed of clover, bordering the little brook that whimpered by his school-house, and there con over old Mather's direful tales, until the gathering dusk of the evening made the printed page a mere mist before his eyes. Then, as he wended his way by swamp and stream and awful woodland, to the farm-house where he happened to be quartered, every sound of nature, at that witching hour, fluttered his excited imagination: the moan of the whip-poor-will[1] from the hill-side; the boding cry of the tree-toad, that harbinger of storm; the dreary hooting of the screech-owl, or the sudden rustling in the thicket of birds frightened from their roost. The fireflies, too, which sparkled most vividly in the darkest places, now and then startled him, as one of uncommon brightness would stream across his path; and if by chance a huge blackhead of a beetle came winging his blundering flight against him, the poor varlet was ready to give up the ghost, with the idea that he was struck with a witch's token. His only resource on such occasions, either to drown thought or drive away evil spirits, was to sing psalm tunes;—and the good people of Sleepy Hollow, as they sat by their doors of an evening, were often filled with awe at hearing his nasal melody, "in linked sweetness long drawn out," floating from the distant hill, or along the dusky road.

Another of his sources of fearful pleasure was, to pass long winter evenings with the old Dutch wives, as they sat spinning by the fire, with a row of apples roasting and spluttering along the hearth, and listen to their marvellous tales of ghosts and goblins, and haunted fields, and haunted brooks, and haunted bridges, and haunted houses, and particularly of the headless horseman, or Galloping Hessian of the Hollow, as they sometimes called him. He would delight them equally by his anecdotes of witchcraft, and of the direful omens and portentous sights and sounds in the air, which prevailed in the earlier times of Connecticut; and would frighten them wofully with

[1]The whip-poor-will is a bird which is only heard at night. It receives its name from its note, which is thought to resemble those words.

speculations upon comets and shooting stars; and with the alarming fact that the world did absolutely turn round, and that they were half the time topsy-turvy!

But if there was a pleasure in all this, while snugly cuddling in the chimney-corner of a chamber that was all of a ruddy glow from the crackling wood fire, and where, of course, no spectre dared to show its face, it was dearly purchased by the terrors of his subsequent walk homewards. What fearful shapes and shadows beset his path amidst the dim and ghastly glare of a snowy night!—With what wistful look did he eye every trembling ray of light streaming across the waste fields from some distant window!—How often was he appalled by some shrub covered with snow, which, like a sheeted spectre, beset his very path!—How often did he shrink with curdling awe at the sound of his own steps on the frosty crust beneath his feet! and dread to look over his shoulder, lest he should behold some uncouth being tramping close behind him!—and how often was he thrown into complete dismay by some rushing blast, howling among the trees, in the idea that it was the Galloping Hessian on one of his nightly scourings!

All these, however, were mere terrors of the night, phantoms of the mind that walk in darkness; and though he had seen many spectres in his time, and been more than once beset by Satan in divers shapes, in his lonely perambulations, yet daylight put an end to all these evils; and he would have passed a pleasant life of it, in despite of the devil and all his works, if his path had not been crossed by a being that causes more perplexity to mortal man than ghosts, goblins, and the whole race of witches put together, and that was—a woman.

Among the musical disciples who assembled one evening in each week to receive his instructions in psalmody, was Katrina Van Tassel, the daughter and only child of a substantial Dutch farmer. She was a blooming lass of fresh eighteen; plump as a partridge; ripe and melting and rosy-cheeked as one of her father's peaches, and universally famed, not merely for her beauty, but her vast expectations. She was, withal, a little of a coquette, as might be perceived even in her dress, which was a mixture of ancient and modern fashions, as most suited to set off her charms. She wore the ornaments of pure yellow gold, which her great-great-grandmother had brought over from Saardam; the tempting stomacher of the olden time; and withal a provokingly short petticoat, to display the prettiest foot and ankle in the country round.

Ichabod Crane had a soft and foolish heart towards the sex, and it is not to be wondered at that so tempting a morsel soon found favour in his eyes, more especially after he had visited her in her paternal mansion. Old Baltus Van Tassel was a perfect picture of a thriving, contented, liberal-hearted farmer. He seldom, it is true, sent either his eyes or his thoughts beyond the boundaries of his own farm; but within those, everything was snug, happy, and well-conditioned. He was satisfied with his wealth, but not proud of it; and piqued himself upon the hearty abundance, rather than the style in which he lived. His stronghold was situated on the banks of the Hudson, in one of those green, sheltered, fertile nooks, in which the Dutch farmers are so fond of nestling. A great elm-tree spread its broad branches over it, at the foot of which bubbled up a spring of the softest and sweetest water, in a little well formed of a barrel, and then stole sparkling away through the grass to a neighbouring brook that bubbled along among alders and dwarf willows. Hard by the farm-house was a vast barn that might have served for a church, every window and crevice of which seemed bursting forth with the treasures of the farm; the flail was busily resounding within it from morning to night; swallows and martins skimmed twittering about the eaves; and rows of pigeons, some with one eye turned up, as if watching the weather, some with their heads under their wings, or buried in their bosoms, and others swelling, and cooing, and bowing about their dames, were enjoying the sunshine on the roof. Sleek unwieldy porkers were grunting in the repose and abundance of their pens, whence sallied forth now and then troops of sucking pigs, as if to snuff the air. A stately squadron of snowy geese were riding in an adjoining pond, convoying whole fleets of ducks; regiments of turkeys were gobbling through the farm-yard, and guinea-fowls fretting about it, like ill-tempered housewives, with their peevish, discontented cry. Before the barn door strutted the gallant cock, that pattern of a husband, a warrior, and a fine gentleman, clapping his burnished wings, and crowing in the pride and gladness of his heart—sometimes tearing up the earth with his feet, and then generously calling his ever-hungry family of wives and children to enjoy the rich morsel which he had discovered.

The pedagogue's mouth watered as he looked upon his sumptuous promise of luxurious winter fare. In his devouring mind's eye he pictured to himself every roasting-pig running about with a pudding in his belly, and an apple in his mouth; the pigeons were snugly put to bed in a comfortable pie, and tucked in with a coverlet of crust; the geese were swimming in their own gravy; and the ducks pairing cosily in dishes, like snug married couples, with a decent competency of onion sauce. In the porkers he saw carved out the future sleek side of bacon and juicy relishing ham; not a turkey but he beheld daintily trussed-up, with its gizzard under its wing, and, peradventure, a necklace of savoury sausages; and even bright chanticleer himself lay sprawling on his back in a side dish, with uplifted claws, as if craving that quarter which his chivalrous spirit disdained to ask while living.

As the enraptured Ichabod fancied all this, and as he rolled his great green eyes over the fat meadow-lands, the rich fields of wheat, of rye, of buckwheat, and Indian corn, and the orchards burthened with ruddy fruit, which surrounded the warm tenement of Van Tassel, his heart yearned after the damsel who was to inherit these domains, and his imagination expanded with the idea, how they might be readily turned into cash, and the money invested in immense tracts of wild land, and shingle palaces in the wilderness. Nay, his busy fancy already realised his hopes, and presented to him the blooming Katrina, with a whole family of children, mounted on the top of a waggon loaded with household trumpery, with pots and kettles dangling beneath; and he beheld himself bestriding a pacing mare, with a colt at her heels, setting out for Kentucky, Tennessee, or the Lord knows where.

When he entered the house, the conquest of his heart was complete. It was one of those spacious farm-houses, with high-ridged, but lowly-sloping roofs, built in the style handed down from the first Dutch settlers; the low projecting eaves forming a piazza along the front, capable of being closed up in bad weather. Under this were hung flails, harness, various utensils of husbandry, and nets for fishing in the neighbouring river. Benches were built along the sides for summer use; and a great spinning-wheel at one end, and a churn at the other, showed the various uses to which this important porch might be devoted. From this piazza the wondering Ichabod entered the hall, which formed the centre of the mansion and the place of usual residence. Here rows of resplendent pewter, ranged on a long dresser, dazzled his eyes. In one corner stood a huge bag of wool ready to be spun; in another, a quantity of linsey-woolsey just from the loom; ears of Indian corn, and strings of dried apples and peaches, hung in gay festoons along the wall, mingled with the gaud of red peppers; and a door left ajar gave him a peep into the best parlour, where the claw-footed chairs and dark mahogany tables shone like mirrors; and irons, with their accompanying shovel and tongs, glistened from their covert of asparagus tops; mock oranges and conch-shells decorated the mantelpiece; strings of various coloured birds' eggs were suspended above it; a great ostrich egg was hung from the centre of the room, and a corner-cupboard, knowingly left open, displayed immense treasures of old silver and well-mended china.

From the moment Ichabod laid his eyes upon these regions of delight, the peace of his mind was at an end, and his only study was how to gain the affections of the peerless daughter of Van Tassel. In this enterprise, however, he had more real difficulties than generally fell to the lot of a knight-errant of yore, who seldom had anything but giants, enchanters, fiery dragons, and such like easily conquered adversaries, to contend with; and had to make his way merely through gates of iron and brass, and walls of adamant, to the castle keep, where the lady of his heart was confined; all which he achieved as easily as a man would carve his way to the centre of a Christmas pie, and then the lady gave him her hand as a matter of course. Ichabod, on the contrary, had to win his way to the heart of a country coquette, beset with a labyrinth of whims and caprices, which were for ever presenting new difficulties and impediments; and he had to encounter a host of fearful adversaries of real flesh and blood, the numerous rustic admirers who beset every portal to her heart, keeping a watchful and angry eye upon each other, but ready to fly out in the common cause against any new competitor.

Among these the most formidable was a burly, roaring, roistering blade, of the name of Abraham, or, according to the Dutch abbreviation, Brom Van Brunt, the hero of the country round, which rang with his feats of strength and hardihood. He was broad-shouldered and double-jointed, with short curly black hair, and a bluff but not unpleasant countenance, having a mingled air of fun and arrogance. From his Herculean frame and great powers of limb, he had received the nickname of Brom Bones, by which he was universally known. He was famed for great knowledge and skill in horsemanship, being as dexterous on horseback as a Tartar. He was foremost at all races and cock-fights, and, with the ascendency which bodily strength acquires in rustic life, was the umpire in all disputes, setting his hat on one side, and giving his decisions with an air and tone admitting of no gainsay or appeal. He was always ready for either a fight or frolic, but had more mischief than ill-will in his composition; and, with all his overbearing roughness, there was a strong dash of waggish good humour at bottom. He had three or four boon companions, who regarded him as their model, and at the head of whom he scoured the country, attending every scene of feud or merriment for miles round. In cold weather he was distinguished by a fur cap, surmounted with a flaunting fox's tail; and when the folks at a country gathering descried this well-known crest at a distance, whisking about among a squad of hard riders, they always stood by for a squall. Sometimes his crew would be heard dashing along past the farmhouses at midnight, with hoop and halloo, like a troop of Don Cossacks, and the old dames, startled out of their sleep, would listen for a moment, till the hurry-scurry had clattered by, and then exclaim, "Ay, there goes Brom Bones and his gang!" The neighbours looked upon him with a mixture of awe, admiration, and good-will; and when any madcap prank or rustic brawl occurred in the vicinity, always shook their heads and warranted Brom Bones was at the bottom of it.

This rantipole hero had for some time singled out the blooming Katrina for the object of his uncouth gallantries, and though his amorous toyings were something like the gentle caresses and endearments of a bear, yet it was whispered that she did not altogether discourage his hopes. Certain it is, his advances were signals for rival candidates to retire, who felt no inclination to cross a lion in his amours; insomuch that when his horse was seen tied to Van Tassel's paling on a Sunday night, a sure sign that his master was courting, or, as it is termed, "sparking," within, all other suitors passed by in despair, and carried the war into other quarters.

Such was the formidable rival with whom Ichabod Crane had to contend, and, considering all things, a stouter man that he would have shrank from the competition, and a wiser man would have despaired. He had, however, a happy mixture of pliability and perseverance in his nature; he was in form and spirit like a supple-jack,—yielding, but tough; though he bent, he never broke; and though he bowed beneath the slightest pressure, yet, the moment it was away—jerk! he was as erect, and carried his head as high as ever.

To have taken the field openly against his rival would have been madness; for he was not a man to be thwarted in his amours, any more than that stormy lover, Achilles. Ichabod, therefore, made his advances in a quiet and gently-insinuating manner. Under cover of his character of singing-master, he made frequent visits at the farm-house; not that he had anything to apprehend from the meddlesome interference of parents, which is so often a stumbling-block in the path of lovers. Balt Van Tassel was an easy, indulgent soul; he loved his daughter better even than his pipe, and, like a reasonable man and an excellent father, let her have her way in everything. His notable little wife, too, had enough to do to attend to her housekeeping, and manage her poultry; for, as she sagely observed, ducks and geese are foolish things, and must be looked after, but girls can take care of themselves. Thus, while the busy dame bustled about the house, or plied her spinning-wheel at one end of the piazza, honest Balt would sit smoking his evening pipe at the other, watching the achievements of a little wooden warrior, who, armed with a sword in each hand, was most valiantly fighting the wind on the pinnacle of the barn. In the meantime, Ichabod would carry on his suit with the daughter by the side of the spring under the great elm, or sauntering along in the twilight, that hour so favourable to the lover's eloquence.

I profess not to know how women's hearts are wooed and won. To me they have always been matters of riddle and admiration. Some seem to have but one vulnerable point, or door of access; while others have a thousand avenues, and may be captured in a thousand different ways. It is a great triumph of skill to gain the former, but a still greater proof of generalship to maintain possession of the latter, for a man must battle for his fortress at every door and window. He who wins a thousand common hearts is therefore entitled to some renown; but he who keeps undisputed sway over the heart of a coquette, is indeed a hero. Certain it is, this was not the case with the redoubtable Brom Bones; and from the moment Ichabod Crane made his advances, the interests of the former evidently declined; his horse was no longer seen tied at the palings on Sunday nights, and a deadly feud gradually arose between him and the preceptor of Sleepy Hollow.

Brom, who had a degree of rough chivalry in his nature, would fain have carried matters to open warfare, and have settled their pretensions to the lady, according to the mode of those most concise and simple reasoners, the knights-errant of yore—by single combat; but Ichabod was too conscious of the superior might of his adversary to enter the lists against him; he had overheard a boast of Bones, that he "would double the school-master up, and lay him on a shelf of his own school-house"; and he was too wary to give him an opportunity. There was something extremely provoking in this obstinately pacific system; it left Brom no alternative but to draw upon the funds of rustic waggery in his disposition, and to play off boorish practical jokes upon his rival. Ichabod became the object of whimsical persecution to Bones and his gang of rough riders. They harried his hitherto peaceful domains; smoked out his singing-school, by stopping up the chimney; broke into the school-house at night, in spite of his formidable fastenings of withe and window stakes, and turned everything topsy-turvy; so that the poor schoolmaster began to think all the witches in the country held their meetings there. But what was still more annoying, Brom took all opportunities of turning him into ridicule in presence of his mistress, and had a scoundrel dog whom he taught to whine in the most ludicrous manner, and introduced as a rival of Ichabod's to instruct her in psalmody.

In this way matters went on for some time, without producing any material effect on the relative situation of the contending powers. On a fine autumnal afternoon, Ichabod, in pensive mood, sat enthroned on the lofty stool whence he usually watched all the concerns of his little literary realm. In his hand he swayed a ferule, that sceptre of despotic power; the birch of justice reposed on three nails behind the throne, a constant terror to evil-doers; while on the desk before him might be seen sundry contraband articles and prohibited weapons, detected upon the persons of idle urchins; such as half-munched apples, pop-guns, whirligigs, fly-cages, and whole legions of rampant little paper game-cocks. Apparently there had been some appalling act of justice recently inflicted, for his scholars were all busily intent upon their books, or slyly whispering behind them with one eye kept upon the master; and a kind of buzzing stillness reigned throughout the school-room. It was suddenly interrupted by the appearance of a negro, in tow-cloth jacket and trousers, a round-crowned fragment of a hat, like the cap of Mercury, and mounted on the back of a ragged, wild, half-broken colt, which he managed with a rope by way of halter. He came clattering up to the school door with an invitation to Ichabod to attend a merry-making, or "quilting frolic," to be held that evening at Mynheer Van Tassel's; and having delivered his message with that air of importance and effort at fine language which a negro is apt to display on petty embassies of the kind, he dashed over the brook, and was seen scampering away up the hollow, full of the importance and hurry of his mission.

All was now bustle and hubbub in the late quiet school-room. The scholars were hurried through their lessons without stopping at trifles; those who were nimble skipped over half with impunity, and those who were tardy had a smart application now and then in the rear, to quicken their speed, or help them over a tall word. Books were flung aside without being put away on the shelves; inkstands were overturned, benches thrown down, and the whole school was turned loose an hour before the usual time, bursting forth like a legion of young imps, yelping and racketing about the green in joy at their early emancipation.

The gallant Ichabod now spent at least an extra half-hour at his toilet, brushing and furbishing up his best, and indeed only suit of rusty black, and arranging his locks by a bit of broken looking-glass that hung up in the school-house. That he might make his appearance before his mistress in the true style of a cavalier, he borrowed a horse from the farmer with whom he was domiciliated, a choleric old Dutchman, of the name of Hans Van Ripper, and, thus gallantly mounted, issued forth like a knight-errant in quest of adventures. But it is meet I should, in the true spirit of romantic story, give some account of the looks and equipments of my hero and his steed. The animal he bestrode was a broken-down plough-horse that had outlived almost everything but his viciousness. He was gaunt and shagged, with a ewe neck and a head like a hammer; his rusty main and tail were tangled and knotted with burrs; one eye had lost its pupil, and was glaring and spectral; but the other had the gleam of a genuine devil in it. Still he must have had fire and mettle in his day, if we may judge from the name he bore of Gunpowder. He had, in fact, been a favourite steed of his master's, the choleric Van Ripper, who was a furious rider, and had infused, very probably, some of his own spirit into the animal; for, old and broken-down as he looked, there was more of the lurking devil in him than in any young filly in the country.

Ichabod was a suitable figure for such a steed. He rode with short stirrups, which brought his knees nearly up to the pommel of the saddle; his sharp elbows stuck out like grasshoppers; he carried his whip perpendicularly in his hand, like a sceptre, and, as his horse jogged on, the motion of his arms was not unlike the flapping of a pair of wings. A small wool hat rested on the top of his nose, for so his scanty strip of forehead might be called; and the skirts of his black coat fluttered out almost to the horse's tail. Such was the appearance of Ichabod and his steed, as they shambled out of the gate of Hans Van Ripper, and it was altogether such an apparition as is seldom to be met with in broad daylight.

It was, as I have said, a fine autumnal day, the sky was clear and serene, and nature wore that rich and golden livery which we always associate with the idea of abundance. The forests had put on their sober brown and yellow, while some trees of the tenderer kind had been nipped by the frosts into brilliant dyes of orange, purple, and scarlet. Streaming files of wild ducks began to make their appearance high in the air; the bark of the squirrel might be heard from the groves of beech and hickory nuts, and the pensive whistle of the quail at intervals from the neighbouring stubble field.

The small birds were taking their farewell banquets. In the fulness of their revelry, they fluttered, chirping and frolicking, from bush to bush and tree to tree, capricious from the very profusion and variety around them. There was the honest cock-robin, the favourite game of stripling sportsmen, with its loud, querulous note; and the twittering blackbirds flying in sable clouds; and the golden-winged woodpecker, with his crimson crest, his broad black gorget, and splendid plumage; and the cedar-bird, with its red-tipt wings and yellow-tipt tail, and its little monteiro cap of feathers; and the blue jay, that noisy coxcomb, in his gay light-blue coat and white under-clothes; screaming and chattering, nodding and bobbing and bowing, and pretending to be on good terms with every songster of the grove.

As Ichabod jogged slowly on his way, his eye, ever open to every symptom of culinary abundance, ranged with delight over the treasures of jolly autumn. On all sides he beheld vast stores of apples; some hanging in oppressive opulence on the trees; some gathered into baskets and barrels for the market; others heaped up in rich piles for the cider-press. Further on he beheld great fields of Indian corn, with its golden ears peeping from their leafy coverts, and holding out the promise of cakes and hasty-pudding; and the yellow pumpkins lying beneath them, turning up their fair round bellies to the sun, and giving ample prospects of the most luxurious of pies; and anon he passed the fragrant buckwheat fields breathing the odour of the bee-hive, and as he beheld them, soft anticipations stole over his mind of dainty slapjacks, well buttered, and garnished with honey or treacle, by the delicate little dimpled hand of Katrina Van Tassel.

Thus feeding his mind with many sweet thoughts and "sugared suppositions," he journeyed along the sides of a range of hills which look out upon some of the goodliest scenes of the mighty Hudson. The sun gradually wheeled his broad disc down into the west. The wide bosom of the Tappan Zee lay motionless and glassy, except that here and there a gentle undulation waved and prolonged the blue shadow of the distant mountain. A few amber clouds floated in the sky, without a breath of air to move them. The horizon was of a fine golden tint, changing gradually into a pure apple-green, and from that into the deep blue of the mid-heaven. A slanting ray lingered on the woody crests of the precipices that overhung some parts of the river, giving greater depth to the dark-gray and purple of their rocky sides. A sloop was loitering in the distance, dropping slowly down with the tide, her sail hanging uselessly against the mast; and as the reflection of the sky gleamed along the still water, it seemed as if the vessel was suspended in the air.

It was toward evening that Ichabod arrived at the castle of the Heer Van Tassel, which he found thronged with the pride and flower of the adjacent country. Old farmers, a spare leathern-faced race, in homespun coats and breeches, blue stockings, huge shoes, and magnificent pewter buckles. Their brisk withered little dames, in close crimped caps, long-waisted short gowns, homespun petticoats, with scissors and pincushions, and gay calico pockets hanging on the outside. Buxom lasses, almost as antiquated as their mothers, excepting where a straw hat, a fine riband, or perhaps a white frock, gave symptoms of city innovation. The sons, in short square-skirted coats with rows of stupendous brass buttons, and their hair generally queued in the fashion of the times, especially if they could procure an eel-skin for the purpose, it being esteemed throughout the country as a potent nourisher and strengthener of the hair.

Brom Bones, however, was the hero of the scene, having come to the gathering on his favourite steed Daredevil, a creature like himself, full of mettle and mischief, and which no one but himself could manage. He was, in fact, noted for preferring vicious animals, given to all kinds of tricks, which kept the rider in constant risk of his neck, for he held a tractable, well-broken horse as unworthy of a lad of spirit.

Fain would I pause to dwell upon the world of charms that burst upon the enraptured gaze of my hero, as he entered the state parlour of Van Tassel's mansion. Not those of the bevy of buxom lasses, with their luxurious display of red and white; but the ample charms of a genuine Dutch country tea-table in the sumptuous time of autumn. Such heaped-up platters of cakes of various and almost indescribable kinds, known only to experienced Dutch housewives! There was the doughty dough-nut, the tenderer oly koek, and the crisp and crumbling cruller; sweet-cakes and short-cakes, ginger-cakes and honey-cakes, and the whole family of cakes. And then there were apple-pies and peach-pies and pumpkin-pies; besides slices of ham and smoked beef; and, moreover, delectable dishes of preserved plums, and peaches, and pears, and quinces; not to mention broiled shad and roasted chickens; together with bowls of milk and cream, all mingled higgledy-piggledy, pretty much as I have enumerated them, with the motherly tea-pot sending up its clouds of vapour from the midst—Heaven bless the mark! I want breath and time to discuss this banquet as it deserves, and am too eager to get on with my story. Happily, Ichabod Crane was not in so great a hurry as his historian, but did ample justice to every dainty.

He was a kind and thankful creature, whose heart dilated in proportion as his skin was filled with good cheer; and whose spirits rose with eating as some men's do with drink. He could not help, too, rolling his large eyes round him as he ate, and chuckling with the possibility that he might one day be lord of all this scene of almost unimaginable luxury and splendour. Then he thought, how soon he'd turn his back upon the old school-house, snap his fingers in the face of Hans Van Ripper and every other niggardly patron, and kick any itinerant pedagogue out of doors that should dare to call him comrade!

Old Baltus Van Tassel moved about among his guests with a face dilated with content and good humour, round and jolly as the harvest moon. His hospitable attentions were brief, but expressive, being confined to a shake of the hand, a slap on the shoulder, a loud laugh, and a pressing invitation to "fall to, and help themselves."

And now the sound of the music from the common room or hall summoned to the dance. The musician was an old gray-headed negro, who had been the itinerant orchestra of the neighbourhood for more than half a century. His instrument was as old and battered as himself. The greater part of the time he scraped on two or three strings, accompanying every movement of the bow with a motion of the head; bowing almost to the ground, and stamping with his foot whenever a fresh couple were to start.

Ichabod prided himself upon his dancing as much as upon his vocal powers. Not a limb, not a fire about him was idle; and to have seen his loosely-hung frame in full motion, and clattering about the room, you would have thought Saint Vitus himself, that blessed patron of the dance, was figuring before you in person. He was the admiration of all the negroes; who, having gathered, of all ages and sizes, from the farm and the neighbourhood, stood forming a pyramid of shining black faces, at every door and window, gazing with delight at the scene, rolling their white eye-balls, and showing grinning rows of ivory from ear to ear. How could the flogger of urchins be otherwise than animated and joyous? the lady of his heart was his partner in the dance, and smiling graciously in reply to all his amorous oglings; while Brom Bones, sorely smitten with love and jealousy, sat brooding by himself in one corner.

When the dance was at an end, Ichabod was attracted to a knot of the sager folks, who, with old Van Tassel, sat smoking at one end of the piazza, gossiping over former times, and drawing out long stories about the war.

This neighbourhood, at the time of which I am speaking, was one of those highly-favoured places which abound with chronicle and great men. The British and American line had run near it during the war; it had, therefore, been the scene of marauding, and infested with refugees, cow-boys, and all kinds of border chivalry. Just sufficient time had elapsed to enable each storyteller to dress up his tale with a little becoming fiction, and, in the indistinctness of his recollection, to make himself the hero of every exploit.

There was the story of Doffue Martling, a large blue-bearded Dutchman, who had nearly taken a British frigate with an old iron nine-pounder from a mud breastwork, only that his gun burst at the sixth discharge. And there was an old gentleman who shall be nameless, being too rich a mynheer to be lightly mentioned, who, in the battle of Whiteplains, being an excellent master of defence, parried a musket-ball with a small sword, insomuch that he absolutely felt it whiz round the blade, and glance off at the hilt; in proof of which he was ready at any time to show the sword, with the hilt a little bent. There were several more that had been equally great in the field, not one of whom but was persuaded that he had a considerable hand in bringing the war to a happy termination.

But all these were nothing to the tales of ghosts and apparitions that succeeded. The neighbourhood is rich in legendary treasures of the kind. Local tales and superstitions thrive best in these sheltered long-settled retreats; but are trampled under-foot by the shifting throng that forms the population of most of our country places. Besides, there is no encouragement for ghosts in most of our villages, for they have scarcely had time to finish their first nap, and turn themselves in their graves, before their surviving friends have travelled away from the neighbourhood; so that when they turn out at night to walk their rounds, they have no acquaintance left to call upon. This is perhaps the reason why we so seldom hear of ghosts except in our long-established Dutch communities.

The immediate cause, however, of the prevalence of supernatural stories in these parts, was doubtless owing to the vicinity of Sleepy Hollow. There was a contagion in the very air that blew from that haunted region; it breathed forth an atmosphere of dreams and fancies infecting all the land. Several of the Sleepy Hollow people were present at Van Tassel's, and, as usual, were doling out their wild and wonderful legends. Many dismal tales were told about funeral trains, and mourning cries and wailings heard and seen about the great tree where the unfortunate Major André was taken, and which stood in the neighbourhood. Some mention was made also of the woman in white, that haunted the dark glen at Raven Rock, and was often heard to shriek on winter nights before a storm, having perished there in the snow. The chief part of the stories, however, turned upon the favourite spectre of Sleepy Hollow, the headless horseman, who had been heard several times of late, patrolling the country; and, it was said, tether his horse nightly among the graves in the churchyard.

The sequestered situation of this church seems always to have made it a favourite haunt of troubled spirits. It stands on a knoll surrounded by locust-trees and lofty elms, from among which its decent whitewashed walls shine modestly forth, like Christian purity, beaming through the shades of retirement. A gentle slope descends from it to a silver sheet of water, bordered by high trees, between which peeps may be caught at the blue hills of the Hudson. To look upon its grass-grown yard, where the sunbeams seem to sleep so quietly, one would think that there at least the dead might rest in peace. On one side of the church extends a wide woody dell, along which raves a large brook among broken rocks and trunks of fallen trees. Over a deep black part of the stream, not far from the church, was formerly thrown a wooden bridge; the road that led to it, and the bridge itself, were thickly shaded by overhanging trees, which cast a gloom about it, even in the daytime; but occasioned a fearful darkness at night. Such was one of the favourite haunts of the headless horseman, and the place where he was most frequently encountered. The tale was told of old Brouwer, a most heretical disbeliever in ghosts, how he met the horseman returning from his foray into Sleepy Hollow, and was obliged to get up behind him; how they galloped over bush and brake, over hill and swamp, until they reached the bridge; when the horseman suddenly turned into a skeleton, threw old Brouwer into the brook, and sprang away over the tree-tops with a clap of thunder.

This story was immediately matched by a thrice marvellous adventure of Brom Bones, who made light of the Galloping Hessian as an arrant jockey. He affirmed that, on returning one night from the neighbouring village of Sing-Sing, he had been overtaken by this midnight trooper; that he had offered to race with him for a bowl of punch, and should have won it too, for Daredevil beat the goblin horse all hollow, but, just as they came to the church bridge, the Hessian bolted, and vanished in a flash of fire.

All these tales, told in that drowsy under-tone with which men talk in the dark, the countenances of the listeners only now and then receiving a casual gleam from the glare of a pipe, sank deep in the mind of Ichabod. He repaid them in kind, with large extracts from his invaluable author, Cotton Mather, and added many marvellous events that had taken place in his native state of Connecticut, and fearful sights which he had seen in his nightly walks about Sleepy Hollow.

The revel now gradually broke up. The old farmers gathered together their families in their waggons, and were heard for some time rattling along the hollow roads, and over the distant hills. Some of the damsels mounted on pillions behind their favourite swains, and their light-hearted laughter, mingling with the clatter of hoofs, echoed along the silent woodlands, sounding fainter and fainter until they gradually died away—and the late scene of noise and frolic was all silent and deserted. Ichabod only lingered behind, according to the custom of country lovers, to have a *tête-à-tête* with the heiress, fully convinced that he was now on the high road to success. What passed at this interview I will not pretend to say, for in fact I do not know. Something, however, I fear me, must have gone wrong, for he certainly sallied forth, after no very great interval, with an air quite desolate and chop-fallen. Oh these women! these women! Could that girl have been playing off any of her coquettish tricks? —Was her encouragement of the poor pedagogue all a mere sham to secure her conquest of his rival?—Heaven only knows, not I!—Let it suffice to say, Ichabod stole forth with the air of one who had been sacking a hen-roost, rather than a fair lady's heart. Without looking to the right or left to notice the scene of rural wealth on which he had so often gloated, he went straight to the stable, and with several hearty cuffs and kicks, roused his steed most uncourteously from the comfortable quarters in which he was soundly sleeping, dreaming of mountains of corn and oats. and whole valleys of timothy and clover.

It was the very witching time of night that Ichabod, heavy-hearted and crest-fallen, pursued his travels homewards, along the sides of the lofty hills which rise above Tarry Town, and which he had traversed so cheerily in the after-noon. The hour was as dismal as himself. Far below him the Tappan Zee spread its dusky and indistinct waste of waters, with here and there the tall mast of a sloop riding quietly at anchor under the land. In the dead hush of midnight he could even hear the barking of the watch-dog from the opposite shore of the Hudson; but it was so vague and faint as only to give an idea of his distance from this faithful companion of man. Now and then, too, the long-drawn crow-ing of a cock, accidentally awakened, would sound far, far off, from some farm-house away among the hills—but it was like a dreaming sound in his ear. No signs of life occurred near him, but occasionally the melancholy chirp of a cricket, or perhaps the guttural twang of a bull-frog, from a neighbouring marsh, as if sleeping uncomfortably, and turning suddenly in his bed.

All the stories of ghosts and goblins that he had heard in the afternoon now came crowding upon his recollection. The night grew darker and darker; the stars seemed to sink deeper in the sky, and driving clouds occasionally hid them from his sight. He had never felt so lonely and dismal. He was, moreover, approaching the very place where many of the scenes of the ghost-stories had been laid. In the centre of the road stood an enormous tulip-tree, which towered like a giant above all the other trees of the neighbourhood, and formed a kind of landmark. Its limbs were gnarled and fantastic, large enough to form trunks for ordinary trees, twisting down almost to the earth, and rising again into the air. It was connected with the tragical story of the unfortunate André, who had been taken prisoner hard by; and was universally known by the name of Major André's tree. The common people regarded it with a mixture of respect and superstition, partly out of sympathy for the fate of its ill-starred namesake and partly from the tales of strange sights and doleful lamentations told con-cerning it.

As Ichabod approached this fearful tree, he began to whistle; he thought his whistle was answered; it was but a blast sweeping sharply through the dry branches. As he approached a little nearer, he thought he saw something white hanging in the midst of the tree—he paused and ceased whistling; but on looking more narrowly, perceived that it was a place where the tree had been scathed by lightning, and the white wood laid bare. Suddenly he heard a groan—his teeth chattered, and his knees smote against the saddle; it was but the rubbing of one huge bough upon another, as they were swayed about by the breeze. He passed the tree in safety, but new perils lay before him.

About two hundred yards from the tree a small brook crossed the road, and ran into a marshy and thickly-wooded glen, known by the name of Wiley's Swamp. A few rough logs, laid side by side, served for a bridge over this stream. On that side of the road where the brook entered the wood, a group of oaks and chestnuts, matted thick with wild grape-vines, threw a cavernous gloom over it. To pass this bridge was the severest trial. It was at this identical spot that the unfortunate André was captured, and under the covert of those chest-nuts and vines were the sturdy yeomen concealed who surprised him. This has ever since been considered a haunted stream, and fearful are the feelings of the schoolboy who has to pass it alone after dark.

As he approached the stream, his heart began to thump; he summoned up, however, all his resolution, gave his horse half a score of kicks in the ribs, and attempted to dash briskly across the bridge; but instead of starting forward, the perverse old animal made a lateral movement, and ran broadside against the fence. Ichabod, whose fears increased with the delay, jerked the reins on the other side, and kicked lustily with the contrary foot: it was all in vain; his steed started, it is true, but it was only to plunge to the opposite side of the road into a thicket of brambles and alder-bushes. The schoolmaster now bestowed both whip and heel upon the starveling ribs of old Gunpowder, who dashed forward, snuffling and snorting, but came to a stand just by the bridge, with a suddenness that had nearly sent his rider sprawling over his head. Just at this moment a plashy tramp by the side of the bridge caught the sensitive ear of Ichabod. In the dark shadow of the grove, on the margin of the brook, he beheld something huge, misshapen, black and towering. It stirred not, but seemed gathered up in the gloom, like some gigantic monster ready to spring upon the traveller.

The hair of the affrighted pedagogue rose upon his head with terror. What was to be done? To turn and fly was now too late; and besides, what chance was there of escaping ghost or goblin, if such it was, which could ride upon the wings of the wind? Summoning up, therefore, a show of courage, he demanded in stammering accents—"Who are you?" He received no reply. He repeated his demand in a still more agitated voice. Still there was no answer. Once more he cudgelled the sides of the inflexible Gunpowder, and, shutting his eyes, broke forth with involuntary fervour into a psalm tune. Just then the shadowy object of alarm put itself in motion, and with a scramble and a bound, stood at once in the middle of the road. Though the night was dark and dismal, yet the form of the unknown might now in some degree be ascertained. He appeared to be a horseman of large dimensions, and mounted on a black horse of powerful frame. He made no offer of molestation or sociability, but kept aloof on one side of the road, jogging along on the blind side of old Gunpowder, who had now got over his fright and waywardness.

Ichabod, who had no relish for this strange midnight companion, and bethought himself of the adventure of Brom Bones with the Galloping Hessian, now quickened his steed, in hopes of leaving him behind. The stranger, however, quickened his horse to an equal pace. Ichabod pulled up, and fell into a walk, thinking to lag behind—the other did the same. His heart began to sink within him; he endeavoured to resume his psalm tune, but his parched tongue clove to the roof of his mouth, and he could not utter a stave. There was something in the moody and dogged silence of this pertinacious companion that was mysterious and appalling. It was soon fearfully accounted for. On mounting a rising ground, which brought the figure of his fellow-traveller in relief against the sky, gigantic in height, and muffled in a cloak, Ichabod was horror-struck on perceiving that he was headless!—but his horror was still more increased on observing that the head, which should have rested on his shoulders, was carried before him on the pommel of the saddle: his terror rose to desperation; he rained a shower of kicks and blows upon Gunpowder, hoping, by a sudden movement, to give his companion the slip—but the spectre started full jump with him. Away then they dashed, through thick and thin; stones flying and sparks flashing at every bound. Ichabod's flimsy garments fluttered in the air, as he stretched his long lank body away over his horse's head, in the eagerness of his flight.

They had now reached the road which turns off to Sleepy Hollow; but Gunpowder, who seemed possessed with a demon, instead of keeping up it, made an opposite turn, and plunged headlong down the hill to the left. This road leads through a sandy hollow, shaded by trees for about a quarter of a mile, where it crosses the bridge famous in goblin story, and just beyond swells the green knoll on which stands the whitewashed church.

As yet the panic of the steed had given his unskilful rider an apparent advantage in the chase; but just as he had got half way through the hollow, the girths of the saddle gave way, and he felt it slipping from under him. He seized it by the pommel, and endeavoured to hold it firm, but in vain; and had just time to save himself by clasping old Gunpowder round the neck, when the saddle fell to the earth, and he heard it trampled under-foot by his pursuer. For a moment the terror of Hans Van Ripper's wrath passed across his mind—for it was his Sunday saddle; but this was no time for petty fears; the goblin was hard on his haunches; and (unskilful rider that he was!) he had much ado to maintain his seat; sometimes slipping on one side, sometimes on the other, and sometimes jolted on the high ridge of his horse's back-bone, with a violence that he verily feared would cleave him asunder.

An opening in the trees now cheered him with the hopes that the church bridge was at hand. The wavering reflection of a silver star in the bosom of the brook told him that he was not mistaken. He saw the walls of the church dimly glaring under the trees beyond. He recollected the place where Brom Bones' ghostly competitor had disappeared. "If I can but reach that bridge," thought Ichabod, "I am safe." Just then he heard the black steed panting and blowing close behind him; he even fancied that he felt his hot breath. Another convulsive kick in the ribs, and old Gunpowder sprang upon the bridge; he thundered over the resounding planks; he gained the opposite side; and now Ichabod cast a look behind to see if his pursuer should vanish, according to rule, in a flash of fire and brimstone. Just then he saw the goblin rising in his stirrups, and in the very act of hurling his head at him. Ichabod endeavoured to dodge the horrible missile, but too late. It encountered his cranium with a tremendous crash—he was tumbled headlong into the dust, and Gunpowder, the black steed, and the goblin rider passed by like a whirlwind.

The next morning the old horse was found without his saddle, and with the bridle under his feet, soberly cropping the grass at his master's gate. Ichabod did not make his appearance at breakfast—dinner-hour came, but no Ichabod. The boys assembled at the school-house, and strolled idly about the banks of the brook; but no school-master. Hans Van Ripper now began to feel some uneasiness about the fate of poor Ichabod and his saddle. An inquiry was set on foot, and after diligent investigation they came upon his traces. In one part of the road leading to the church was found the saddle trampled in the dirt; the tracks of horses' hoofs deeply dented in the road, and evidently at furious speed, were traced to the bridge, beyond which, on the bank of a broad part of the brook, where the water ran deep and black, was found the hat of the unfortunate Ichabod, and close beside it a shattered pumpkin.

The brook was searched, but the body of the school-master was not to be discovered. Hans Van Ripper, as executor of his estate, examined the bundle, which contained all his worldly effects. They consisted of two shirts and a half; two stocks for the neck; a pair or two of worsted stockings; an old pair of corduroy small-clothes; a rusty razor; a book of psalm tunes, full of dog's ears; and a broken pitch-pipe. As to the books and furniture of the school-house, they belonged to the community, excepting Cotton Mather's *History of Witchcraft*, a New England Almanac, and a book of dreams and fortune-telling; in which last was a sheet of foolscap much scribbled and blotted in several fruitless attempts to make a copy of verses in honour of the heiress of Van Tassel. These magic books and the poetic scrawl were forthwith consigned to the flames by Hans Van Ripper; who from that time forward determined to send his children no more to school, observing, that he never knew any good come of this same reading and writing. Whatever money the schoolmaster possessed, and he had received his quarter's pay but a day or two before, he must have had about his person at the time of his disappearance.

The mysterious event caused much speculation at the church on the following Sunday. Knots of gazers and gossips were collected in the churchyard, at the bridge, and at the spot where the hat and pumpkin had been found. The stories of Brouwer, of Bones, and a whole budget of others, were called to mind; and when they had diligently considered them all, and compared them with the symptoms of the present case, they shook their heads, and came to the conclusion that Ichabod had been carried off by the Galloping Hessian. As he was a bachelor, and in nobody's debt, nobody troubled his head any more about him: the school was removed to a different quarter of the Hollow, and another pedagogue reigned in his stead.

It is true, an old farmer, who had been down to New York on a visit several years after, and from whom this account of the ghostly adventure was received, brought home the intelligence that Ichabod Crane was still alive; that he had left the neighbourhood, partly through fear of the goblin and Hans Van Ripper, and partly in mortification at having been suddenly dismissed by the heiress; that he had changed his quarters to a distant part of the country; had kept school and studied law at the same time; had been admitted to the bar, turned politician, electioneered, written for the newspapers, and finally had been made a justice of the Ten-pound Court. Brom Bones, too, who shortly after his rival's disappearance conducted the blooming Katrina in triumph to the altar, was observed to look exceedingly knowing whenever the story of Ichabod was related, and always burst into a hearty laugh at the mention of the pumpkin; which led some to suspect that he knew more about the matter than he chose to tell.

The old country wives, however, who are the best judges of these matters, maintain to this day that Ichabod was spirited away by supernatural means; and it is a favourite story often told about the neighbourhood round the winter evening fire. The bridge became more than ever an object of superstitious awe, and that may be the reason why the road has been altered of late years, so as to approach the church by the border of the mill-pond. The school-house being deserted, soon fell to decay, and was reported to be haunted by the ghost of the unfortunate pedagogue; and the plough-boy, loitering homeward of a still summer evening, has often fancied his voice at a distance, chanting a melancholy psalm tune among the tranquil solitudes of Sleepy Hollow.

POSTSCRIPT

FOUND IN THE HANDWRITING OF MR. KNICKERBOCKER

THE preceding tale is given, almost in the precise words in which I heard it related at a Corporation meeting of the ancient city of Manhattoes, at which were present many of its sagest and most illustrious burghers. The narrator was a pleasant, shabby, gentlemanly old fellow, in pepper-and-salt clothes, with a sadly humorous face; and one whom I strongly suspected of being poor,—he made such efforts to be entertaining. When his story was concluded, there was much laughter and approbation, particularly from two or three deputy aldermen, who had been asleep the greater part of the time. There was, however, one tall, dry-looking old gentleman, with beetling eyebrows, who maintained a grave and rather a severe face throughout: now and then folding his arms, inclining his head, and looking down upon the floor, as if turning a doubt over in his mind. He was one of your wary men, who never laugh, but upon good grounds—when they have reason and the law on their side. When the mirth of the rest of the company had subsided, and silence was restored, he leaned one arm on the elbow of his chair, and sticking the other a-kimbo, demanded, with a slight but exceedingly sage motion of the head, and contraction of the brow, what was the moral of the story, and what it went to prove?

The story-teller, who was just putting a glass of wine to his lips, as a refreshment after his toils, paused for a moment, looked at his inquirer with an air of infinite deference, and, lowering the glass slowly to the table, observed that the story was intended most logically to prove:—

"That there is no situation in life but has its advantages and pleasures—provided we will but take a joke as we find it:

"That, therefore, he that runs races with goblin troopers is likely to have rough riding of it.

"Ergo, for a country schoolmaster to be refused the hand of a Dutch heiress is a certain step to high preferment in the state."

The cautious old gentleman knit his brows tenfold closer after this explanation, being sorely puzzled by the ratiocination of the syllogism: while, methought, the one in pepper-and-salt eyed him with something of a triumphant leer. At length he observed that all this was very well; but still he thought the story a little on the extravagant—there were one or two points on which he had his doubts.

"Faith, sir," replied the story-teller, "as to that matter, I don't believe one half of it myself."

D. K.